2009
Yearbook of
Astronomy

2009
Yearbook of Astronomy

edited by
Patrick Moore

co-editor
John Mason

MACMILLAN

First published 2008 by Macmillan
an imprint of Pan Macmillan Ltd
Pan Macmillan, 20 New Wharf Road, London N1 9RR
Basingstoke and Oxford
Associated companies throughout the world
www.panmacmillan.com

ISBN 978-0-230-71441-0

9 8 7 6 5 4 3 2 1

A CIP catalogue record for this book is available from
the British Library.

Typeset by Rowland Phototypesetting Ltd, Bury St Edmunds, Suffolk
Printed and bound in the UK by CPI Mackays, Chatham ME5 8TD

Visit **www.panmacmillan.com** to read more about all our books
and to buy them. You will also find features, author interviews and
news of any author events, and you can sign up for e-newsletters
so that you're always first to hear about our new releases.

Contents

Editors' Foreword

It is noteworthy that 2009 has been designated 'The International Year of Astronomy', or IYA2009. This will be a global celebration of astronomy and its contributions to society and culture, highlighted by the 400th anniversary of the first telescopic observations made by the Italian astronomer Galileo Galilei. In Britain, we shall also be remembering the Englishman, Thomas Harriot, who observed the Moon on 26 July 1609 from Syon House, and it is likely that this was the first astronomical observation made with a telescope. Harriot's telescopic drawings of the Moon predate those made by Galileo by some months. The aim of IYA2009 is to stimulate worldwide interest, among people of all ages, in astronomy and science under the central theme 'The Universe, Yours to Discover'. IYA activities will take place locally, regionally and nationally in each participating country, with professional and amateur astronomers, science centres and science communicators all taking part.

We hope that many people will be encouraged to take up an interest in astronomy by the events held during IYA2009. We also hope that these newcomers and those who have been interested in the subject for much longer will find something of interest in this book. The *2009 Yearbook* follows the traditional pattern, with contributions to the articles section from both our regular authors and some welcome newcomers. As usual, we have done our best to cover a wide range, both of subject and of technical level. Gordon Taylor has, as always, produced the material for the monthly notes, and John Isles and Bob Argyle have provided the information on variable stars and double stars, respectively.

PATRICK MOORE
JOHN MASON
Selsey, August 2008

Preface

New readers will find that all the information in this *Yearbook* is given in diagrammatic or descriptive form; the positions of the planets may easily be found from the specially designed star charts, while the monthly notes describe the movements of the planets and give details of other astronomical phenomena visible in both in the Northern and Southern Hemispheres. Two sets of star charts are provided. The **Northern Charts** (pp.17 to 41) are designed for use at latitude 52°N, but may be used without alteration throughout the British Isles, and (except in the case of eclipses and occultations) in other countries of similar northerly latitude. The **Southern Charts** (pp.43 to 67) are drawn for latitude 35°S, and are suitable for use in South Africa, Australia and New Zealand, and other locations in approximately the same southerly latitude. The reader who needs more detailed information will find *Norton's Star Atlas* an invaluable guide, while more precise positions of the planets and their satellites, together with predictions of occultations, meteor showers and periodic comets, may be found in the *Handbook* of the British Astronomical Association. Readers will also find details of forthcoming events given in the American monthly magazine *Sky & Telescope* and the British periodicals *The Sky at Night*, *Astronomy Now* and *Astronomy and Space*.

Important note

The times given on the star charts and in the Monthly Notes are generally given as local times, using the 24-hour clock, the day beginning at midnight. All the dates, and the times of a few events (e.g. eclipses) are given in Greenwich Mean Time (GMT), which is related to local time by the formula

Local Mean Time = GMT – west longitude

In practice, small differences in longitude are ignored, and the observer will use local clock time, which will be the appropriate Standard (or Zone) Time. As the formula indicates, places in west longitude will have a Standard Time slow on GMT, while places in east longitude will have a Standard Time fast on GMT. As examples we have:

Standard Time in

New Zealand	GMT + 12 hours
Victoria, NSW	GMT + 10 hours
Western Australia	GMT + 8 hours
South Africa	GMT + 2 hours
British Isles	GMT
Eastern ST	GMT − 5 hours
Central ST	GMT − 6 hours, etc.

If Summer Time is in use, the clocks will have been advanced by one hour, and this hour must be subtracted from the clock time to give Standard Time.

Part I

Monthly Charts and Astronomical Phenomena

Notes on the Star Charts

The stars, together with the Sun, Moon and planets, seem to be set on the surface of the celestial sphere, which appears to rotate about the Earth from east to west. Since it is impossible to represent a curved surface accurately on a plane, any kind of star map is bound to contain some form of distortion.

Most of the monthly star charts which appear in the various journals and some national newspapers are drawn in circular form. This is perfectly accurate, but it can make the charts awkward to use. For the star charts in this volume, we have preferred to give two hemispherical maps for each month of the year, one showing the northern aspect of the sky and the other showing the southern aspect. Two sets of monthly charts are provided, one for observers in the Northern Hemisphere and one for those in the Southern Hemisphere.

Unfortunately the constellations near the overhead point (the zenith) on these hemispherical charts can be rather distorted. This would be a serious drawback for precision charts, but what we have done is to give maps which are best suited to star recognition. We have also refrained from putting in too many stars, so that the main patterns stand out clearly. To help observers with any distortions near the zenith, and the lack of overlap between the charts of each pair, we have also included two circular maps, one showing all the constellations in the northern half of the sky, and one those in the southern half. Incidentally, there is a curious illusion that stars at an altitude of 60° or more are actually overhead, and beginners may often feel that they are leaning over backwards in trying to see them.

The charts show all stars down to the fourth magnitude, together with a number of fainter stars which are necessary to define the shapes of constellations. There is no standard system for representing the outlines of the constellations, and triangles and other simple figures have been used to give outlines which are easy to trace with the naked eye. The names of the constellations are given, together with the proper names of the brighter stars. The apparent magnitudes of the stars are indicated roughly by using different sizes of dot, the larger dots representing the brighter stars.

The two sets of star charts – one each for Northern and Southern Hemisphere observers – are similar in design. At each opening there is a single circular chart which shows all the constellations in that hemisphere of the sky. (These two charts are centred on the North and South Celestial Poles, respectively.) Then there are twelve double-page spreads, showing the northern and southern aspects for each month of the year for observers in that hemisphere. In the **Northern Charts** (drawn for latitude 52°N) the left-hand chart of each spread shows the northern half of the sky (lettered 1N, 2N, 3N ... 12N), and the corresponding right-hand chart shows the southern half of the sky (lettered 1S, 2S, 3S ... 12S). The arrangement and lettering of the charts is exactly the same for the **Southern Charts** (drawn for latitude 35°S).

Because the sidereal day is shorter than the solar day, the stars appear to rise and set about four minutes earlier each day, and this amounts to two hours in a month. Hence the twelve pairs of charts in each set are sufficient to give the appearance of the sky throughout the day at intervals of two hours, or at the same time of night at monthly intervals throughout the year. For example, charts 1N and 1S here are drawn for 23 hours on 6 January. The view will also be the same on 6 October at 05 hours; 6 November at 03 hours; 6 December at 01 hours and 6 February at 21 hours. The actual range of dates and times when the stars on the charts are visible is indicated on each page. Each pair of charts is numbered in bold type, and the number to be used for any given month and time may be found from the following table:

Local Time	18h	20h	22h	0h	2h	4h	6h
January	11	12	1	2	3	4	5
February	12	1	2	3	4	5	6
March	1	2	3	4	5	6	7
April	2	3	4	5	6	7	8
May	3	4	5	6	7	8	9
June	4	5	6	7	8	9	10
July	5	6	7	8	9	10	11
August	6	7	8	9	10	11	12
September	7	8	9	10	11	12	1

Local Time	18h	20h	22h	0h	2h	4h	6h
October	8	9	10	11	12	1	2
November	9	10	11	12	1	2	3
December	10	11	12	1	2	3	4

On these charts, the ecliptic is drawn as a broken line on which longitude is marked every 10°. The positions of the planets are then easily found by reference to the table on p.74. It will be noticed that on the **Southern Charts** the ecliptic may reach an altitude in excess of 62.5° on the star charts showing the northern aspect (5N to 9N). The continuations of the broken line will be found on the corresponding charts for the southern aspect (5S, 6S, 8S and 9S).

Northern Star Charts

Northern Hemisphere

Note that the markers at 0ʰ, 6ʰ, 12ʰ and 18ʰ
indicate hours of Right Ascension.

1N

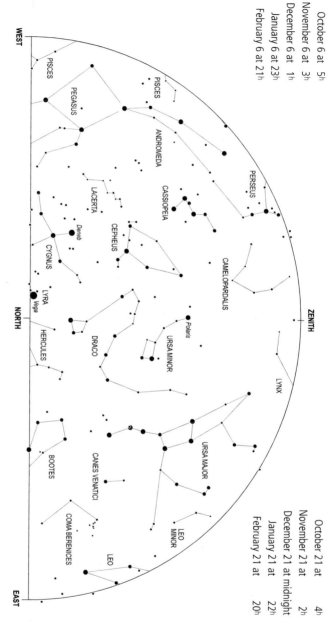

October 6 at   5h
November 6 at   3h
December 6 at   1h
January 6 at 23h
February 6 at 21h

October 21 at   4h
November 21 at   2h
December 21 at midnight
January 21 at   22h
February 21 at 20h

WEST

NORTH

EAST

ZENITH

PISCES

PEGASUS

PISCES

ANDROMEDA

PERSEUS

LACERTA

CASSIOPEIA

CEPHEUS

CAMELOPARDALIS

Deneb

CYGNUS

LYRA
Vega

HERCULES

DRACO

URSA MINOR

Polaris

LYNX

BOOTES

CANES VENATICI

URSA MAJOR

COMA BERENICES

LEO
MINOR

LEO

1S

October 21 at   4ʰ
November 21 at   2ʰ
December 21 at midnight
January 21 at   22ʰ
February 21 at   20ʰ

October 6 at   5ʰ
November 6 at   3ʰ
December 6 at   1ʰ
January 6 at   23ʰ
February 6 at   21ʰ

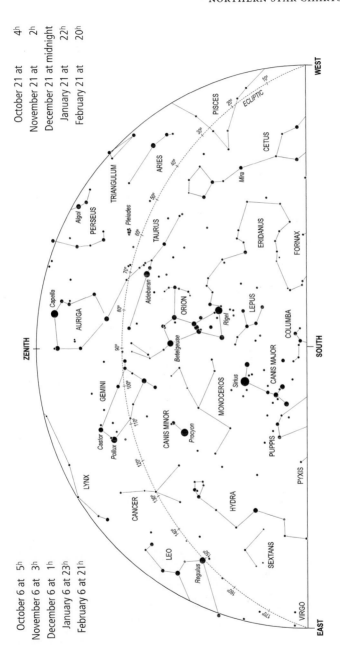

2N

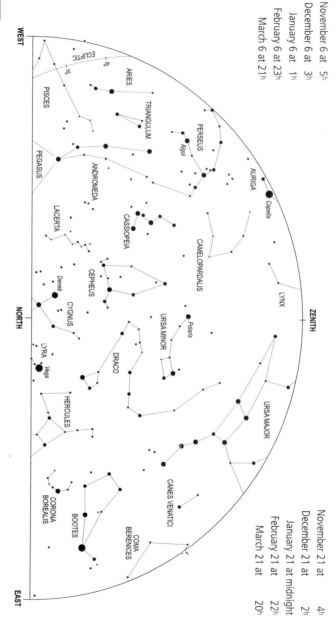

November 6 at 5h
December 6 at 3h
January 6 at 1h
February 6 at 23h
March 6 at 21h

November 21 at 4h
December 21 at 2h
January 21 at midnight
February 21 at 22h
March 21 at 20h

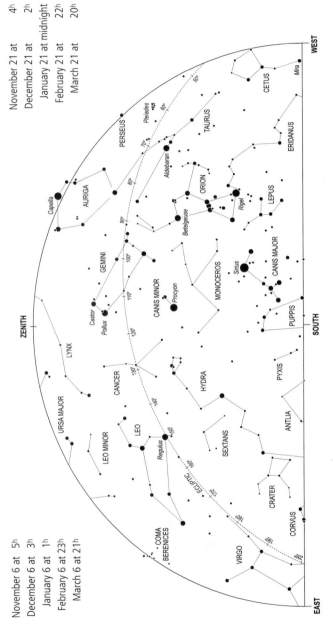

November 21 at   4ʰ
December 21 at   2ʰ
January 21 at midnight
February 21 at   22ʰ
March 21 at   20ʰ

November 6 at   5ʰ
December 6 at   3ʰ
January 6 at   1ʰ
February 6 at 23ʰ
March 6 at 21ʰ

3N

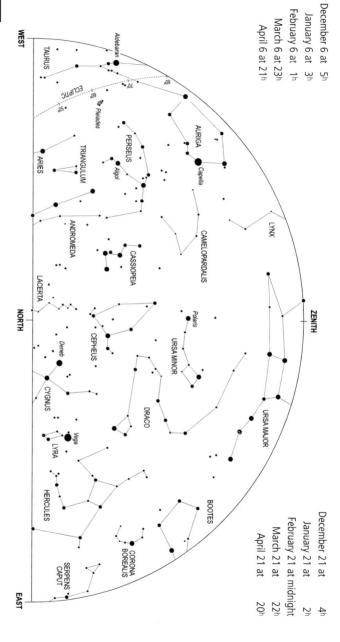

December 6 at 5ʰ
January 6 at 3ʰ
February 6 at 1ʰ
March 6 at 23ʰ
April 6 at 21ʰ

December 21 at   4ʰ
January 21 at   2ʰ
February 21 at midnight
March 21 at   22ʰ
April 21 at   20ʰ

3S

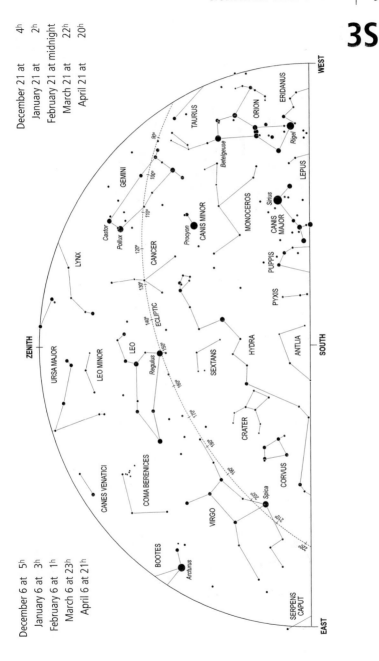

December 21 at 4ʰ
January 21 at 2ʰ
February 21 at midnight
March 21 at 22ʰ
April 21 at 20ʰ

December 6 at 5ʰ
January 6 at 3ʰ
February 6 at 1ʰ
March 6 at 23ʰ
April 6 at 21ʰ

WEST

ERIDANUS
ORION
TAURUS
Betelgeuse
Rigel
GEMINI
LEPUS
Castor
Pollux
CANIS MINOR
Procyon
MONOCEROS
Sirius
CANIS MAJOR
LYNX
CANCER
PUPPIS
ECLIPTIC
PYXIS
ANTLIA
ZENITH
URSA MAJOR
LEO MINOR
LEO
Regulus
SEXTANS
HYDRA
SOUTH
CANES VENATICI
COMA BERENICES
CRATER
CORVUS
Spica
VIRGO
BOOTES
Arcturus
SERPENS
CAPUT
EAST

90°
100°
110°
120°
130°
140°
150°
160°
170°
180°
190°
200°
210°
220°

4N

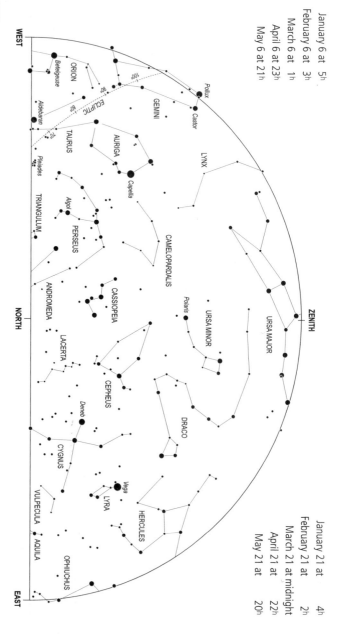

January 6 at 5h
February 6 at 3h
March 6 at 1h
April 6 at 23h
May 6 at 21h

January 21 at 4h
February 21 at 2h
March 21 at midnight
April 21 at 22h
May 21 at 20h

January 21 at 4ʰ
February 21 at 2ʰ
March 21 at midnight
April 21 at 22ʰ
May 21 at 20ʰ

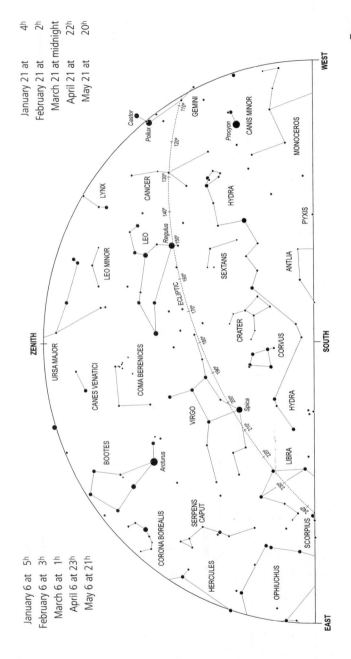

WEST

Castor
Pollux
Procyon
Spica
Regulus
Arcturus

GEMINI
CANIS MINOR
MONOCEROS
LYNX
CANCER
HYDRA
PYXIS
LEO
LEO MINOR
SEXTANS
ANTLIA
ZENITH
ECLIPTIC
CRATER
URSA MAJOR
CORVUS
CANES VENATICI
COMA BERENICES
VIRGO
HYDRA
BOOTES
LIBRA
SERPENS CAPUT
CORONA BOREALIS
SCORPIUS
HERCULES
OPHIUCHUS

SOUTH

EAST

110°
120°
130°
140°
150°
160°
170°
180°
190°
200°
210°
220°
230°
240°

January 6 at 5ʰ
February 6 at 3ʰ
March 6 at 1ʰ
April 6 at 23ʰ
May 6 at 21ʰ

5N

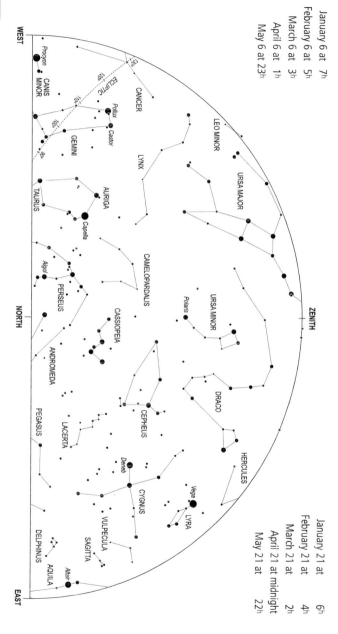

January 6 at 7h
February 6 at 5h
March 6 at 3h
April 6 at 1h
May 6 at 23h

January 21 at 6h
February 21 at 4h
March 21 at 2h
April 21 at midnight
May 21 at 22h

5S

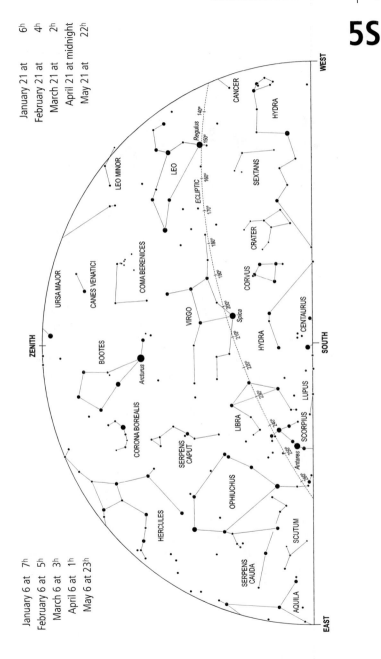

6N

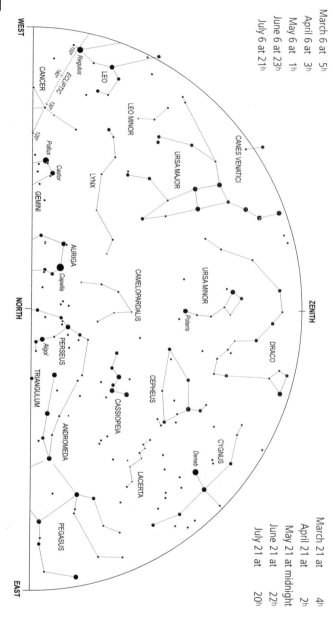

WEST

March 6 at 5h
April 6 at 3h
May 6 at 1h
June 6 at 23h
July 6 at 21h

ZENITH

NORTH

EAST

March 21 at 4h
April 21 at 2h
May 21 at midnight
June 21 at 22h
July 21 at 20h

6S

March 21 at 4ʰ
April 21 at 2ʰ
May 21 at midnight
June 21 at 22ʰ
July 21 at 20ʰ

March 6 at 5ʰ
April 6 at 3ʰ
May 6 at 1ʰ
June 6 at 23ʰ
July 6 at 21ʰ

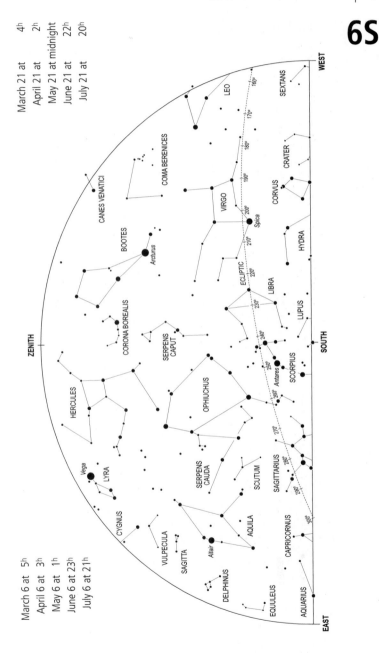

7N

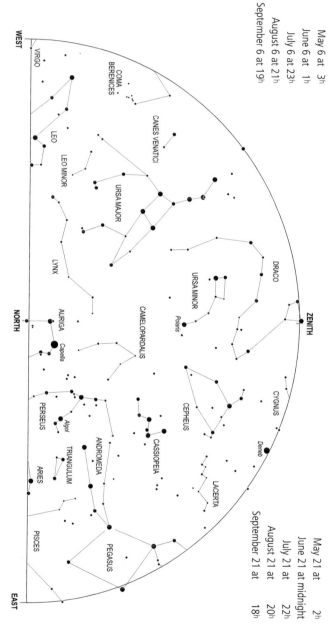

May 6 at 3h
June 6 at 1h
July 6 at 23h
August 6 at 21h
September 6 at 19h

May 21 at 2h
June 21 at midnight
July 21 at 22h
August 21 at 20h
September 21 at 18h

WEST

VIRGO

COMA BERENICES

CANES VENATICI

LEO

LEO MINOR

URSA MAJOR

DRACO

LYNX

URSA MINOR

Polaris

CAMELOPARDALIS

AURIGA

Capella

NORTH

ZENITH

CYGNUS

Deneb

PERSEUS

Algol

CEPHEUS

CASSIOPEIA

TRIANGULUM

ANDROMEDA

LACERTA

ARIES

PISCES

PEGASUS

EAST

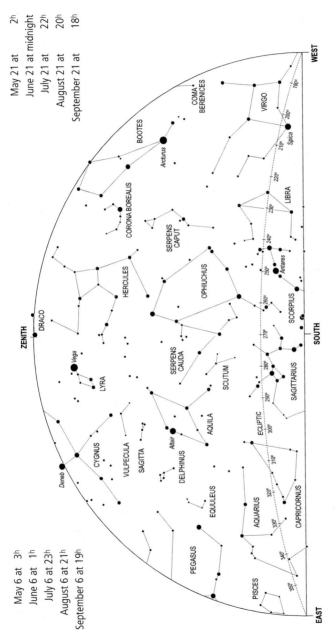

May 21 at 2ʰ
June 21 at midnight
July 21 at 22ʰ
August 21 at 20ʰ
September 21 at 18ʰ

May 6 at 3ʰ
June 6 at 1ʰ
July 6 at 23ʰ
August 6 at 21ʰ
September 6 at 19ʰ

8N

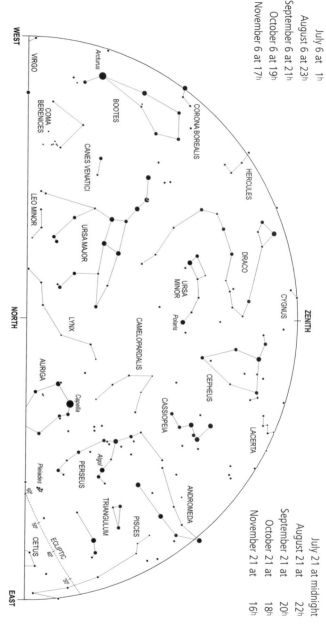

WEST

July 6 at 1h
August 6 at 23h
September 6 at 21h
October 6 at 19h
November 6 at 17h

VIRGO

Arcturus

COMA BERENICES

BOOTES

CORONA BOREALIS

CANES VENATICI

HERCULES

LEO MINOR

URSA MAJOR

DRACO

URSA MINOR

Polaris

CYGNUS

ZENITH

NORTH

LYNX

CAMELOPARDALIS

CEPHEUS

AURIGA

Capella

CASSIOPEIA

LACERTA

Algol

PERSEUS

Pleiades

60°

50°

ECLIPTIC

40°

CETUS

30°

ANDROMEDA

TRIANGULUM

PISCES

EAST

July 21 at midnight
August 21 at 22h
September 21 at 20h
October 21 at 18h
November 21 at 16h

8S

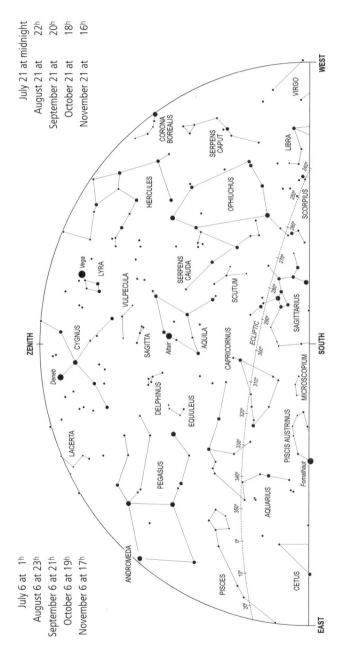

July 21 at midnight
August 21 at 22h
September 21 at 20h
October 21 at 18h
November 21 at 16h

July 6 at 1h
August 6 at 23h
September 6 at 21h
October 6 at 19h
November 6 at 17h

9N

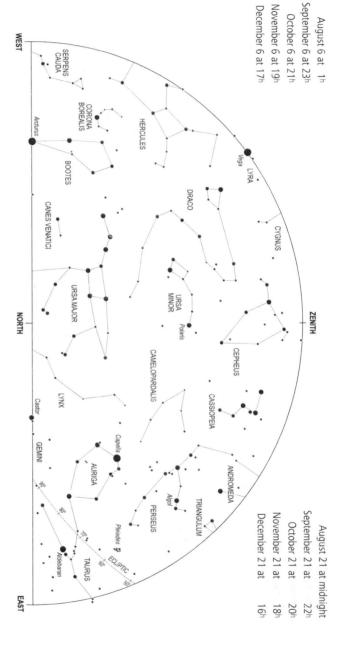

August 6 at 1ʰ
September 6 at 23ʰ
October 6 at 21ʰ
November 6 at 19ʰ
December 6 at 17ʰ

August 21 at midnight
September 21 at 22ʰ
October 21 at 20ʰ
November 21 at 18ʰ
December 21 at 16ʰ

9S

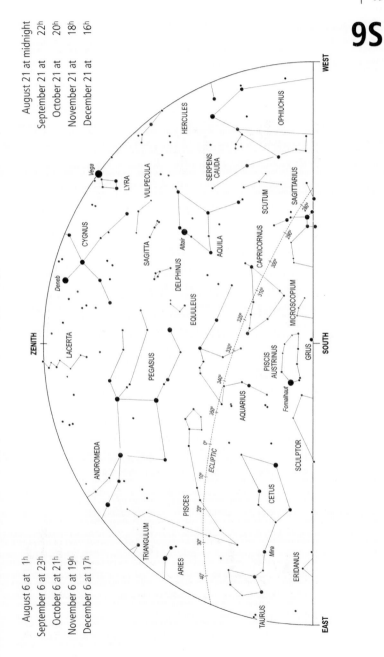

August 6 at 1ʰ
September 6 at 23ʰ
October 6 at 21ʰ
November 6 at 19ʰ
December 6 at 17ʰ

August 21 at midnight
September 21 at 22ʰ
October 21 at 20ʰ
November 21 at 18ʰ
December 21 at 16ʰ

WEST

ZENITH

SOUTH

EAST

HERCULES
OPHIUCHUS
Vega
LYRA
VULPECULA
SERPENS CAUDA
CYGNUS
SCUTUM
SAGITTARIUS
Deneb
SAGITTA
DELPHINUS
Altair
AQUILA
CAPRICORNUS
LACERTA
EQUULEUS
MICROSCOPIUM
PEGASUS
PISCIS AUSTRINUS
GRUS
ANDROMEDA
AQUARIUS
Fomalhaut
SCULPTOR
PISCES
TRIANGULUM
CETUS
ARIES
Mira
ERIDANUS
TAURUS

ECLIPTIC

10N

August 6 at 3h
September 6 at 1h
October 6 at 23h
November 6 at 21h
December 6 at 19h

August 21 at 2h
September 21 at midnight
October 21 at 22h
November 21 at 20h
December 21 at 18h

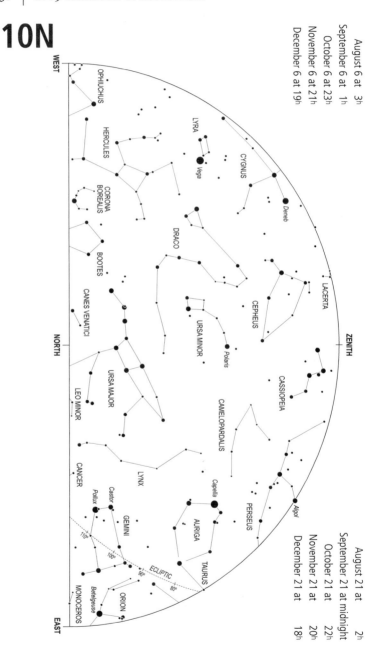

10S

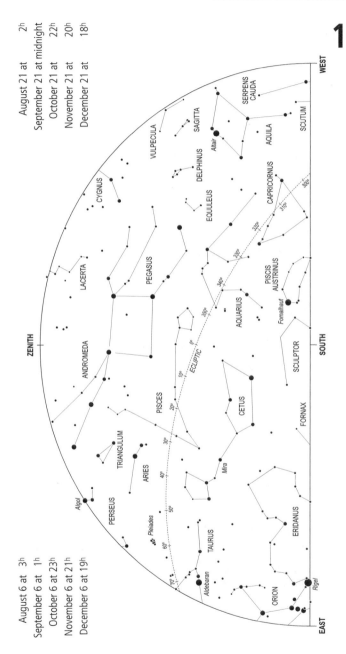

August 6 at 3h
September 6 at 1h
October 6 at 23h
November 6 at 21h
December 6 at 19h

11N

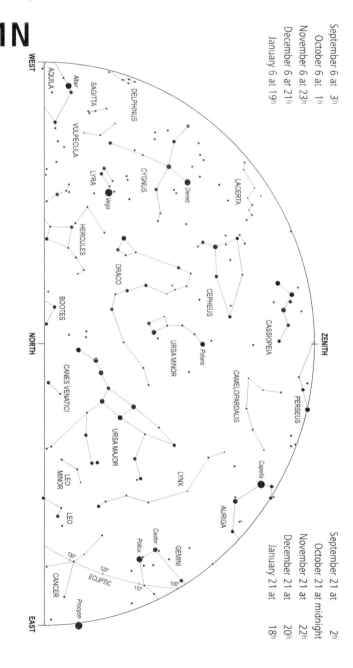

September 6 at 3h
October 6 at 1h
November 6 at 23h
December 6 at 21h
January 6 at 19h

September 21 at 2h
October 21 at midnight
November 21 at 22h
December 21 at 20h
January 21 at 18h

11S

September 21 at 2ʰ
October 21 at midnight
November 21 at 22ʰ
December 21 at 20ʰ
January 21 at 18ʰ

September 6 at 3ʰ
October 6 at 1ʰ
November 6 at 23ʰ
December 6 at 21ʰ
January 6 at 19ʰ

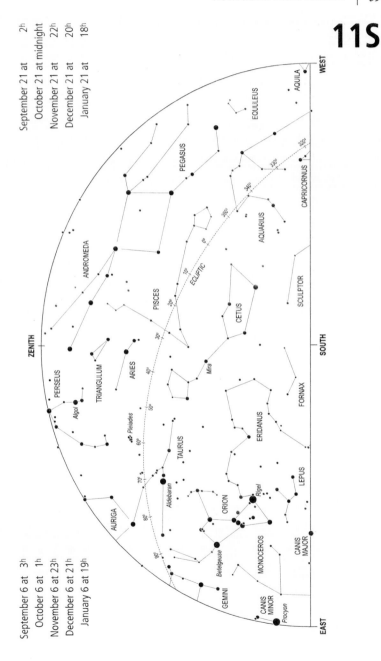

ZENITH

WEST

EAST

SOUTH

AQUILA

EQUULEUS

PEGASUS

CAPRICORNUS

AQUARIUS

ANDROMEDA

SCULPTOR

PISCES

ECLIPTIC

CETUS

PERSEUS

TRIANGULUM

ARIES

Algol

Mira

Pleiades

TAURUS

FORNAX

ERIDANUS

Aldebaran

AURIGA

ORION

LEPUS

Rigel

Betelgeuse

MONOCEROS

CANIS
MAJOR

GEMINI

CANIS
MINOR

Procyon

12N

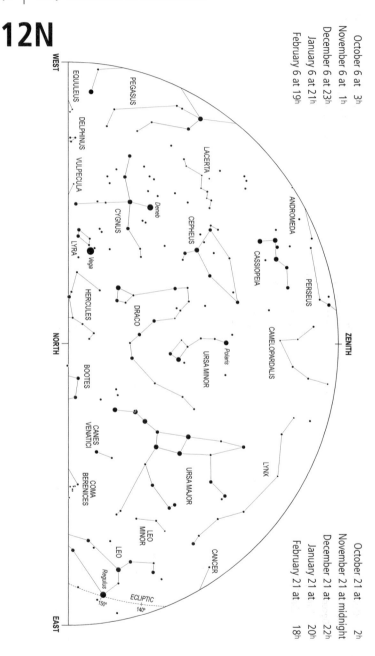

October 6 at 3h
November 6 at 1h
December 6 at 23h
January 6 at 21h
February 6 at 19h

October 21 at 2h
November 21 at midnight
December 21 at 22h
January 21 at 20h
February 21 at 18h

12S

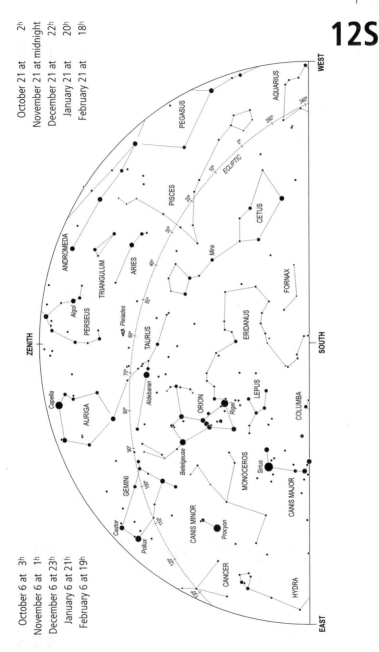

Southern Star Charts

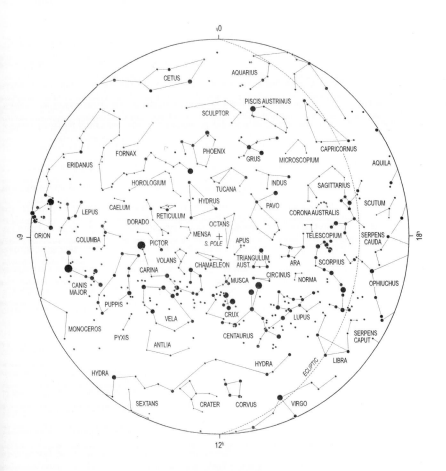

Southern Hemisphere

Note that the markers at 0ʰ, 6ʰ, 12ʰ and 18ʰ
indicate hours of Right Ascension.

1N

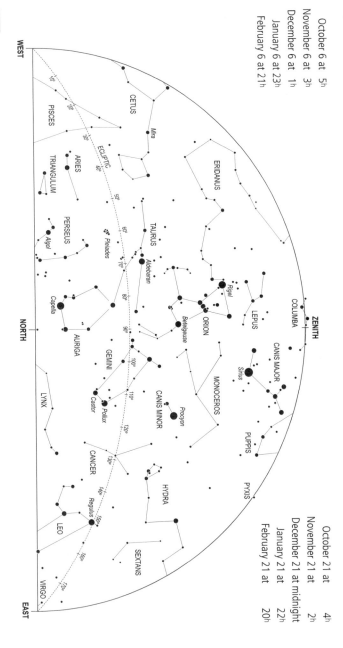

October 6 at 5h
November 6 at 3h
December 6 at 1h
January 6 at 23h
February 6 at 21h

WEST

NORTH

EAST

ZENITH

CETUS
PISCES
Mira
TRIANGULUM
ARIES
ECLIPTIC
PERSEUS
Algol
Capella
AURIGA
LYNX
TAURUS
Pleiades
Aldebaran
GEMINI
Castor
Pollux
CANCER
LEO
Regulus
VIRGO
ERIDANUS
Rigel
Betelgeuse
ORION
LEPUS
COLUMBA
CANIS MAJOR
Sirius
MONOCEROS
CANIS MINOR
Procyon
SEXTANS
HYDRA
PUPPIS
PYXIS

October 21 at   4h
November 21 at   2h
December 21 at midnight
January 21 at   22h
February 21 at   20h

October 21 at 4ʰ
November 21 at 2ʰ
December 21 at midnight
January 21 at 22ʰ
February 21 at 20ʰ

October 6 at 5ʰ
November 6 at 3ʰ
December 6 at 1ʰ
January 6 at 23ʰ
February 6 at 21ʰ

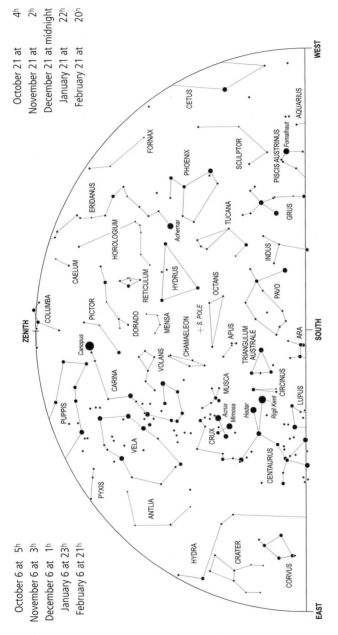

2N

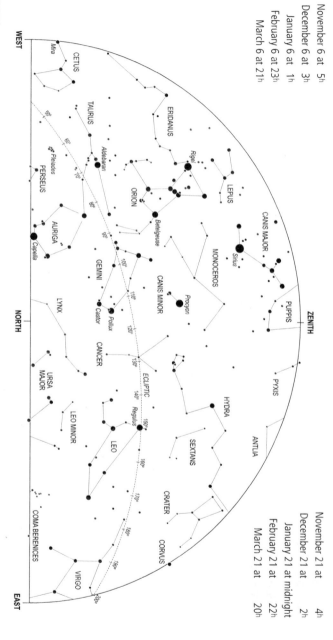

November 6 at 5h
December 6 at 3h
January 6 at 1h
February 6 at 23h
March 6 at 21h

November 21 at 4h
December 21 at 2h
January 21 at midnight
February 21 at 22h
March 21 at 20h

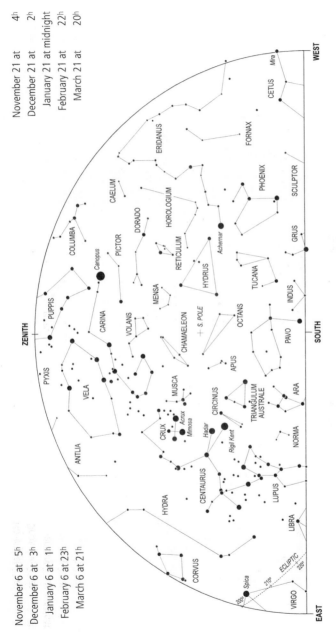

November 21 at 4h
December 21 at 2h
January 21 at midnight
February 21 at 22h
March 21 at 20h

November 6 at 5h
December 6 at 3h
January 6 at 1h
February 6 at 23h
March 6 at 21h

WEST

Mira

CETUS

ERIDANUS

FORNAX

SCULPTOR

CAELUM

PHOENIX

DORADO

PICTOR

HOROLOGIUM

RETICULUM

Achernar

GRUS

COLUMBA

Canopus

CARINA

MENSA

HYDRUS

TUCANA

INDUS

PUPPIS

VOLANS

CHAMAELEON

+ S. POLE

OCTANS

PAVO

SOUTH

ZENITH

PYXIS

VELA

APUS

ANTLIA

MUSCA

CIRCINUS

TRIANGULUM
AUSTRALE

ARA

CRUX

Acrux

Mimosa

Hadar

Rigil Kent

CENTAURUS

NORMA

LUPUS

HYDRA

LIBRA

CORVUS

ECLIPTIC

210°

220°

Spica

200°

VIRGO

EAST

3N

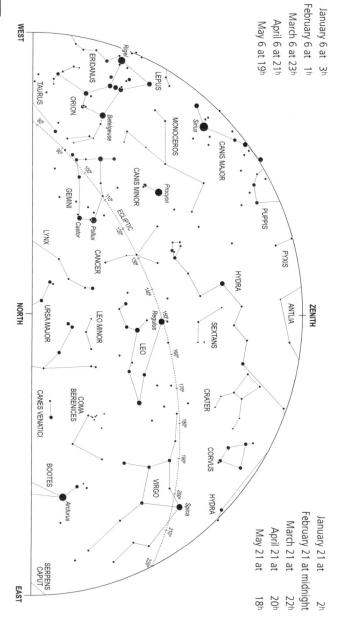

January 6 at 3h
February 6 at 1h
March 6 at 23h
April 6 at 21h
May 6 at 19h

January 21 at 2h
February 21 at midnight
March 21 at 22h
April 21 at 20h
May 21 at 18h

3S

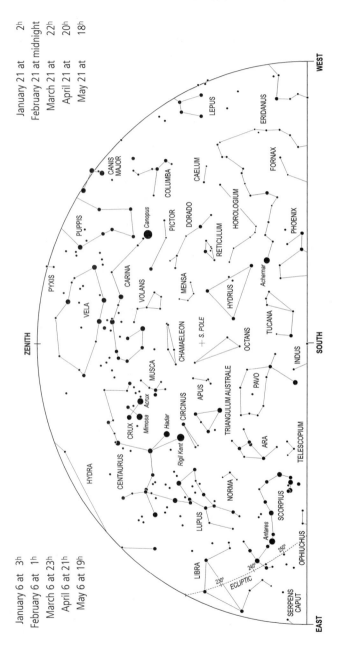

January 21 at 2ʰ
February 21 at midnight
March 21 at 22ʰ
April 21 at 20ʰ
May 21 at 18ʰ

WEST

LEPUS
ERIDANUS
CANIS MAJOR
COLUMBA
CAELUM
FORNAX
PUPPIS
Canopus
PICTOR
DORADO
HOROLOGIUM
PHOENIX
PYXIS
CARINA
VOLANS
MENSA
RETICULUM
HYDRUS
Achernar
ZENITH
VELA
CHAMAELEON
+ S. POLE
OCTANS
TUCANA
SOUTH
MUSCA
Acrux
APUS
INDUS
CRUX
Mimosa
Hadar
CIRCINUS
TRIANGULUM AUSTRALE
PAVO
CENTAURUS
Rigil Kent
ARA
TELESCOPIUM
HYDRA
NORMA
LUPUS
SCORPIUS
Antares
230°
240°
250°
ECLIPTIC
OPHIUCHUS
LIBRA
SERPENS CAPUT
EAST

January 6 at 3ʰ
February 6 at 1ʰ
March 6 at 23ʰ
April 6 at 21ʰ
May 6 at 19ʰ

4N

February 6 at 3ʰ
March 6 at 1ʰ
April 6 at 23ʰ
May 6 at 21ʰ
June 6 at 19ʰ

February 21 at 2ʰ
March 21 at midnight
April 21 at 22ʰ
May 21 at 20ʰ
June 21 at 18ʰ

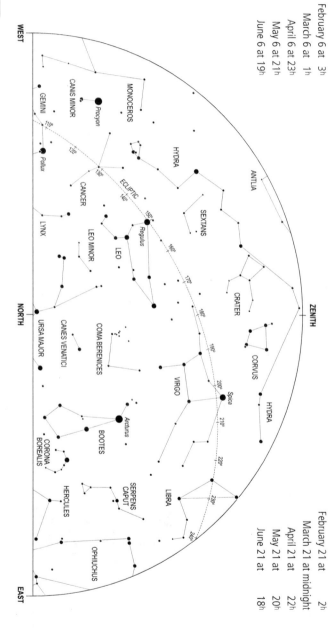

February 21 at 2ʰ
March 21 at midnight
April 21 at 22ʰ
May 21 at 20ʰ
June 21 at 18ʰ

February 6 at 3ʰ
March 6 at 1ʰ
April 6 at 23ʰ
May 6 at 21ʰ
June 6 at 19ʰ

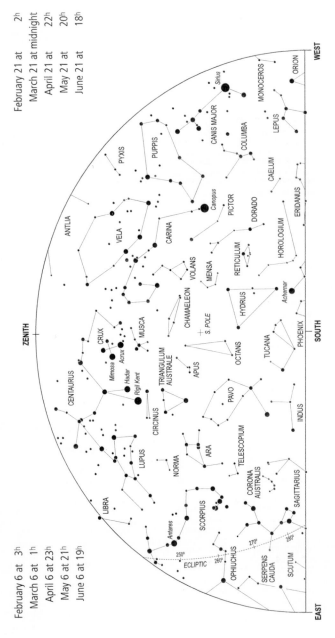

WEST

ZENITH

SOUTH

EAST

ORION
MONOCEROS
Sirius
CANIS MAJOR
LEPUS
COLUMBA
PYXIS
PUPPIS
CAELUM
ERIDANUS
Canopus
PICTOR
ANTLIA
CARINA
DORADO
VELA
HOROLOGIUM
VOLANS
MENSA
RETICULUM
Achernar
CHAMAELEON
HYDRUS
PHOENIX
CRUX
MUSCA
S. POLE
OCTANS
TUCANA
Mimosa
Acrux
CENTAURUS
TRIANGULUM
AUSTRALE
Hadar
APUS
Rigil Kent
PAVO
INDUS
CIRCINUS
ARA
NORMA
LUPUS
TELESCOPIUM
LIBRA
CORONA
AUSTRALIS
SAGITTARIUS
Antares
SCORPIUS
270°
280°
250°
260°
ECLIPTIC
OPHIUCHUS
SERPENS
CAUDA
SCUTUM

5N

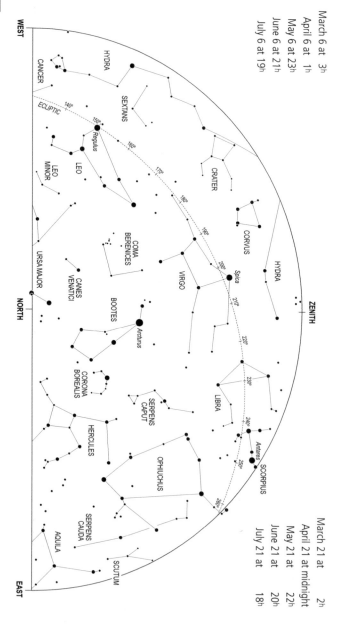

5S

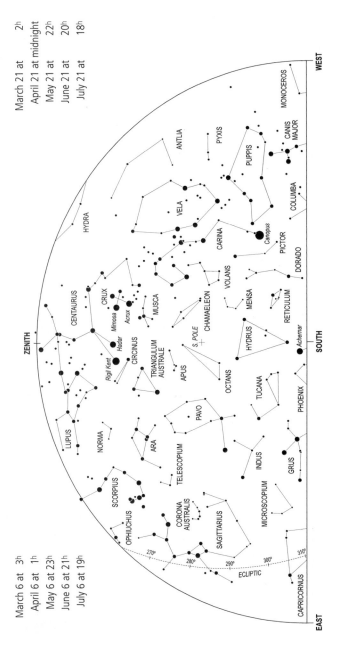

March 21 at 2ʰ
April 21 at midnight
May 21 at 22ʰ
June 21 at 20ʰ
July 21 at 18ʰ

March 6 at 3ʰ
April 6 at 1ʰ
May 6 at 23ʰ
June 6 at 21ʰ
July 6 at 19ʰ

WEST

ZENITH

SOUTH

EAST

MONOCEROS
CANIS MAJOR
PYXIS
PUPPIS
ANTLIA
VELA
COLUMBA
Canopus
PICTOR
CARINA
DORADO
HYDRA
VOLANS
CENTAURUS
CRUX
Mimosa
Acrux
MUSCA
CHAMAELEON
MENSA
RETICULUM
Achernar
Rigil Kent
Hadar
CIRCINUS
S. POLE
HYDRUS
TRIANGULUM AUSTRALE
APUS
OCTANS
LUPUS
NORMA
ARA
PAVO
TUCANA
PHOENIX
INDUS
GRUS
SCORPIUS
TELESCOPIUM
OPHIUCHUS
CORONA AUSTRALIS
SAGITTARIUS
MICROSCOPIUM
270°
280°
290°
300°
310°
ECLIPTIC
CAPRICORNUS

6N

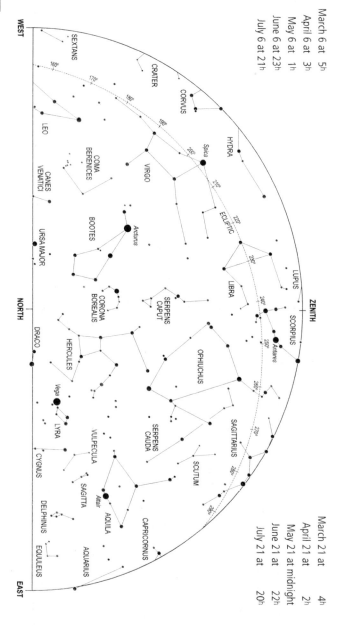

6S

March 21 at 4ʰ
April 21 at 2ʰ
May 21 at midnight
June 21 at 22ʰ
July 21 at 20ʰ

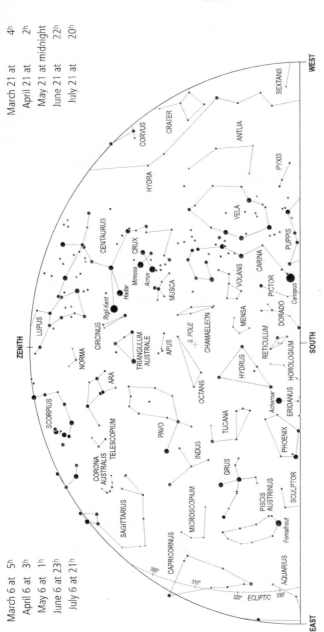

March 6 at 5ʰ
April 6 at 3ʰ
May 6 at 1ʰ
June 6 at 23ʰ
July 6 at 21ʰ

7N

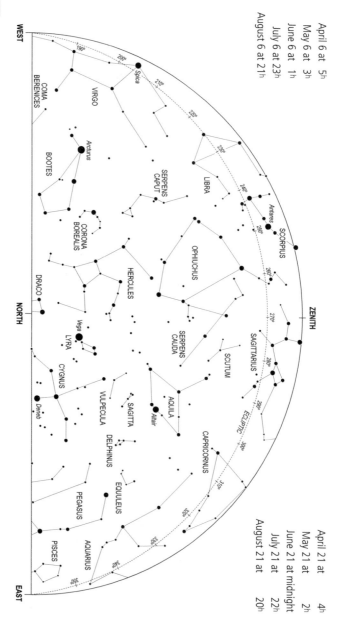

April 6 at 5h
May 6 at 3h
June 6 at 1h
July 6 at 23h
August 6 at 21h

April 21 at 4h
May 21 at 2h
June 21 at midnight
July 21 at 22h
August 21 at 20h

7S

April 21 at 4h
May 21 at 2h
June 21 at midnight
July 21 at 22h
August 21 at 20h

April 6 at 5h
May 6 at 3h
June 6 at 1h
July 6 at 23h
August 6 at 21h

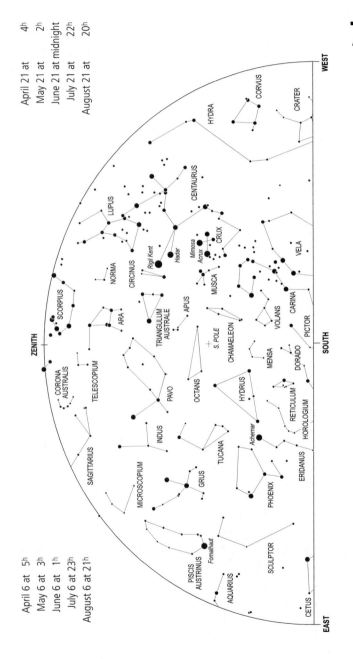

WEST

CORVUS

CRATER

HYDRA

CENTAURUS

LUPUS

Mimosa
CRUX
Acrux

Rigil Kent
Hadar

CIRCINUS
NORMA

MUSCA

VELA

SCORPIUS

ARA

APUS

TRIANGULUM
AUSTRALE

CARINA

VOLANS

CARINA

PICTOR

ZENITH

S. POLE

CHAMAELEON

MENSA

DORADO

SOUTH

CORONA
AUSTRALIS

TELESCOPIUM

PAVO

OCTANS

HYDRUS

RETICULUM

HOROLOGIUM

SAGITTARIUS

INDUS

Achernar

ERIDANUS

MICROSCOPIUM

TUCANA

GRUS

PHOENIX

Fomalhaut

SCULPTOR

PISCIS
AUSTRINUS

AQUARIUS

CETUS

EAST

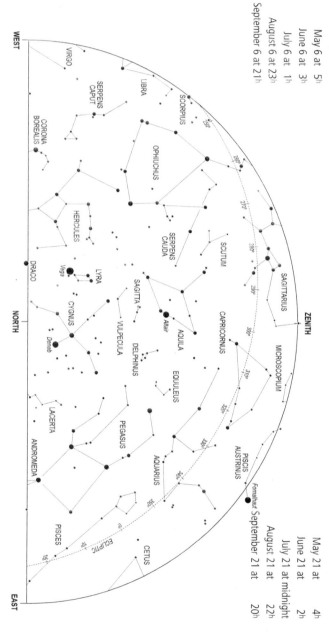

8S

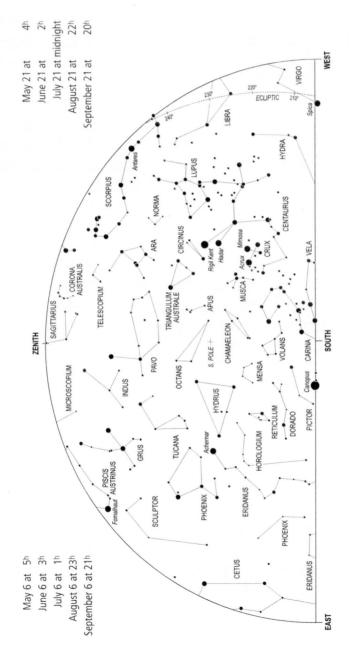

May 21 at   4ʰ
June 21 at   2ʰ
July 21 at midnight
August 21 at   22ʰ
September 21 at 20ʰ

May 6 at   5ʰ
June 6 at   3ʰ
July 6 at   1ʰ
August 6 at   23ʰ
September 6 at 21ʰ

WEST

ZENITH

SOUTH

EAST

VIRGO
ECLIPTIC
Spica
220°
230°
210°
240°
LIBRA
HYDRA
ANTARES
LUPUS
SCORPIUS
NORMA
CENTAURUS
ARA
CIRCINUS
Rigil Kent
Hadar
Mimosa
Acrux
CRUX
VELA
CORONA AUSTRALIS
TELESCOPIUM
TRIANGULUM AUSTRALE
APUS
MUSCA
SAGITTARIUS
PAVO
S. POLE
CHAMAELEON
VOLANS
CARINA
MICROSCOPIUM
INDUS
OCTANS
HYDRUS
MENSA
Canopus
PICTOR
GRUS
TUCANA
Achernar
RETICULUM
DORADO
HOROLOGIUM
PISCIS AUSTRINUS
Fomalhaut
SCULPTOR
PHOENIX
ERIDANUS
PHOENIX
CETUS
ERIDANUS

9N

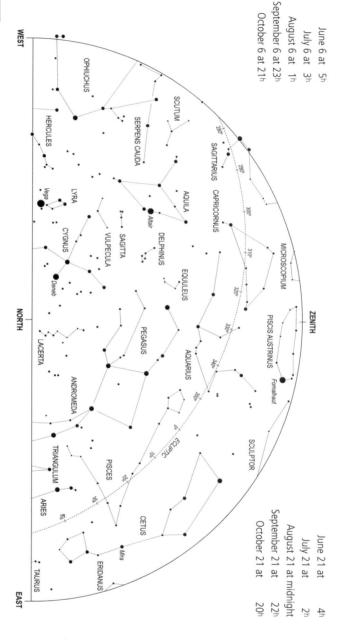

June 6 at 5h
July 6 at 3h
August 6 at 1h
September 6 at 23h
October 6 at 21h

WEST

OPHIUCHUS

HERCULES

SCUTIUM

SERPENS CAUDA

SAGITTARIUS

CAPRICORNUS

280°

290°

MICROSCOPIUM

300°

AQUILA

Vega

LYRA

Altair

310°

CYGNUS

SAGITTA

DELPHINUS

320°

VULPECULA

Deneb

EQUULEUS

PISCIS AUSTRINUS

ZENITH

330°

NORTH

PEGASUS

AQUARIUS

340°

Fomalhaut

LACERTA

350°

ANDROMEDA

SCULPTOR

0°

ECLIPTIC

10°

TRIANGULUM

PISCES

20°

ARIES

30°

CETUS

TAURUS

Mira

40°

ERIDANUS

EAST

June 21 at 4h
July 21 at 2h
August 21 at midnight
September 21 at 22h
October 21 at 20h

9S

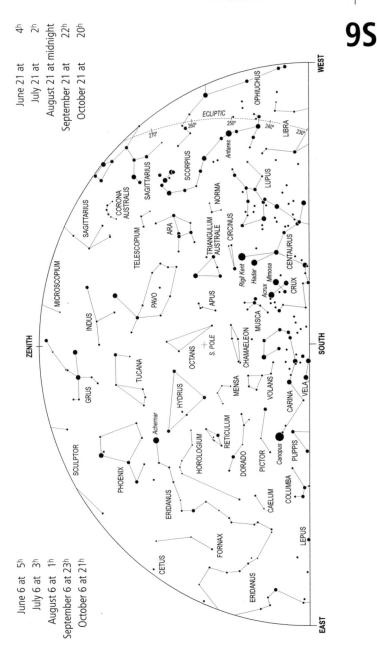

WEST

EAST

SOUTH

ZENITH

ECLIPTIC

OPHIUCHUS
LIBRA
230°
240°
250°
260°
270°
Antares
SCORPIUS
SAGITTARIUS
LUPUS
CORONA AUSTRALIS
NORMA
TRIANGULUM AUSTRALE
CIRCINUS
ARA
TELESCOPIUM
CENTAURUS
Rigil Kent
Hadar
Acrux
Mimosa
CRUX
SAGITTARIUS
APUS
PAVO
MUSCA
MICROSCOPIUM
INDUS
OCTANS
S. POLE
CHAMAELEON
TUCANA
VOLANS
CARINA
VELA
GRUS
HYDRUS
MENSA
RETICULUM
PICTOR
Canopus
PUPPIS
Achernar
HOROLOGIUM
DORADO
SCULPTOR
PHOENIX
ERIDANUS
CAELUM
COLUMBA
FORNAX
LEPUS
CETUS
ERIDANUS

10N

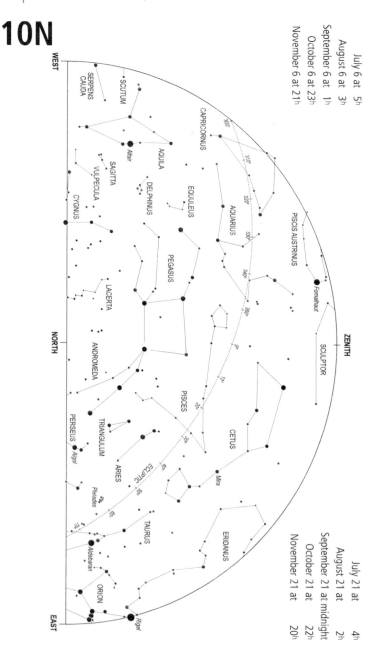

July 6 at 5h
August 6 at 3h
September 6 at 1h
October 6 at 23h
November 6 at 21h

WEST

SERPENS CAUDA
SCUTUM
CAPRICORNUS
300°
310°
320°
330°
340°
AQUILA
Altair
SAGITTA
VULPECULA
DELPHINUS
EQUULEUS
AQUARIUS
350°
CYGNUS
PEGASUS
PISCIS AUSTRINUS
Fomalhaut
0°
ZENITH
SCULPTOR
LACERTA
10°
NORTH
ANDROMEDA
20°
PISCES
30°
CETUS
PERSEUS
Algol
TRIANGULUM
ARIES
40°
Mira
ECLIPTIC
50°
Pleiades
60°
70°
TAURUS
ERIDANUS
Aldebaran
ORION
EAST
Rigel

July 21 at 4h
August 21 at 2h
September 21 at midnight
October 21 at 22h
November 21 at 20h

10S

July 21 at 4ʰ
August 21 at 2ʰ
September 21 at midnight
October 21 at 22ʰ
November 21 at 20ʰ

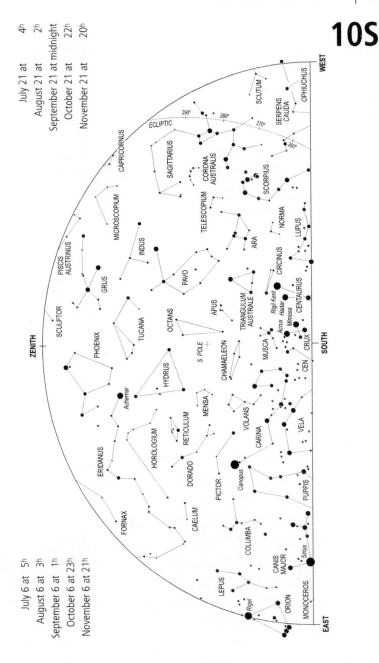

July 6 at 5ʰ
August 6 at 3ʰ
September 6 at 1ʰ
October 6 at 23ʰ
November 6 at 21ʰ

11N

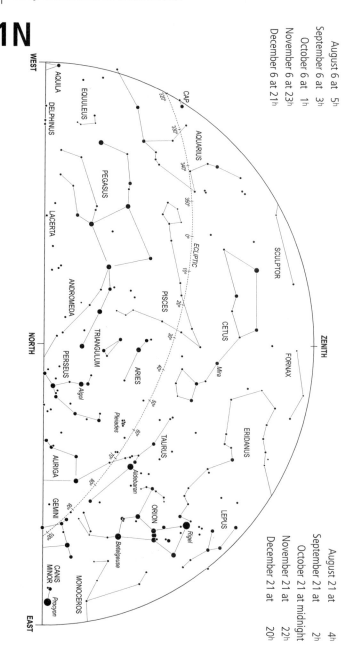

August 6 at 5h
September 6 at 3h
October 6 at 1h
November 6 at 23h
December 6 at 21h

August 21 at 4h
September 21 at 2h
October 21 at midnight
November 21 at 22h
December 21 at 20h

11S

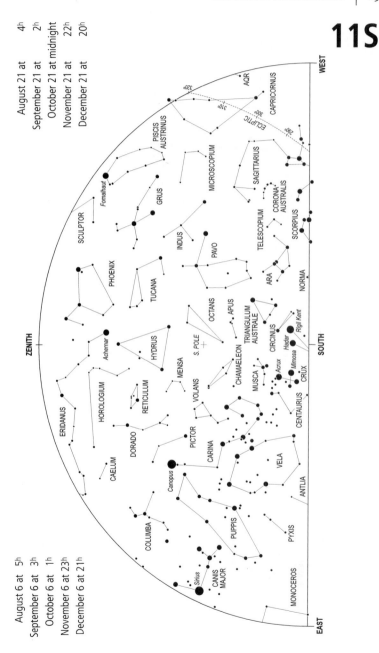

August 21 at 4ʰ
September 21 at 2ʰ
October 21 at midnight
November 21 at 22ʰ
December 21 at 20ʰ

August 6 at 5ʰ
September 6 at 3ʰ
October 6 at 1ʰ
November 6 at 23ʰ
December 6 at 21ʰ

WEST

ZENITH

SOUTH

EAST

AQR
CAPRICORNUS
ECLIPTIC
320°
310°
300°
290°
PISCIS AUSTRINUS
MICROSCOPIUM
SAGITTARIUS
Fomalhaut
GRUS
CORONA AUSTRALIS
SCULPTOR
INDUS
PAVO
TELESCOPIUM
SCORPIUS
PHOENIX
TUCANA
ARA
NORMA
Achernar
HYDRUS
OCTANS
APUS
TRIANGULUM AUSTRALE
CIRCINUS
Rigil Kent
ERIDANUS
HOROLOGIUM
MENSA
S. POLE
CHAMAELEON
MUSCA
Acrux
Hadar
Mimosa
CRUX
RETICULUM
VOLANS
CENTAURUS
CAELUM
DORADO
PICTOR
CARINA
VELA
COLUMBA
Canopus
ANTLIA
PUPPIS
PYXIS
Sirius
CANIS MAJOR
MONOCEROS

12N

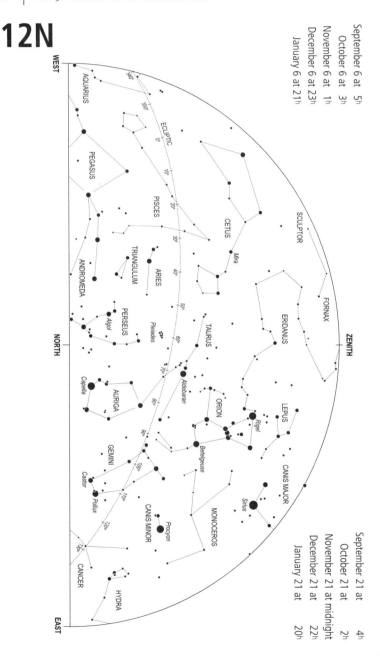

September 21 at 4ʰ
October 21 at 2ʰ
November 21 at midnight
December 21 at 22ʰ
January 21 at 20ʰ

September 21 at 4ʰ
October 21 at 2ʰ
November 21 at midnight
December 21 at 22ʰ
January 21 at 20ʰ

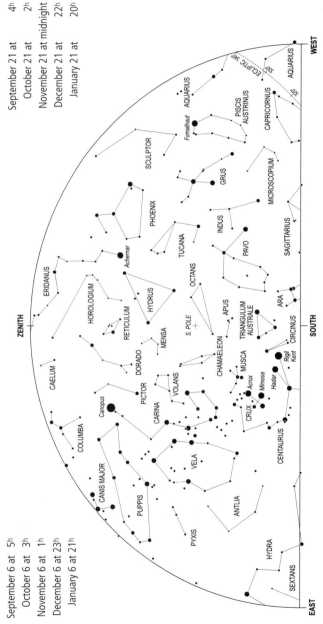

September 6 at 5ʰ
October 6 at 3ʰ
November 6 at 1ʰ
December 6 at 23ʰ
January 6 at 21ʰ

The Planets and the Ecliptic

The paths of the planets about the Sun all lie close to the plane of the ecliptic, which is marked for us in the sky by the apparent path of the Sun among the stars, and is shown on the star charts by a broken line. The Moon and naked-eye planets will always be found close to this line, never departing from it by more than about 7°. Thus the planets are most favourably placed for observation when the ecliptic is well displayed, and this means that it should be as high in the sky as possible. This avoids the difficulty of finding a clear horizon, and also overcomes the problem of atmospheric absorption, which greatly reduces the light of the stars. Thus a star at an altitude of 10° suffers a loss of 60 per cent of its light, which corresponds to a whole magnitude; at an altitude of only 4°, the loss may amount to two magnitudes.

The position of the ecliptic in the sky is therefore of great importance, and since it is tilted at about 23.5° to the Equator, it is only at certain times of the day or year that it is displayed to the best advantage. It will be realized that the Sun (and therefore the ecliptic) is at its highest in the sky at noon in midsummer, and at its lowest at noon in midwinter. Allowing for the daily motion of the sky, it follows that the ecliptic is highest at midnight in winter, at sunset in the spring, at noon in summer and at sunrise in the autumn. Hence these are the best times to see the planets. Thus, if Venus is an evening object in the western sky after sunset, it will be seen to best advantage if this occurs in the spring, when the ecliptic is high in the sky and slopes down steeply to the horizon. This means that the planet is not only higher in the sky, but will remain for a much longer period above the horizon. For similar reasons, a morning object will be seen at its best on autumn mornings before sunrise, when the ecliptic is high in the east. The outer planets, which can come to opposition (i.e. opposite the Sun), are best seen when opposition occurs in the winter months, when the ecliptic is high in the sky at midnight.

The seasons are reversed in the Southern Hemisphere, spring beginning at the September Equinox, when the Sun crosses the Equator on its way south, summer beginning at the December Solstice, when the

Sun is highest in the southern sky, and so on. Thus, the times when the ecliptic is highest in the sky, and therefore best placed for observing the planets, may be summarized as follows:

	Midnight	Sunrise	Noon	Sunset
Northern latitudes	December	September	June	March
Southern latitudes	June	March	December	September

In addition to the daily rotation of the celestial sphere from east to west, the planets have a motion of their own among the stars. The apparent movement is generally *direct*, i.e. to the east, in the direction of increasing longitude, but for a certain period (which depends on the distance of the planet) this apparent motion is reversed. With the outer planets this *retrograde* motion occurs about the time of opposition. Owing to the different inclination of the orbits of these planets, the actual effect is to cause the apparent path to form a loop, or sometimes an S-shaped curve. The same effect is present in the motion of the inferior planets, Mercury and Venus, but it is not so obvious, since it always occurs at the time of inferior conjunction.

The *inferior planets*, Mercury and Venus, move in smaller orbits than that of the Earth, and so are always seen near the Sun. They are most obvious at the times of greatest angular distance from the Sun (greatest elongation), which may reach 28° for Mercury, and 47° for Venus. They are seen as evening objects in the western sky after sunset (at eastern elongations) or as morning objects in the eastern sky before sunrise (at western elongations). The succession of phenomena, conjunctions and elongations, always follows the same order, but the intervals between them are not equal. Thus, if either planet is moving round the far side of its orbit its motion will be to the east, in the same direction in which the Sun appears to be moving. It therefore takes much longer for the planet to overtake the Sun – that is, to come to superior conjunction – than it does when moving round to inferior conjunction, between Sun and Earth. The intervals given in the table at the top of p.70 are average values; they remain fairly constant in the case of Venus, which travels in an almost circular orbit. In the case of Mercury, however, conditions vary widely because of the great eccentricity and inclination of the planet's orbit.

		Mercury	Venus
Inferior Conjunction	to Elongation West	22 days	72 days
Elongation West	to Superior Conjunction	36 days	220 days
Superior Conjunction	to Elongation East	35 days	220 days
Elongation East	to Inferior Conjunction	22 days	72 days

The greatest brilliancy of Venus always occurs about 36 days before or after inferior conjunction. This will be about a month after greatest eastern elongation (as an evening object), or a month before greatest western elongation (as a morning object). No such rule can be given for Mercury, because its distances from the Earth and the Sun can vary over a wide range.

Mercury is not likely to be seen unless a clear horizon is available. It is seldom as much as 10° above the horizon in the twilight sky in northern temperate latitudes, but this figure is often exceeded in the Southern Hemisphere. This favourable condition arises because the maximum elongation of 28° can occur only when the planet is at aphelion (farthest from the Sun), and it then lies well south of the Equator. Northern observers must be content with smaller elongations, which may be as little as 18° at perihelion (closest to the Sun). In general, it may be said that the most favourable times for seeing Mercury as an evening object will be in spring, some days before greatest eastern elongation; in autumn, it may be seen as a morning object some days after greatest western elongation.

Venus is the brightest of the planets and may be seen on occasions in broad daylight. Like Mercury, it is alternately a morning and an evening object, and it will be highest in the sky when it is a morning object in autumn, or an evening object in spring. Venus is to be seen at its best as an evening object in northern latitudes when eastern elongation occurs in June. The planet is then well north of the Sun in the preceding spring months, and is a brilliant object in the evening sky over a long period. In the Southern Hemisphere a November elongation is best. For similar reasons, Venus gives a prolonged display as a morning object in the months following western elongation in October (in northern latitudes) or in June (in the Southern Hemisphere).

The *superior planets*, which travel in orbits larger than that of the Earth, differ from Mercury and Venus in that they can be seen opposite the Sun in the sky. The superior planets are morning objects after conjunction with the Sun, rising earlier each day until they come to opposition. They will then be nearest to the Earth (and therefore at their brightest), and will be on the meridian at midnight, due south in northern latitudes, but due north in the Southern Hemisphere. After opposition they are evening objects, setting earlier each evening until they set in the west with the Sun at the next conjunction. The difference in brightness from one opposition to another is most noticeable in the case of Mars, whose distance from Earth can vary considerably and rapidly. The other superior planets are at such great distances that there is very little change in brightness from one opposition to the next. The effect of altitude is, however, of some importance, for at a December opposition in northern latitudes the planets will be among the stars of Taurus or Gemini, and can then be at an altitude of more than 60° in southern England. At a summer opposition, when the planet is in Sagittarius, it may only rise to about 15° above the southern horizon, and so makes a less impressive appearance. In the Southern Hemisphere the reverse conditions apply, a June opposition being the best, with the planet in Sagittarius at an altitude which can reach 80° above the northern horizon for observers in South Africa.

Mars, whose orbit is appreciably eccentric, comes nearest to the Earth at oppositions at the end of August. It may then be brighter even than Jupiter, but rather low in the sky in Aquarius for northern observers, though very well placed for those in southern latitudes. These favourable oppositions occur every fifteen or seventeen years (e.g. in 1988, 2003 and 2018). In the Northern Hemisphere the planet is probably better seen at oppositions in the autumn or winter months, when it is higher in the sky – such as in 2005 when opposition was in early November. Oppositions of Mars occur at an average interval of 780 days, and during this time the planet makes a complete circuit of the sky.

Jupiter is always a bright planet, and comes to opposition a month later each year, having moved, roughly speaking, from one zodiacal constellation to the next.

Saturn moves much more slowly than Jupiter, and may remain in the same constellation for several years. The brightness of Saturn depends on the aspects of its rings, as well as on the distance from Earth and Sun. The Earth passed through the plane of Saturn's rings in 1995 and 1996, when they appeared edge-on; we saw them at maximum opening, and Saturn at its brightest, in 2002. The rings will next appear edge-on in 2009.

Uranus and *Neptune* are both visible with binoculars or a small telescope, but you will need a finder chart to help locate them (such as those reproduced in this *Yearbook* on pages 123 and 128). *Pluto* (now officially classified as a 'dwarf planet') is hardly likely to attract the attention of observers without adequate telescopes.

Phases of the Moon in 2009

New Moon				First Quarter				Full Moon				Last Quarter			
	d	h	m		d	h	m		d	h	m		d	h	m
				Jan	4	11	56	Jan	11	03	27	Jan	18	02	46
Jan	26	07	55	Feb	2	23	13	Feb	9	14	49	Feb	16	21	37
Feb	25	01	35	Mar	4	07	46	Mar	11	02	38	Mar	18	17	47
Mar	26	16	06	Apr	2	14	34	Apr	9	14	56	Apr	17	13	36
Apr	25	03	23	May	1	20	44	May	9	04	01	May	17	07	26
May	24	12	11	May	31	03	22	June	7	18	12	June	15	22	15
June	22	19	35	June	29	11	28	July	7	09	21	July	15	09	53
July	22	02	35	July	28	22	00	Aug	6	00	55	Aug	13	18	55
Aug	20	10	02	Aug	27	11	42	Sept	4	16	03	Sept	12	02	16
Sept	18	18	44	Sept	26	04	50	Oct	4	06	10	Oct	11	08	56
Oct	18	05	33	Oct	26	00	42	Nov	2	19	14	Nov	9	15	56
Nov	16	19	14	Nov	24	21	39	Dec	2	07	30	Dec	9	00	13
Dec	16	12	02	Dec	24	17	36	Dec	31	19	13				

All times are GMT

Longitudes of the Sun, Moon and Planets in 2009

Date		Sun °	Moon °	Venus °	Mars °	Jupiter °	Saturn °
January	6	286	35	333	277	300	172
	21	301	243	348	289	304	171
February	6	317	88	2	301	307	171
	21	332	287	12	313	311	170
March	6	346	98	15	323	314	169
	21	1	295	11	335	317	167
April	6	16	151	2	347	320	166
	21	31	339	359	359	323	165
May	6	46	188	5	10	325	165
	21	60	14	15	22	326	165
June	6	75	236	30	34	327	165
	21	90	64	45	45	327	166
July	6	104	269	61	56	326	167
	21	118	103	77	66	325	168
August	6	134	313	96	77	323	170
	21	148	156	113	87	321	172
September	6	164	359	132	97	319	174
	21	178	207	151	106	318	175
October	6	193	34	169	114	317	177
	21	208	242	188	122	317	179
November	6	224	85	207	129	318	181
	21	239	287	226	135	320	182
December	6	254	124	245	138	322	183
	21	269	318	264	140	324	184

Longitude of	*Uranus*	354°	*Moon:* Longitude of ascending node
	Neptune	325°	Jan 1: 311° Dec 31: 293°

Mercury moves so quickly among the stars that it is not possible to indicate its position on the star charts at convenient intervals. The monthly notes must be consulted for the best times at which the planet may be seen.

The positions of the other planets are given in the table on p.74. This gives the apparent longitudes on dates which correspond to those of the star charts, and the position of the planet may at once be found near the ecliptic at the given longitude.

EXAMPLES

In low northern latitudes two planets are seen in the morning about an hour before sunrise, in the north-eastern sky early in July. Identify them.

The northern chart 9N (for 6 July at 03^h) shows longitudes 50° to 90° along the ecliptic. Reference to the table on p.74 for 6 July gives the longitude of Mars as 56° and that of Venus as 61°, Venus being lower down in the sky than Mars, and also very much brighter than Mars.

The positions of the Sun and Moon can be plotted on the star maps in the same manner as for the planets. The average daily motion of the Sun is 1°, and of the Moon 13°. For the Moon an indication of its position relative to the ecliptic may be obtained from a consideration of its longitude relative to that of the ascending node. The latter changes only slowly during the year, as will be seen from the values given on p.74. Let us denote by d the difference in longitude between the Moon and its ascending node. Then if $d = 0°,180°$ or $360°$, the Moon is on the ecliptic. If $d = 90°$ the Moon is 5° north of the ecliptic, and if $d = 270°$ the Moon is 5° south of the ecliptic.

On 6 January, the Moon's longitude is given in the table on p.74 as 35° and the longitude of the ascending node is found by interpolation to be about 311°. Thus $d = 84°$ and the Moon is about 5° north of the ecliptic. Its position may be plotted on northern star charts 1S, 9S, 10S and 12S, and on southern star charts 1N, 9N, 10N, 11N, and 12N.

Some Events in 2009

Jan   4   *Earth* at Perihelion
          4   *Mercury* at Greatest Eastern Elongation (19°)
        11   Full Moon
        14   *Venus* at Greatest Eastern Elongation (47°)
        20   *Mercury* at Inferior Conjunction
        24   *Jupiter* in Conjunction with Sun
        26   New Moon
        26   Annular Eclipse of the Sun

Feb   9   Full Moon
          9   Penumbral Eclipse of the Moon
        13   *Mercury* at Greatest Western Elongation (26°)
        19   *Venus* attains its greatest brilliancy (magnitude −4.6)
        25   New Moon

Mar   8   *Saturn* at Opposition in Leo
        11   Full Moon
        20   Equinox (Spring Equinox in Northern Hemisphere)
        26   New Moon
        27   *Venus* at Inferior Conjunction
        31   *Mercury* at Superior Conjunction

Apr   9   Full Moon
        25   New Moon
        26   *Mercury* at Greatest Eastern Elongation (20°)

May   2   *Venus* attains its greatest brilliancy (magnitude −4.5)
          9   Full Moon
        18   *Mercury* at Inferior Conjunction
        24   New Moon

Jun   5   *Venus* at Greatest Western Elongation (46°)
          7   Full Moon

13 *Mercury* at Greatest Western Elongation (24°)
21 Solstice (Summer Solstice in Northern Hemisphere)
22 New Moon
23 *Pluto* at Opposition in Sagittarius

Jul 4 *Earth* at Aphelion
7 Full Moon
14 *Mercury* at Superior Conjunction
22 New Moon
22 Total Eclipse of the Sun

Aug 6 Full Moon
6 Penumbral Eclipse of the Moon
14 *Jupiter* at Opposition in Capricornus
17 *Neptune* at Opposition in Capricornus
20 New Moon
24 *Mercury* at Greatest Eastern Elongation (27°)

Sep 4 Full Moon
17 *Saturn* in Conjunction with Sun
17 *Uranus* at Opposition in Pisces
18 New Moon
20 *Mercury* at Inferior Conjunction
22 Equinox (Autumn Equinox in Northern Hemisphere)

Oct 4 Full Moon
6 *Mercury* at Greatest Western Elongation (18°)
18 New Moon

Nov 2 Full Moon
5 *Mercury* at Superior Conjunction
16 New Moon

Dec 2 Full Moon
16 New Moon
18 *Mercury* at Greatest Eastern Elongation (20°)
21 Solstice (Winter Solstice in Northern Hemisphere)
31 Full Moon
31 Partial Eclipse of the Moon

Monthly Notes 2009

January

New Moon: 26 January   *Full Moon*: 11 January

EARTH is at perihelion (nearest to the Sun) on 4 January at a distance of 147 million kilometres (91.3 million miles).

MERCURY reaches greatest eastern elongation (19°) on 4 January. For observers in equatorial and northern latitudes it is visible in the early evenings for the first two weeks of the month, though only for about the first ten days for observers further south. It may be seen low above the south-western horizon at the end of evening civil twilight. The magnitude of the planet fades from −0.7 to +1.2 during this period. Mercury passes through inferior conjunction on 20 January and on the last two days of the month observers south of the tropics may be able to spot the planet low above the east-south-eastern horizon in the mornings about half an hour before sunrise: its magnitude is then +1.0. Mars, at almost the same magnitude, may be detected only a few degrees to the right and above Mercury.

VENUS, magnitude −4.4, reaches its greatest eastern elongation of 47 degrees on 14 January and is visible as a brilliant evening object, completely dominating the western evening sky for several hours after sunset.

MARS will not be suitably placed for observation until next month, except for observers in southern latitudes: see the note above for Mercury.

JUPITER, magnitude −1.9, is no longer visible in the evening skies for observers in the latitudes of the British Isles, while those in southern temperate latitudes are only likely to see it for the first few days of the year, low above the western horizon about half an hour after sunset. Those in tropical latitudes should be able to observe it during the first half of the month, low in the western sky as soon as the sky is dark enough after sunset, but only for a short while. After passing through conjunction on 24 January, Jupiter reappears in the morning skies next month.

SATURN, magnitude +0.8, begins the year moving retrograde in Leo, some way below the three stars making up the triangle at the eastern end of the constellation: Beta (Denebola), Delta, and Theta Leonis. Technically, Saturn is a morning object, but can now be seen low in the eastern sky before midnight. The angular width of the rings is only about one arcsecond so they will be difficult or impossible to observe even in moderately sized instruments. The Earth passes through the ring-plane later in the year. The last time this occurred was back in 1995. The path of Saturn among the stars during the year is shown in Figure 15 included with the notes for May.

Mercury: Taking a Second Look. On 14 January 2008, the MESSEN-GER probe became only the second spacecraft to fly past Mercury. Its only predecessor had been Mariner 10 (Figure 1), which made three successive passes of the planet in 1974 and 1975. Contact with Mariner 10 was finally lost on 24 March 1975, and though the probe is no doubt still orbiting the Sun and making regular close approaches to Mercury we have no hope of contacting it again.

From Earth it is not easy to observe Mercury, because it always stays close to the Sun in the sky. Telescopes used by amateurs can show the phase easily (indeed, phase changes were definitely seen by Giovanni Zupus as long ago as 1639), but surface markings are very elusive. The best pre-space age map was drawn by E. M. Antoniadi, with the 33-inch refractor at the Meudon Observatory in Paris. In my Moon-mapping days (over half a century ago now) I turned the 33-inch towards Mercury several times, but I could only see a few darkish areas. Of course, this had to be done in the daytime, when Mercury was at a respectable altitude above the horizon.

I have often been asked: 'What does the Hubble Space Telescope show on Mercury?' The answer is that Hubble has never been used to look at Mercury – the planet is always so close to the Sun that the Sun's light could permanently damage the telescope's sensitive optics and electronics.

When MESSENGER (an abbreviation of Mercury Surface, Space Environment, Geochemistry and Ranging) passed just 200 kilometres

Figure 1. The Mariner 10 spacecraft being prepared prior to its November 1973 launch. Mariner 10 was the seventh successful launch in the Mariner series and the first spacecraft to visit Mercury. It was also the first spacecraft to use the gravitational pull of one planet (Venus) to reach another (Mercury), and the first mission to visit two planets. (Image courtesy of NASA/JPL.)

above the surface of Mercury in January 2008 (Figure 2), it sent back over 1200 images and data from seven on-board instruments, revealing a large portion of the planet's surface that had never been seen by Mariner 10 (Figure 3). Some of the images support the case that ancient volcanoes are scattered across Mercury's surface and that the planet is shrinking as it gets older, forming wrinkle-like ridges. But other images are surprising and puzzling. In some ways the surface of Mercury resembles that of our Moon – there are mountains, valleys, ridges and, of course, craters – but the craters seem different from those on the Moon, and some exhibit features that appear unique to Mercury. One of these – a remarkable feature known as 'The Spider' – is surrounded by more than a hundred narrow, flat-floored troughs radiating outwards from a complex central crater (Figure 4). Now that

Figure 2. Artist's impression of the Mercury Surface, Space ENvironment, GEochemistry, and Ranging (MESSENGER) spacecraft during a flyby of the planet Mercury. MESSENGER, launched from Cape Canaveral Air Force Station on 3 August 2004, will begin a year-long orbital study of Mercury in March 2011. (Image courtesy of NASA/Johns Hopkins University Applied Physics Laboratory/Carnegie Institution of Washington.)

MESSENGER has revealed the full extent of the large, multi-ringed impact structure known as the Caloris Basin, its diameter has been revised upwards from the Mariner 10 estimate of 1300 kilometres to perhaps as large as 1550 kilometres from rim to rim. The plains inside the Caloris Basin are distinctive and more reflective than the exterior plains. Impact basins on the Moon have opposite characteristics.

There also seems to be enormous interest in the possibility of finding ice on the floors of craters on Mercury (and on the Moon), which are always in shadow, so they remain bitterly cold. But how could any ice have got there? Ice cannot be truly Mercurian, so the only explanation must be cometary impact, but the heat caused by such a collision would be considerable, to put it mildly. The search for ice on the Moon and Mercury will no doubt continue, but I am confident that the results will be negative. Without doubt, MESSENGER's first fly-by of Mercury has whetted scientists' appetite for more information

Figure 3. Craters on Mercury, imaged during MESSENGER's flyby of the planet on 14 January 2008. This image was taken 13 minutes after MESSENGER's closest approach, by which time the spacecraft was about 3000 kilometres from Mercury. (Image courtesy of NASA/Johns Hopkins University Applied Physics Laboratory/Carnegie Institution of Washington.)

about this enigmatic little world. The probe is set to make two more passes of Mercury, in October 2008 and September 2009, before finally settling into orbit around the planet in 2011. We may expect these encounters to yield further surprises – and if any ice is found, I will make a suitable apology!

Like Venus, but unlike Mars, Mercury is a solitary traveller in space. There was a flurry of excitement in 1974, when Mariner 10 reported a small satellite, but the object turned out to be an ordinary star, 31 Crateris. If there were a satellite of appreciable size it would surely

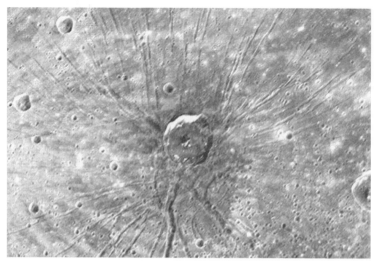

Figure 4. Researchers once thought Mercury to be much like Earth's Moon, but MESSEN-GER has found many differences. For instance, the spacecraft revealed impact craters that appear very different from lunar craters. One particularly curious crater has been dubbed 'The Spider'. It lies in the middle of the Caloris Basin, and consists of more than 100 narrow, flat-floored troughs radiating out from a complex central region. (Image courtesy of NASA/Johns Hopkins University Applied Physics Laboratory/Carnegie Institution of Washington.)

have been found by now, and no deliberate search has been scheduled for MESSENGER.

Muliphen. The constellation of Canis Major, the Great Dog, is of course dominated by Sirius, the brightest star in the entire sky, 25 times as luminous as our Sun, and a mere 8.6 light years distant. But appearances can be deceptive. Look for Muliphen (or Muliphein), Gamma Canis Majoris, not far from Sirius. Muliphen is not a particularly obvious star in the constellation, since it is below fourth magnitude. However, it is a class B (B8II) bluish-white giant, similar in colour to many stars in the Canis Major–Orion region, and lying just over 400 light years away. Its luminosity is equivalent to almost 700 Suns. This means that in round figures it is 30 times as luminous as Sirius, and over 45 times as far away. Were it as close as Sirius, it would indeed be a magnificent object in our sky.

Most of the brighter stars were assigned their first scientific names by the German astronomer Johann Bayer at the beginning of the seventeenth century, but it is indeed curious why Bayer assigned the star Muliphen the Greek letter designation Gamma Canis Majoris. This indicates that it should be the third brightest star in the constellation, after Alpha (Sirius) and Beta (Mirzam). In fact, since Muliphen is below fourth magnitude (mag. 4.12), it ranks as only the fourteenth brightest star in Canis Major! This fact has led some to propose that Muliphen has actually faded in brightness since Bayer's time, but this seems highly unlikely. Indeed there was a claim that in 1670 the star disappeared and was not seen again until 1693, but such assertions should be taken with a very large pinch of cosmic salt!

February

MERCURY is visible in the morning skies for observers in the tropics and the Southern Hemisphere. It will be seen in the south-eastern skies around the time of the beginning of morning civil twilight, its magnitude brightening from +0.7 to −0.1 during the month. On 13 February it attains a greatest western elongation of 26°. For observers in southern latitudes this will be the most favourable morning apparition of the year. Figure 5 shows, for observers in latitude 35°S, the changes in azimuth (true bearing from the north through east, south and west) and altitude of Mercury on successive evenings when the Sun is 6° below the horizon. This condition is known as the beginning of morning civil twilight and in this latitude and at this time of year occurs about 25 minutes before sunrise. The changes in the brightness of the planet are indicated by the relative sizes of the circles marking Mercury's position at five-day intervals. It will be noticed that Mercury is at its brightest after it reaches greatest western elongation. The diagram gives positions for a time at the beginning of morning civil twilight on the Greenwich meridian, on the stated date. Observers in different longitudes should note that the actual positions of Mercury in azimuth and altitude will differ slightly from those shown in the diagram. This change will be much greater still for the Moon, if it is shown, as its motion is about 0.5° per hour.

VENUS, magnitude −4.6, attains its greatest brilliancy on 19 February and continues to dominate the western sky in the evenings after sunset.

MARS, magnitude +1.2, becomes visible as a morning object at the beginning of the month, though only to observers in the tropics and in the Southern Hemisphere. The planet will then be visible low above the eastern horizon for a short while before the brightening twilight inhibits observation. Mars is moving eastwards in the constellation of Capricornus. Observers in the latitudes of the British Isles will not be

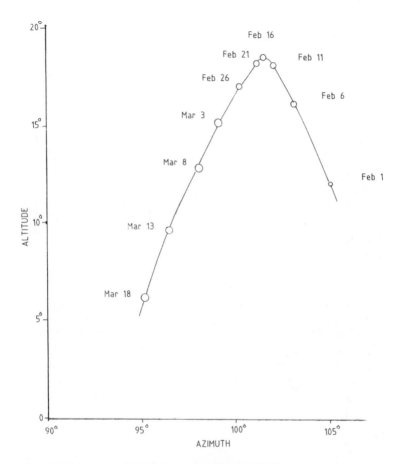

Figure 5. Morning apparition of Mercury, from latitude 35°S. The planet reaches greatest western elongation on 13 February. It will be at its brightest later in the month, after elongation.

able to see Mars before the middle of June at the earliest. Mars passes 0.6° south of Jupiter on 17 February.

JUPITER, magnitude −1.9, becomes visible in the morning skies shortly before dawn, low above the eastern horizon, after the first week of the month, though not to those as far north as the latitudes of the British Isles. Mercury passes 0.6° south of Jupiter on 24 February.

SATURN, magnitude +0.6, may be seen rising in the eastern sky as soon as darkness falls. By the end of the month it will be crossing the meridian shortly after midnight.

Venus: the Half-Forgotten Observer. Venus is at its best this month, reaching magnitude −4.6 in the middle of February. Inferior conjunction will not be passed until 27 March, but as Edmund Halley first pointed out, Venus, unlike Mercury, is at its brightest during the crescent stage, when about 30 per cent of the daylit hemisphere is turned toward us. It was also Halley who suggested that making observations of transits of Venus would lead on to an evaluation of the length of the astronomical unit, or Earth–Sun distance. In theory he was right, but he never saw a transit; they are depressingly rare. The last occurred on 8 June 2004, and I saw it beautifully (Figure 6); at my Selsey observatory we had a 'transit party', which was most enjoyable – there was something of a carnival atmosphere about it. Sadly, the next transit visible from Selsey is not due until 11 December 2117, and I do

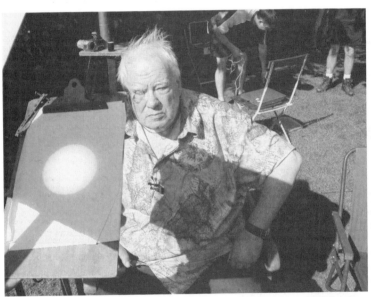

Figure 6. The Editor watching the transit of Venus on 8 June 2004 from the garden of his home in Selsey. Venus can be seen as the distinct black dot visible against the projected disc of the Sun centre left. (Picture courtesy of Martin Mobberley.)

not really expect to see this – I will by then have reached the age of one hundred and ninety-four . . .

The first transit to be observed, or at least recorded, was that of 4 December 1639. Predictions had been made by Jeremiah Horrocks, a young Englishman who would undoubtedly have made great discoveries if he had not died at the age of 22. Horrocks did not finish his calculations until shortly before the transit, so there was little time to spread the word, but he did manage to alert another amateur, William Crabtree. Horrocks and Crabtree both observed the transit, which allowed them to accurately measure the apparent diameter of the planet; so far as we know, nobody else saw it. All astronomical historians remember Horrocks, but Crabtree is largely forgotten – so who was he?

He was born in 1610 in Broughton, near Manchester, now part of Salford, and was educated in local schools. He made a happy marriage, and worked as a merchant; apparently there were no money problems, and he was able to follow his hobbies of astronomy and mathematics. He corresponded with Horrocks, who also lived near Manchester, and

Figure 7. William Crabtree watching the Transit of Venus on 4 December 1639, as depicted in the Manchester Murals, a series of twelve paintings by Ford Madox Brown on the history of Manchester, England, in Manchester Town Hall. The murals were begun in 1879, towards the end of Brown's career, but were not completed until 1893, the year he died. (Image courtesy of Manchester City Council, Manchester Town Hall, and Ford Madox Brown.)

with other enthusiasts, notably William Gascoigne, inventor of the micrometer. Whether Horrocks and Crabtree ever met face to face is not known. They arranged to do so, and fixed a date, but Horrocks died the day before the meeting was due to take place. Crabtree continued with his astronomical work, but he died in 1644, and is now remembered almost solely for his observation of the 1639 transit. There is an interesting picture, by the artist Ford Madox Brown, showing Crabtree watching the transit (Figure 7). It is one of twelve paintings in the Manchester Murals, depicting the history of Manchester, in Manchester Town Hall. It may not be scientifically accurate, but at least it is a fitting tribute to him.

Gascoigne, another member of the group, was born near Leeds and may have graduated from Oxford University; his invention of the micrometer was of the greatest value to science. He probably met Crabtree, and certainly corresponded with him and with Horrocks, but then civil war broke out, and he became an officer in the Royalist army; on 2 July 1644 he was killed at the Battle of Marston Moor. Most of his papers were lost either then or in the Great Fire of London. Those which survived are kept in the Bodleian Library in Oxford.

March

New Moon: 26 March   *Full Moon*: 11 March

Equinox: 20 March

Summer Time in the United Kingdom commences on 29 March.

MERCURY, for observers in tropical and southern latitudes, is visible in the morning skies around the time of beginning of civil twilight until the middle of the month (and a few days later for observers in southern latitudes). During this period its magnitude brightens from −0.1 to −0.7. On 2 March, Mercury passes 0.6° south of Mars. On 31 March the planet passes through superior conjunction.

VENUS continues to be visible as a brilliant object in the western sky in the early evenings after sunset. The visibility period varies considerably with the latitude of the observer: those in southern latitudes will only see it for about the first ten days of the month, those in tropical latitudes for double that period, and those in the latitudes of the British Isles for all but the last week of the month. Because of the high northern ecliptic latitude of the planet at this time, the last-mentioned observers will have the opportunity of seeing Venus low in the eastern sky in the mornings shortly before dawn for about the last ten days of March even though Venus passes through inferior conjunction on 27 March. By the end of the month its magnitude has faded slightly, to −4.1.

MARS is not visible from the latitudes of the British Isles, but observers further south will be able to see it above the eastern horizon for a while before the brightening twilight inhibits observation. The magnitude of Mars is +1.2. The path of Mars among the stars during the first part of the year is given in Figure 8. Mars could be used as a guide to locating Neptune as it passes 0.76° south of that planet on

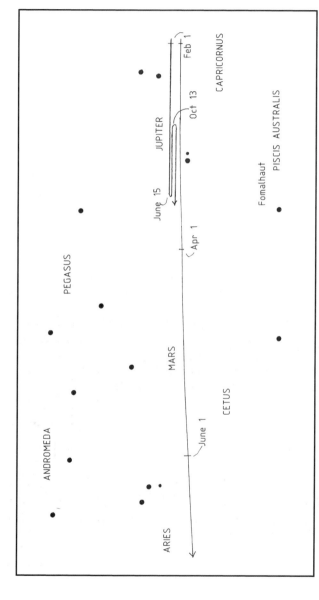

Figure 8. The path of Mars as it moves through the Zodiacal constellations from Capricornus to Aries during the first six months of 2009. Also shown is the path of Jupiter in Capricornus for the whole year.

8 March. A map showing the position of Neptune is given with the notes for August (Figure 22).

JUPITER is becoming easier to locate in the eastern sky in the early mornings, though observers in the latitudes of the British Isles are unlikely to see it before the last ten days of the month. Its magnitude is −2.0. Figure 8 also shows the path of Jupiter among the stars during the year.

SATURN is now visible throughout the hours of darkness as it reaches opposition on 8 March, magnitude +0.5. Although the angular width of the rings has increased slightly since January, to 3 arcseconds, this is as wide as they get during the year, and will still not be easy to observe in small instruments. At closest approach Saturn is 1,256 million kilometres (780 million miles) from the Earth.

Saturn's Strange Inner Moons. Saturn is at opposition this month. Temporarily it has lost its beauty, because the rings are more or less edgewise-on; this last happened in 1995 (Figure 9), and will next occur in 2025. Small telescopes will show the rings only with difficulty, and

Figure 9. This image of Saturn with its rings barely visible was acquired by the Hubble Space Telescope on 6 August 1995, when Earth was almost in the plane of the rings. In this view, Saturn's largest moon, Titan, is casting a shadow on Saturn. (Image courtesy of Erich Karkoschka (University of Arizona Lunar & Planetary Lab.) and NASA/STScI.)

then only as an extremely thin line of light. In 1995, I was able to follow them with my 15½-inch reflector, but it was not easy.

However, there are compensations, because this is an ideal time for observing the satellites – and here I must tell a story against myself. When the rings were edge-on in 1966, I followed them with the 10-inch refractor at Armagh Observatory (I was then Director of the Armagh Planetarium; the only professional post I have ever held). I made notes of the inner satellites, and later found that I had recorded two pre-discovery observations of Janus. As I did not recognize it as being new, I can claim absolutely no credit!

Janus (Figure 10a) and another small, irregularly shaped moon, Epimetheus (Figure 10b), share the same orbit of 151,450 kilometres from Saturn's centre – about 91,000 kilometres above the planet's cloud tops. They may be the remains of a larger body which was broken up a long time ago. Their orbits around Saturn differ in size by only about 50 kilometres. As these two satellites approach each other they exchange a little momentum and swap orbits; the inner satellite becomes the outer one and vice versa. This exchange happens about once every four years. The changeover takes about a hundred days.

The Cassini spacecraft arrived at Saturn in July 2004, and from that time until January 2006, Epimetheus was the innermost of the two satellites. Being closer to Saturn, Epimetheus orbited at a slightly faster angular rate than Janus, with the result that Epimetheus slowly caught up Janus. As the two approach each other in their orbits, Epimetheus tugs on Janus from behind as Janus tugs on Epimetheus with equal and opposite force. This mutual attraction causes them to exchange angular momentum. Epimetheus gains momentum and rises in orbit as Janus loses an equivalent amount of momentum and falls. Because Janus (diameter 180 kilometres) is nearly four times more massive than Epimetheus (diameter 120 kilometres), it falls four times less than Epimetheus rises. The switch in orbital altitudes now makes Janus the faster of the two. As a result, Janus moves slowly ahead of Epimetheus – and will continue to do so, until it catches up from behind in four more years.

The main inner satellites are Mimas and Enceladus, both found in 1789 by William Herschel with his 49-inch reflector. Incidentally, these were the only notable discoveries made with this telescope; almost all Herschel's work was carried out with much smaller instruments. The official magnitudes are 11.7 for Enceladus and 12.9 for Mimas, so that

Figure 10a. The Cassini spacecraft's narrow-angle camera provided this dramatic view of Saturn's small moon Janus against the cloud-streaked backdrop of the planet. Janus is potato-shaped with many craters, and has a surface that looks as though it has been smoothed by some process; Janus may be covered with a mantle of fine dust-sized, icy material.

Figure 10b. A close-up view of Saturn's small moon Epimetheus from Cassini's narrow-angle camera. The depression at lower left is a crater named Pollux. The large crater just below centre is Hilairea, which is about 33 kilometres across. With a diameter of 120 kilometres, Epimetheus is slightly smaller than its companion moon, Janus (180 kilometres across), which orbits at essentially the same distance from Saturn. (Both images courtesy of NASA/JPL/Space Science Institute.)

Enceladus is much easier to see. Both are very small, and before the Space Age were assumed to be rocky and probably cratered. The first close-range views were obtained by the Voyager probes in 1980–81, and now of course we have Cassini, orbiting Saturn and sending back breathtaking images of the planet and its satellite family. Mimas (Figure 11) measures 415 × 394 × 381 kilometres, and is only slightly denser than water, so that ice must be a major constituent of its globe. There is one huge crater, named Herschel, nearly 140 kilometres across and 10 kilometres deep, with a lofty central peak 6 kilometres high. Given that Herschel is about one-third the size of Mimas itself, the

Figure 11. Saturn's moon Mimas, as seen by the Cassini spacecraft's narrow-angle camera. Herschel crater, a 140-kilometre-wide impact feature with a prominent central peak, is shown to the upper right of this image. (Image courtesy of NASA/JPL/Space Science Institute.)

Figure 12. Cassini spacecraft images of Saturn's icy moon Enceladus backlit by the Sun show the fountain-like sources of the fine spray of material that extends far above the south polar region. It is thought that the jets are geysers erupting from pressurized subsurface reservoirs of liquid water. (Image courtesy of NASA/JPL/Space Science Institute.)

impact which produced it must have come close to shattering Mimas completely.

Enceladus is as different as it could possibly be. It is larger than Mimas, but again not perfectly spherical; it measures 513 × 503 × 497 kilometres. Craters exist in many areas, but there are plains which are crater-free, so that they must have been resurfaced comparatively recently. Amazingly, Enceladus is active. Plumes of ice particles and water vapour gush out from cracks in the icy crust near the south pole (Figure 12), and these particles replenish Saturn's E ring; they may be entirely responsible for it. So can there be water below the crust? It sounds improbable, but all other explanations sound even more improbable. At present we simply cannot explain the geysers of Enceladus.

Take advantage of the virtual absence of the rings, and seek out this tiny, mysterious world. I do not find it really difficult with my 12½-inch reflector, and with my 15½-inch it is easy.

The Intergalactic Tramp. For Northern Hemisphere observers, the somewhat obscure pattern of Lynx (the Lynx) is almost overhead during March evenings. It adjoins Ursa Major, but has only one brightish star, the reddish Alpha (magnitude 3.8). Telescope-users may care to look for the globular cluster NGC 2419 (Caldwell 25). It is only of magnitude 10.4, but is interesting because it may be escaping from the Galaxy; it has been nicknamed the Intergalactic Tramp. It is the fifth most distant globular cluster known (lying about 275,000 light years from us, and slightly further from the galactic centre), and one of six so-called 'extreme halo' globular clusters. Its position is RA 7 h 38.1 m, Dec +38° 52.9'.

April

New Moon: 25 April   *Full Moon*: 9 April

MERCURY becomes visible low in the western sky in the evenings after about the first ten days of the month for observers in tropical and northern latitudes. Particularly for Northern Hemisphere observers this is the most favourable evening apparition of the year. Figure 13 shows, for observers in latitude 52°N, the changes in azimuth (true

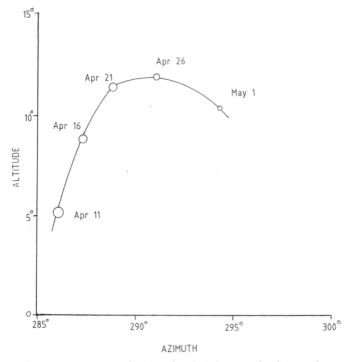

Figure 13. Evening apparition of Mercury, from latitude 52°N. The planet reaches greatest eastern elongation on 26 April. It will be at its brightest earlier in the month, before elongation.

bearing from the north through east, south and west) and altitude of Mercury on successive evenings when the Sun is 6° below the horizon. This condition is known as the end of evening civil twilight and in this latitude and at this time of year occurs about 35 minutes after sunset. During its period of visibility Mercury's magnitude fades from −1.2 to +1.0. The changes in the brightness of the planet are indicated by the relative sizes of the circles marking Mercury's position at five-day intervals. It will be noticed that Mercury is at its brightest before it reaches its greatest eastern elongation of 20° on 26 April. The diagram gives positions for a time at the beginning of evening civil twilight on the Greenwich meridian on the stated date. Observers in different longitudes should note that the actual positions of Mercury in azimuth and altitude will differ slightly from those given in the diagram due to the motion of the planet. This change will be much greater still for the Moon, if it is shown, as its motion is about 0.5° per hour.

VENUS is now visible in the eastern sky in the mornings, before sunrise, its magnitude brightening slowly during the month from −4.1 to −4.5. During the second part of the month Venus and Mars are within a few degrees of each other, being 4–5° apart on 21–22 April.

MARS, magnitude +1.2, continues to be visible in the eastern sky in the early mornings, crossing the meridian well before dawn. Unfortunately for observers in northern higher temperate latitudes Mars is still too close to the Sun in the lengthening twilight for it to be observed. A few days before the end of April, Mars, now in the constellation of Pisces, crosses the Equator from south to north. Mars passes 0.43° south of Uranus on 15 April and could serve as a useful guide to locating that planet. A diagram showing the position of Uranus among the stars is given with the notes for September (Figure 24).

JUPITER continues to be visible in the eastern sky in the early mornings, magnitude −2.1.

SATURN, magnitude +0.5, is still visible as soon as darkness falls in the evening right through until the early morning. Saturn is in Leo.

Leo and the Mystery of Denebola. Leo, the Lion, is dominant in the April sky; it cannot be overlooked, and this year it is also graced by the presence of Saturn. If you are in any doubt, find the Pointers in the Great Bear and use them to point in the direction away from the Pole Star. After crossing a relatively faint area, you will arrive in the neighbourhood of Leo. In mythology Leo represents the Nemaean Lion, one of Hercules' victims during his twelve labours – but the great cat has taken ample revenge, and in the sky, is far more conspicuous than his hunter! The principal stars of the pattern are shown in Figure 14. The lion's head is made up of a line of stars arranged rather in the shape of a backwards question mark. The brightest of the stars in this so-called 'sickle' is Regulus (magnitude 1.35), usually regarded as the faintest of the stars officially classed as being of the first magnitude; it lies at a distance of 78 light years. Algieba (Gamma Leonis) is a fine double star; magnitudes 2.2 and 3.5, separation 4.4 arcseconds. It is a binary system, with a revolution period of 619 years. The primary K-type giant is obviously orange, while its companion is of type G.

At the other end of the constellation there are three stars making up a triangle: Beta (Denebola) magnitude 2.14, Delta (Zosma) 2.56, and Theta (Chort) 3.34. Denebola's name is shortened from the Arabic *Deneb Alased*, which means 'tail of the lion', a description appropriate to its place in the constellation of Leo. Denebola is nearly a magnitude

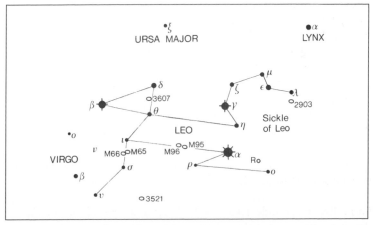

Figure 14. The principal stars of Leo, the Lion. Beta Leonis (also known as Denebola, the "tail of the lion") is towards the left on this chart. Denebola is nearly a magnitude fainter than Alpha Leonis, and almost the equal of Gamma, but there have been suggestions that in historic times Denebola used to be brighter than it is today.

fainter than Regulus, and almost the equal of Algieba, but there have been suggestions that in historic times it used to be more brilliant than it is now. A thousand years ago the Arab astronomer Al-Sûfi, who drew up an excellent star catalogue, described it as 'the great and glorious star in the lion's tail'. So what kind of star is Denebola, and has it really dimmed since Al-Sûfi wrote those words?

We know that Denebola is 36 light years away, and 15 times as luminous as the Sun; the spectral type is A3, so that it is decidedly hotter than the Sun. Its diameter is about 1.7 times that of the Sun, and it is white in colour. It is thought to be a relatively young star, with an estimated age of around 400 million years, and there is nothing outwardly special about it. Indeed it is just an ordinary Main Sequence star. Like many stars, Denebola is slightly variable; it is a Delta Scuti type variable star, so its brightness varies over a period of a few hours, but the changes in magnitude are much too slight to be discernible by the naked eye. Denebola today is certainly not a 'great and glorious' star.

Main Sequence stars do not show marked and permanent changes over periods of a few human lifetimes or a few tens of lifetimes. There have been other reported changes; for example Castor in Gemini is now considerably fainter than the other Twin, Pollux, rather than brighter – and Megrez, one of the seven stars making up the Plough pattern in Ursa Major, is now almost a magnitude fainter than the other six instead of being equal to them. But it is never wise to place too much reliance on old naked-eye estimates, and in all probability the alleged changes are due to errors in observation or interpretation.

Many years ago I made a long series of observations of Denebola, comparing it carefully with Algieba and other suitable stars. I found no variations at all, and I very much doubt whether Denebola will surprise us in the foreseeable future. Still, I suppose that one never knows!

Where Can You See the Southern Cross? Of all the constellations in the sky, the two most famous are probably Ursa Major (the Great Bear), containing the familiar stars of the Plough, in the Northern Hemisphere, and Crux Australis (the Southern Cross) in the Southern. During April, Crux is very well placed in the late evening for observers in countries such as Australia and South Africa, but in Europe it cannot be seen at all. Indeed, there are many people who believe that in order to see the Southern Cross you must travel south of the Equator.

This is not so. The declination of Acrux or Alpha Crucis, the brightest star in the Cross, is −63°. This means that in theory it rises from any latitude south of 27°N, while from any location south of latitude 27°S, it is circumpolar – i.e. it never sets. Of course, the effects of atmospheric refraction complicate this somewhat, and in any case it is never easy to see a star when it is only a degree or two above the horizon, but the principles are straightforward enough.

For example, the island of La Palma in the Canary Islands, where one of the Northern Hemisphere's major observatories is sited, is at latitude 28°N, so that Alpha Crucis cannot be seen. Gamma Crucis (declination −57°) technically rises, but is not easy to glimpse. From Hilo in Hawaii (latitude 20°N) Alpha Crucis is easy. From Johannesburg (latitude 26°S) it is above the horizon for most of the time, and from Sydney, Montevideo, and Cape Town (latitude 34°S) it is circumpolar. On April evenings, from places near the Equator, it is fascinating to see the Great Bear and the Southern Cross above the horizon at the same time.

May

New Moon: 24 May   *Full Moon*: 9 May

MERCURY passes through inferior conjunction on 18 May and remains too close to the Sun for observation to be possible throughout the month.

VENUS attains its greatest brilliancy, magnitude −4.5, on 2 May and therefore continues to be visible in the eastern sky in the early mornings before dawn. Observers in the latitudes of the British Isles will only be able to see it for about an hour before sunrise, but those further south will enjoy a longer period of visibility.

MARS is still not visible to observers in the latitudes of the British Isles, but can be seen as a morning object in the eastern sky by those further south. Its magnitude is +1.2.

JUPITER, magnitude −2.3, is still visible as a brilliant object in the eastern sky, in the constellation of Capricornus, for several hours before sunrise. On 25 May, Jupiter, moving eastwards, passes only 0.4° south of Neptune, a useful guide for observers wishing to locate the fainter planet, though the glare of Jupiter itself may prove overpowering in poor conditions. A diagram showing the path of Neptune among the stars is given with the notes for August (Figure 22).

SATURN is still visible as an evening object in the western sky in the evenings, magnitude +0.9. On 17 May, Saturn reaches its second stationary point, resuming its direct motion. Figure 15 shows the path of Saturn among the stars during the year.

Crushed Spacecraft! Venus reaches its greatest brilliancy this month, although from Britain it does not rise much more than an hour before the Sun; it does not reach greatest western elongation until early next month. Unlike Mercury, it is brightest during the crescent stage.

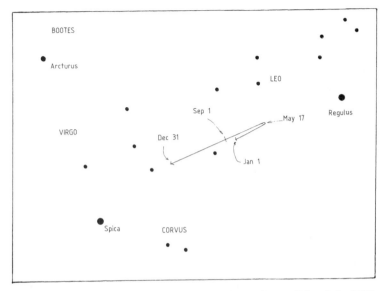

Figure 15. The path of Saturn against the background stars of Leo and Virgo during 2009.

Before the Space Age, Venus was regarded as the planet of mystery; our telescopes could not show us what lay below the clouds, and we had no real idea what the surface conditions were like. Astronomers as eminent as Fred Whipple and Don Menzel believed that the climate would be tolerable, and that there could be broad oceans, and if this had been true there was a strong chance that life might exist, so that Venus might eventually become friendly and Earth-like. Hopes of life were dashed by the first fly-by probes, which showed that the surface temperature was like a furnace (approaching 500°C), and that the main atmospheric constituent was carbon dioxide; also, the clouds were rich in droplets of sulphuric acid. However, it was clearly important to have information from ground level, and the Russians attempted this with Venera 5, which was launched on 5 January 1969 and landed on Venus 40 years ago this month, on 16 May 1969.

Unfortunately, Venera 5 was not a complete success. It was launched successfully by a Molniya launch vehicle, the actual lander being carried in a spacecraft known as the Tyazheliy Sputnik. Near the top of Venus' atmosphere the 405-kg capsule containing scientific instruments was ejected, to end the journey on its own. A parachute was deployed, and during the descent, for 53 minutes, data were returned from the dangling capsule, indicating an atmosphere composed of 93–97 per cent carbon dioxide, 2–5 per cent nitrogen, and less than 4 per cent oxygen. The probe returned data down to within 30 kilometres of the surface and then transmissions ceased. The trouble was that the density of Venus' lower atmosphere had been underestimated, and before reaching the ground the luckless capsule was literally crushed. (The atmospheric pressure at the surface of Venus is about 90 times greater than that of the Earth's air at sea level.) No doubt Venera 5 landed, at around latitude 3 degrees south, longitude 18 degrees east, but nothing was heard from it after arrival. The spacecraft also carried a medallion bearing the coat-of-arms of the USSR, plus the obligatory bas-relief of V.I. Lenin . . . By this time a twin vehicle, Venera 6, was on its way; it had been launched on 10 January 1969. Exactly the same thing happened; parachute, signals, and then silence. This time the landing was at latitude 5 south 23 east.

The Russians soon set to work to put matters right. On 17 August 1970 they launched Venera 7, and made it much tougher than its predecessors. It followed the same procedure, this time with success; it came down on 15 December 1970, and transmitted for over half an hour during the descent, and for 23 minutes after landing, before contact was lost. For the first time we had measurements direct from the surface; this intensely hostile planet could not have been less like the pleasant world pictured by Whipple and Menzel. All thoughts of a manned expedition there were jettisoned, and the main attention of the space-planners swung back to Mars, where it has really remained ever since.

All the same, Venus is a fascinating place. Turn your telescope towards it this month, and spare a thought for the two unmanned probes which were so cruelly squashed forty years ago.

The Celestial Crow. This is a good time to look for Corvus, the Crow, which adjoins Hydra. The four main stars, all around the third magnitude, make up a well-defined quadrilateral, which may be fairly easily located to the south and west of the first magnitude star Spica (Alpha Virginis). In mythology the god Apollo became enamoured of Coronis, mother of the great doctor Aesculapius, and sent the crow to watch her and report on her behaviour. Frankly, the report was decidedly unfavourable, but Apollo rewarded the obliging bird with a place in the sky! The four stars making up the quadrilateral are Gamma (magnitude 2.6), Beta (2.7), Delta (2.9), and Epsilon (3.0). Rather curiously, the star Alpha Corvi is more than a magnitude fainter than any of these.

Phases of the Inner Planets. Although it is often stated in textbooks that the inner planets, Mercury and Venus, show phases like the Moon, it is seldom made clear that these take place in the reverse order (Figure 16). From Europe or North America, we are accustomed to seeing our Moon as a thin crescent in the western sky at sunset, with the horns pointing to the left (east). This phase is followed by First Quarter, Full Moon and Last Quarter, a succession of phases which is summed up by the words *waxing* and *waning*.

The inner planets certainly do the same thing, but the Moon moves eastwards around the Earth, while the planets move westwards from inferior conjunction. They appear soon after conjunction in the morning sky before dawn, first showing a thin crescent with the horns pointing to the right (west). The crescent grows larger until the planet is at western elongation, when it appears half illuminated, like the Moon at Last Quarter (Figure 16). Then follows the gibbous phase, with the phase increasing until the planet reaches superior conjunction on the far side of its orbit (as viewed from Earth), when the phase appears like a Full Moon. The planet then moves out into the evening sky, becoming visible at dusk, and the illuminated portion steadily diminishes. At eastern elongation, it appears half illuminated again, but it is now like the First Quarter Moon. After this time, the planet shows a gradually reducing crescent phase, but the horns of the crescent now point to the east.

In 2009, Venus starts the year in the evening sky approaching half phase. It appears as a rapidly thinning crescent during late January, February, and early March, passing through inferior conjunction on 27 March. It reappears, this time in the morning sky, as a very thin crescent, which rapidly increases until Venus reaches half phase again in early June. For the rest of the year, the planet will display a gibbous phase, although the apparent size of the disc decreases as the distance of Venus from the Earth increases.

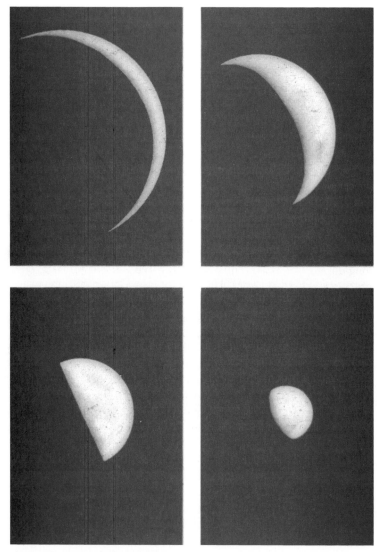

Figure 16. A series of telescopic drawings showing the changing phase of Venus. The view is inverted in an astronomical telescope. From a large, but very thin crescent (upper left), the phase steadily increases to a fatter crescent, then half phase (dichotomy), and finally a small, gibbous disc, as the distance of Venus from Earth steadily increases. (Drawings courtesy of the Editor.)

June

New Moon: 22 June   *Full Moon*: 7 June

Solstice: 21 June

MERCURY becomes visible in the eastern morning sky after the first week of the month for observers in tropical and southern latitudes. During its period of visibility its magnitude brightens from +1.0 to −0.9. It passes 3° north of Aldebaran (Alpha Tauri) on 22 June. Mercury reaches its greatest western elongation of 23° on 13 June. Unfortunately for observers in the latitudes of the British Isles the long duration of twilight means that it remains unsuitably placed for observation throughout the month.

VENUS, magnitude −4.2, continues to be visible in the eastern sky in the early morning skies before sunrise. On 5 June it attains its greatest western elongation of 46° from the Sun. Venus passes 2° south of Mars on 21 June.

MARS, already visible by observers from tropical and southern latitudes, becomes visible to observers from all northern temperate latitudes during the second half of the month: for them it will be a difficult object to detect, very low above the eastern horizon for a short while about two hours before dawn. Its magnitude remains at +1.1.

JUPITER continues to be visible as a conspicuous object in the night sky, crossing the meridian around midnight by the middle of the month. On 15 June, Jupiter reaches its first stationary point on the borders of Aquarius and Capricornus, when it begins its retrograde motion. Its magnitude is −2.6.

SATURN, magnitude +1.1, continues to be visible in the western sky in the evenings, still moving slowly eastwards in the constellation of Leo.

PLUTO reaches opposition on 23 June, in the constellation of Sagittarius, at a distance of 4,586 million kilometres (2,849 million miles). It is visible only with a moderate-sized telescope since its magnitude is +14.

Pluto – The Arguments Continue. Books published between 1930 and very recent times state that the Solar System contains nine planets. More recently the number has been reduced to eight. The rejected member is, of course, Pluto, which is now officially classed as a 'dwarf planet'. Perhaps I may be allowed to make a few points here, because I was a friend of Clyde Tombaugh, discoverer of Pluto, and in 1980 – fifty years after the discovery – he paid me the great honour of inviting me to be the co-author of his book. We called it *Out of the Darkness: The Planet Pluto.* It seemed to be the obvious title.

Although there had been a few earlier fruitless searches for a planet beyond Neptune, the first systematic photographic and visual search was made by Percival Lowell from Flagstaff, between 1905 and 1907. Sadly, Lowell is remembered now mainly for his belief in an inhabited Mars, and this is a pity, because he made so many contributions in other areas. Neptune was discovered in September 1846 because of its effects upon the movements of Uranus; the work was carried out by Urbain Le Verrier, and the actual discovery was made by Johann Galle and Heinrich D'Arrest. (Yes, I know that John Couch Adams had made similar calculations, but Galle and D'Arrest knew nothing about them.) Lowell believed that there were remaining discrepancies, due presumably to another planet, so using his great 24-inch refractor he began to search for it. He did not succeed, and when he died, in 1916, the planet was still unfound. In 1929, after a long hiatus, Vesto Slipher, Director of the Lowell Observatory in Flagstaff, decided to make a fresh attempt. The new search was entrusted to a young Clyde Tombaugh, using the 13-inch refractor specifically acquired for the purpose, and in 1930 the planet turned up very close to Lowell's predicted position. At the suggestion of an Oxford schoolgirl, Venetia Burney (now Mrs Phair) it was named Pluto.

All seemed well. Pluto was found in the expected place, and initially it was thought to be about the size of Mars – perhaps even larger. It was not a giant and indeed it was much fainter than Lowell had expected; ironically it had actually been recorded on one of Lowell's photographs, but was so dim that it had been overlooked. Pluto's orbit was much more eccentric and had a higher orbital inclination (17.14°) than that of any other planet, but this was not thought to affect its status. Then, however, doubts began to creep in. Improved measurements showed that Pluto was smaller than Earth – then smaller than Mars – then smaller than the Moon. In 1978 it was found to have a companion, Charon, half the diameter of Pluto itself – too large to be regarded as a conventional satellite. We were dealing with a double planet, or perhaps a trans-Neptunian asteroid.

Then came a new development. During the 1990s many other asteroid-sized bodies were found in these remote regions, and it became clear that Pluto is only one member of a vast swarm of trans-Neptunian objects. Such trans-Neptunian objects are classified according to the characteristics of their orbits. Within the gravitational influence of Neptune are the Kuiper Belt objects, which have near-circular orbits that lie close to the plane of the Solar System. There is also a small population of so-called Scattered Disc objects, which are also within the gravitational influence of Neptune, but have eccentric and inclined orbits.

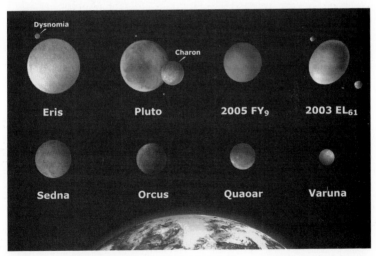

Figure 17. An illustration depicting the relative sizes of some of the largest known trans-Neptunian objects. Eris (upper left), which was first spotted in 2003 by a Palomar Observatory-based team led by Mike Brown but not identified until 2005, is slightly larger than Pluto. (Image courtesy of NASA, ESA, and A. Feild (STScI).)

Since the first was discovered in 1992, the number of known Kuiper Belt objects has increased to over one thousand, and there are perhaps as many as 100,000 such objects, over 100 km in diameter, in this region. The time has come to cast sentiment aside in favour of science. Pluto is not a true planet; it never was. It is a Kuiper Belt object. Yet it is none the less interesting for that. Pluto clearly has far more in common with the other small, icy trans-Neptunian objects (Figure 17) than it does with the major planets lying closer to the Sun.

Pluto is in opposition now, in Sagittarius, and it is of the 14th magnitude, so that it is by no means a difficult object, though it will look like an ordinary faint star. The New Horizons spacecraft (Figure 18) is now on its way there, and in a future *Yearbook* article we hope to tell you what this curious little world is really like.

Figure 18. An artist's impression of the New Horizons spacecraft passing Pluto in July 2015. New Horizons reached an interplanetary milepost on its voyage to Pluto and the icy environs of the Kuiper Belt on 8 June 2008, when it crossed the orbit of Saturn about 1.5 billion kilometres from the Sun, becoming the first spacecraft to journey beyond Saturn's orbit since Voyager 2 passed the ringed planet nearly 27 years earlier. (Image courtesy of Johns Hopkins University Applied Physics Laboratory / Southwest Research Institute.)

July

EARTH is at aphelion (furthest from the Sun) on 4 July at a distance of 152 million kilometres (94.5 million miles).

MERCURY remains unobservable from the latitudes of the British Isles as the planet passes through superior conjunction on 14 July. However, observers in tropical latitudes may still be able to see it low in the east-north-eastern sky around the time of beginning of morning civil twilight, magnitude about −1.1, but only for the first few days of the month. Further south, observers will not be able to see it in the morning skies again until next year. During the last week of the month observers in tropical and southern latitudes will be able to see it in the evenings. It may then be seen low in the western sky around the time of end of civil twilight, at a magnitude of about −0.7.

VENUS continues to be visible as a magnificent morning object in the eastern sky before dawn, magnitude −4.1. On 14 July, Venus passes 3° north of Aldebaran, in Taurus, which will be about a hundred times fainter than the planet.

MARS, magnitude +1.1, may be seen above the eastern horizon for several hours before dawn. The planet passes about 5° north of Aldebaran on 27 July.

JUPITER, magnitude −2.8, is now visible for the greater part of the hours of darkness as it moves towards opposition next month. Jupiter is south of the Equator, but even those in northern temperate latitudes will be able to see it in the eastern sky well before midnight. Jupiter is moving retrograde in the constellation of Capricornus. Around 13 July Jupiter passes only 0.6° south of Neptune, offering a good opportunity for locating the fainter planet, though the glare from Jupiter itself may prove overpowering in poor conditions.

SATURN continues to be visible in the western sky in the evenings in the constellation of Leo, magnitude +1.2, though observers in the latitudes of the British Isles will find it becoming increasingly difficult to observe in the long evening twilight and for them it will be lost to view before the end of July.

Forty Years Ago – The First Men on the Moon. It was the evening of 20 July 1969; Neil Armstrong and Buzz Aldrin, of Apollo 11, landed on the Moon. This is something that will never be forgotten. Do you remember where you were, early the following morning, when Neil stepped down off the ladder on to the rocky surface of the Sea of Tranquillity, and said 'That's one small step for (a) man; one giant leap

Figure 19. The view from Neil Armstrong's window as the Apollo 11 lunar module Eagle descended towards the lunar surface on 20 July 1969, during the first landing on the Moon. The close pair of craters Messier and Messier A appears towards the top of the picture; Messier A is the origin of two slightly divergent light streaks, resembling a comet's tail, which extend over the Mare Fecunditatis. (Image courtesy NASA.)

for mankind.' (It was meant to be 'a man', but the 'a' was indistinct.) I know where I was; I was in Studio 7, Television Centre, carrying out the live commentary for the BBC. I cannot tell you just what I said as Neil came down the ladder, because the BBC has apparently lost all the tapes, but I hope that it was appropriate.

But to me, the most nerve-racking moments had come earlier, as the astronauts prepared to land (Figure 19). Remember, this was an entirely new venture; if the lunar module (nicknamed Eagle) had made a faulty landing, or if it had come down on uneven ground and been tilted sideways, it would have been unable to take off again, and there was no provision for rescue. When I heard Neil's voice: 'Houston, Tranquillity Base here. The Eagle has landed,' my feeling was one of overwhelming relief. It was equally tense when the astronauts were ready to leave the Moon, because the one ascent engine had to work faultlessly, first time – there could be no second chance. Mercifully it did, and the Apollo programme was carried through with no fatalities during the actual missions. It would be folly to send another manned mission to the Moon without making some provision for rescue, difficult though this will undoubtedly be.

There was just a brief period, particularly during the Apollo 13 crisis, when the world seemed united. Naturally this soon wore off, but I hope it will return before the next astronauts set off for the Moon, whatever their nationality might be.

Simon Newcomb. The great Canadian mathematician and astronomer, Simon Newcomb, was born in 1835 and died one hundred years ago this month, on 11 July 1909. He made very important contributions to mathematical astronomy, and was offered the Directorship of the Harvard College Observatory; he declined, because his main interests were not observational, but in 1877 he became Director of the Nautical Almanac office, and undertook a programme of recalculation of all the main astronomical constants. This was of fundamental importance. He did admittedly say that in his opinion it would never be possible to fly in a heavier-than-air machine, apparently unaware that the Wright brothers had already done so, but we all make mistakes. (On the one occasion when I met Orville Wright, I asked him about this. He gave a wry smile!)

Eclipse of the Sun. This month's total eclipse of the Sun on 21–22 July – the latest in the famous Saros Series 136 – should be spectacular, and some of our readers will undoubtedly be hoping to see it. At maximum, the duration of totality will be 6m 39s. For the next total solar eclipse we have only to wait until the following year, 11 July 2010, but to see one with a longer period of totality than the one this month, one has to wait until the eclipse on 13 June 2132 (duration 6m 55s), which belongs to Saros Series 139. For more details see the article by Martin Mobberley elsewhere in this *Yearbook*.

The First Telescopic Observations of the Moon. This month we celebrate the 400th anniversary of the remarkable observations of the Moon by an Englishman, Thomas Harriot (Figure 20). Harriot is an unsung hero of science and astronomy. He was born in 1560 and

Figure 20. A portrait, commonly assumed to be of the remarkable English astronomer Thomas Harriot (1560–1621), now at Trinity College, Oxford.

graduated from Oxford in 1580. His contributions to mathematics, navigation, algebra, optics and shipbuilding were significant achievements of the Elizabethan age. He was on one of the first expeditions to America and collaborated closely with Sir Walter Ralegh.

It is Harriot's remarkable work in astronomy that we shall be remembering in 2009, during the International Year of Astronomy. From 1597, Harriot was living at Syon House, by the River Thames to the west of London, as part of the Ninth Earl of Northumberland's household. He spent his time carrying out numerous scientific investigations, observations and instrument making. His observations included the detailed and meticulous recordings of sunspots. He was observing the moons of Jupiter at the same time as Galileo, and his observations and calculations relating to the comet of 1607 (which would later become known as Halley's Comet) are incredibly close to modern-day computations.

On 26 July 1609, at Syon House, Harriot observed the Moon and it is very likely that this was the first astronomical observation made with a telescope. His telescopic drawings of the Moon predate those made by Galileo by some months. Over the period 1611–1612, Harriot carried out numerous astronomical observations and measurements.

His friendships with Sir Walter Ralegh and Henry Percy, the Ninth Earl of Northumberland (whose association with the Gunpowder Plot led to his imprisonment) placed Harriot in a very intriguing part of Elizabethan society.

Thomas Harriot died in London on 2 July 1621. He was buried at St Christopher le Stock Church on the current site of the Bank of England. The church was destroyed in the Great Fire of London. For many years his incredible scientific achievements remained forgotten. At Syon House on 26 July 2009, as part of the events being arranged for the International Year of Astronomy, there will be a celebration of Harriot's work and particularly his first observation of the Moon with a telescope.

August

New Moon: 20 August   *Full Moon*: 6 August

MERCURY reaches its greatest eastern elongation of 27° on 24 August and, for observers in tropical and southern latitudes, is visible as an evening object throughout the month. For observers in southern latitudes this will be the most favourable evening apparition of the year. Figure 21 shows, for observers in latitude 35°S, the changes in azimuth (true bearing from the north through east, south and west) and altitude of Mercury on successive evenings when the Sun is 6° below the

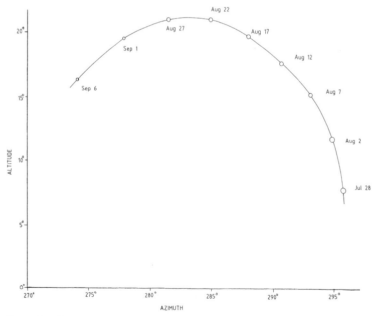

Figure 21. Evening apparition of Mercury, from latitude 35°S. The planet reaches greatest eastern elongation on 24 August. It will be at its brightest earlier in the month, before elongation.

horizon. This condition is known as the end of evening civil twilight and in this latitude and at this time of year occurs about 25 minutes after sunset. The changes in the brightness of the planet are indicated by the relative sizes of the circles marking Mercury's position at five-day intervals. It will be noticed that Mercury is at its brightest before it reaches greatest eastern elongation. The diagram gives positions for a time at the end of evening civil twilight on the Greenwich meridian, on the stated date. Observers in different longitudes should note that the observed positions of Mercury in azimuth and altitude will differ slightly from those shown in the diagram. This change will be much greater still for the Moon, if it is shown, as its motion is about 0.5° per hour. Mercury passes 0.7° north of Regulus (Alpha Leonis) on 2 August. During August its magnitude fades from −0.5 to +0.5. Mercury is not suitably placed for observation during the month for observers in the latitudes of the British Isles.

VENUS continues to be visible as a magnificent object in the east-north-eastern sky in the early mornings before sunrise. Its magnitude is −4.0.

MARS, magnitude +1.0, continues to be visible as a morning object and during the month it is rising above the east-north-eastern horizon around five hours before sunrise. Mars is in Taurus, north-east of Aldebaran, at the beginning of August, but before the end of the month it has entered the constellation of Gemini.

JUPITER, magnitude −2.9, is now at its brightest since it is at opposition on 14 August and therefore available for observation throughout the night wherever you are on the Earth. Jupiter is in the constellation of Capricornus, as will be seen from the diagram given with the notes for March (Figure 8). When closest to the Earth its distance is 603 million kilometres (374 million miles).

SATURN, magnitude +1.2, continues to be visible as an evening object low in the western sky until the end of the month, but only for observers in tropical and southern latitudes. At the end of the month Saturn moves eastwards from Leo into Virgo. On 10 August, the Sun passes through the ring-plane from south to north. As the Earth remains south of this plane until next month, the Sun and the Earth will be on opposite sides of the ring-plane for this time, so the rings would not be visible from the Earth anyway.

NEPTUNE is at opposition on 17 August, in the constellation of Capricornus. It is not visible to the naked eye since its magnitude is +7.9. At closest approach Neptune is 4,341 million kilometres (2,697 million miles) from the Earth. Figure 22 shows the path of Neptune among the stars during the year.

The Sea Goat. Jupiter is at opposition this month, although rather low down in the southern sky from the latitudes of the British Isles. It lies in Capricornus, so why not also take time to look at this ancient if rather inconspicuous Zodiacal constellation?

Capricornus is the sea goat, though its outline does not recall a goat, marine or otherwise. There are no definite Greek mythological legends associated with it (it has sometimes been associated with the demigod Pan), but the pattern is one of the oldest to have been identified – perhaps the oldest – in spite of its dimness; representations of a goat man or goat fish have been found on Babylonian tablets dating back 3,000 years. Capricornus is one of the more obscure constellations in the Zodiac; there are only five stars above the fourth magnitude, and there is no really well-defined pattern (Figure 23). The brightest stars are:

Name	magnitude	spectrum	distance	luminosity
			light years	(Sun=1)
Delta (Deneb Algiedi)	2.87 var	A5	39	9
Beta (Dabih)	3.08	K0+B8	330	600/40
Alpha-2 (Al Giedi)	3.57	G9	109	43
Gamma (Nashira)	3.68	A7	139	47
Zeta (Marakk)	3.74	G4	122	490

Delta Capricorni, whose name Deneb Algiedi means 'the goat's tail', is actually a four-star system. The primary component has a companion that eclipses it every 1,023 days, causing the apparent brightness to drop by about 0.2 magnitudes during eclipses. Two other stars orbit further out in the system.

Beta (Dabih) is a wide double, easy to see in binoculars. The pair have a separation of about 3.5 minutes of arc, the brighter component (Dabih Major) being of magnitude 3.08, and its companion (Dabih

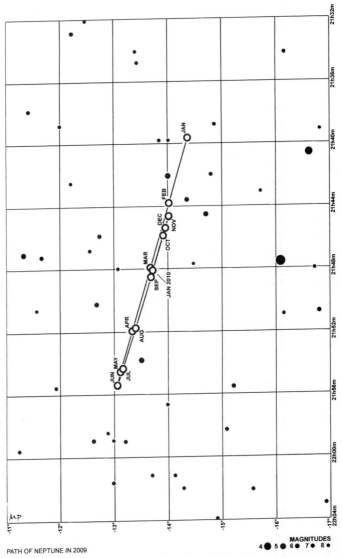

PATH OF NEPTUNE IN 2009

MAGNITUDES
4 ● 5 ● 6 ● 7 ● 8 ●

Figure 22. The path of Neptune against the stars of Capricornus during 2009. The two brightest stars, towards the bottom of the chart, are Gamma Capricorni (magnitude +3.7, RA 21h 40.6m, Dec. −16.6°) and Delta Capricorni (magnitude +2.9, RA 21h 47.6m, Dec. −16.1°).

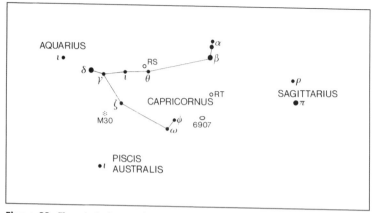

Figure 23. The principal stars of Capricornus, the Sea Goat, which is one of the more obscure constellations of the Zodiac. There are only five stars above the fourth magnitude, and there is no really obvious pattern.

Minor) of magnitude 6.10. Dabih Major and Dabih Minor are themselves double, and one of the components of Dabih Major is also double, so the system is made up of five stars at least.

Alpha Capricorni is an easy naked-eye double; one component (Alpha-2, magnitude 3.6) is noticeably brighter than the other (Alpha-1, magnitude 4.2), and the stars are separated by 6.3 minutes of arc, one-fifth of the angular diameter of the full Moon. There is no colour contrast, since both stars are of spectral type G (yellowish), and the two stars lie at very different distances from us; they make up an 'optical' or line-of-sight double, and there is no real connection between them. Alpha-1, the fainter of the two, is a supergiant star over 900 times more luminous than the Sun, lying 690 light years away (and only seeming fainter because of its greater distance). The brighter component, Alpha-2, is a giant star 43 times the luminosity of the Sun, and only 109 light years distant.

Also in Capricornus, you will find the globular cluster M30, NGC 7099, lying at RA 21h 40m 22s, Dec. −23° 10′ 45′. Its apparent magnitude is 7.5, so that it is straightforward to find, not far to the east of Zeta. It is fairly concentrated towards the core, although the outer parts are easy to resolve, and it is a fine object even in small telescopes. It is 26,000 light years away, and about 90 light years across; its angular diameter is about 12 arcminutes.

John Russell Hind. On 13 August 1847, the large main belt asteroid no. 7, Iris, was discovered by the British astronomer John Russell Hind. Hind spent most of his career at the Royal Greenwich Observatory; Iris was his first asteroid discovery, but it was followed by nine others; the last was 30 Urania, found in July 1854. He was awarded the Gold Medal of the Royal Astronomical Society in 1853, and now has his own asteroid named after him – no. 1897. Asteroid no. 7 Iris can outshine every other member of the main belt apart from Vesta, Ceres, and Pallas, although at typical oppositions it is comparable to Pallas; on rare occasions Iris can rise to magnitude 6.7, which is as bright as Ceres ever gets. Iris is an S-type asteroid, and is 225 × 190 × 190 kilometres in diameter.

Which Way Is The Earth Moving? In addition to sharing the motion of the Sun through space, the Earth also has its own motion due to its annual orbit around the Sun. Since the orbit of the Earth is almost a circle, the point in the sky towards which it is moving – known rather grandly as the Apex of the Earth's Way – is roughly at right-angles to the line joining the Earth and the Sun. This direction will be towards a point on the ecliptic about 90° to the west of the Sun.

So, if you face the Sun at midday, the Apex is setting in the west, and it does not rise again in the east until midnight. At dawn, as the Sun comes up, the Apex will lie to the south (in the northern hemisphere), so one can only look along the line of motion of the Earth against the background stars between midnight and dawn. It is for this reason that visually we see more sporadic meteors after midnight than before it, because it is only in the early morning hours that we are facing that part of space through which the Earth is moving, sweeping up the meteoric dust.

On any date, the Apex will be at its highest altitude above the horizon at sunrise. This altitude will be at its greatest when the ecliptic is high in the sky just before dawn, i.e. around the time when the Sun is on the celestial Equator crossing from north to south. Consequently, the number of sporadic meteors which will be seen visually is usually at its best during pre-dawn hours from the end of August until early October.

September

New Moon: 18 September   *Full Moon*: 4 September

Equinox: 22 September

MERCURY, for the first week of the month, is visible to observers in southern latitudes low in the western sky in the evenings. During this time its magnitude fades from +0.6 to +1.0. It passes rapidly through inferior conjunction on 20 September and may be seen by observers in northern temperate latitudes and also tropical latitudes, low above the eastern horizon in the early mornings before the onset of morning civil twilight, for the last two days of the month. Its magnitude is then +1.0.

VENUS continues to be visible as a brilliant object in the east-north-eastern sky in the mornings before dawn, magnitude −3.9.

MARS continues to be visible as a morning object, though it may be seen rising above the east-north-eastern horizon shortly after midnight. Mars continues its eastward motion through the constellation of Gemini, passing south of Pollux early next month. Its magnitude is +0.9.

JUPITER remains a brilliant object visible during the greater part of the night from shortly after sunset to the early morning twilight, though by the end of the month observers in high northern latitudes will not be able to see it for long after midnight. Jupiter's magnitude is −2.8.

SATURN passes through conjunction on 17 September and therefore continues to be too close to the Sun for observation. In any case the rings would be unobservable as the Earth passes through the ring-plane from south to north on 4 September. In the past, such ring-plane crossings have been the best times to discover new moons around Saturn, using Earth-based telescopes, but the planet will be only 11° east of the Sun on 4 September – too close for that to be feasible this time.

URANUS is at opposition on 17 September, in the constellation of Pisces. The planet is barely visible to the naked eye as its magnitude is +5.7, but it is readily located with only a small optical aid. At closest approach Uranus is 2,856 million kilometres (1,775 million miles) from the Earth. Figure 24 shows the path of Uranus among the stars during the year.

How Was Neptune Missed? In late 1945, when I was newly out of the RAF and had set up my modest observatory at East Grinstead in Sussex, I had a visit from a twelve-year-old boy named John Lockwood. He had become interested in astronomy, and wanted to see through my 12½-inch reflector. We had a good view of the Moon, plus some double stars and various clusters and nebulae, after which we retired to my study for coffee and biscuits. Then he pulled out a notebook. 'Please, I'm puzzled by this. There's something here that looks like a star, but it isn't on my map, and there's something a bit odd about it. What can it be?'

I took out the book and consulted my star atlas. 'John, if you'd done this before 1781 you'd have become world famous. You've made a completely independent discovery of the planet Uranus.'

It was true. John, using binoculars, had found Uranus, and had realized that it was not a star. After that we kept in regular touch – but then, three years later, I had a heartbroken letter from his parents; John had been killed in a road crash. It was a tragic end to a promising career.

I began thinking about discoveries which could have been made, and were not. Take William Herschel, widely regarded as the greatest of all visual observers. He identified Uranus (even though he did at first believe it to be a comet), and he discovered many faint clusters and nebulae. He used high powers on his telescopes. How can he possibly have missed Neptune, which under even a modest magnification appears obviously non-stellar? I do not know. There were other skilled observers, too, and it is hard to see how Neptune was missed for so long. It is in Capricornus now, and with the chart provided here you should not have the slightest difficulty in identifying it. Compare its colour, if you can, with that of Uranus; the two ice-giants are not alike.

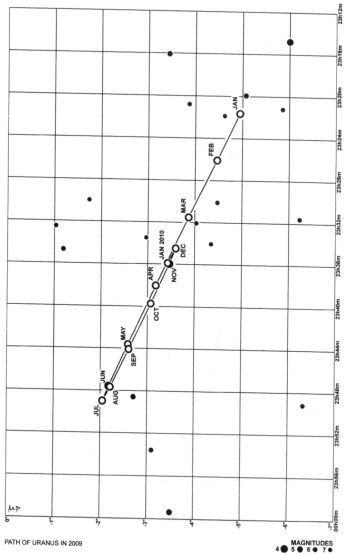

PATH OF URANUS IN 2009

MAGNITUDES
4● 5● 6● 7●

Figure 24. The path of Uranus against the stars of Aquarius during 2009. The brightest stars on the chart are as follows: Phi Aquarii (magnitude +4.2, RA 23h 14.8m, Dec. −6.0°); 96 Aquarii (magnitude +5.6, RA 23h 19.4m, Dec. −5.1°); 20 Piscium (magnitude +5.5, RA 23h 47.9m, Dec. −2.8°); and 27 Piscium (magnitude +4.9, RA 23h 58.7m, Dec. −3.6°).

Problems with Uranus. It is worth looking at Uranus, provided that you have a telescope of fair size; atmospheric markings are very elusive, and you will have to use as high a magnification as you can. I admit that with my 15½-inch I have never had much success, though no doubt keener-sighted observers can do better. The Hubble Space Telescope has obtained some excellent images of the planet, its moons, and extremely narrow rings (Figure 25).

In many ways Uranus is an oddity. It alone of the giant planets seems to have very little by way of an internal heat source, and of course there is the strange tilt of its spin axis with respect to the plane of its orbit – more than a right angle (98°). This leads to a very curious calendar. First one pole, then the other, is plunged into a night lasting for the equivalent of 21 Earth years, with a corresponding period of daylight at the opposite pole – and since Uranus takes 84 years to complete one orbit of the Sun, the seasons are very long.

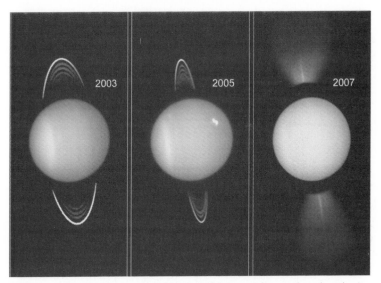

Figure 25. This series of images from NASA's Hubble Space Telescope shows how the ring system around the distant planet Uranus appears at ever more oblique (shallower) tilts as viewed from Earth – culminating in the rings being seen edge-on in three observing opportunities in 2007. The best of these events appears in the far right image taken with Hubble's Wide Field Planetary Camera 2 on 14 August 2007. (Image courtesy of NASA, ESA, and M. Showalter (SETI Institute).)

The reason for the strange axial tilt is unclear. Conventionally it was long assumed that the planet was on the receiving end of a massive impact and literally toppled over, but with a globe more than 51,000 kilometres across, nearly 15 times the mass of the Earth, this does not seem very plausible. Opinion is now veering towards the idea that mutual gravitational interactions between the outer planets were responsible.

The magnetic field of Uranus is probably caused through dynamo action due to electrical currents circulating within the planet's mantle of slushy ices, rather than in the core. Probably for this reason, the planet's magnetic axis (the line linking the north and south magnetic poles) does not pass anywhere near through the centre of the planet. Even stranger, the magnetic axis is tilted by 59° to the planet's axis of rotation and, in common with the other giant planets, has the opposite polarity to that of the Earth. Uranus' magnetic field has a total strength about 50 times that of the Earth's magnetic field, but only 1/400th that of Jupiter's. The extreme tilt causes the magnetic field to gyrate around the planet in a chaotic way as the planet spins on its axis.

It has even been suggested that there may have been planetary migrations, so that at one time, long ago, Uranus may have been further out than Neptune. However, we have to admit there is a great deal that we still do not know about the early history of the Solar System.

October

New Moon: 18 October   ***Full Moon***: 4 October

Summer Time in the United Kingdom ends on 25 October.

MERCURY is visible to observers in northern and tropical latitudes as a morning object during the first half of the month. For observers in the higher northern temperate latitudes this is the best morning apparition of 2009. Figure 26 shows, for observers in latitude 52°N, the

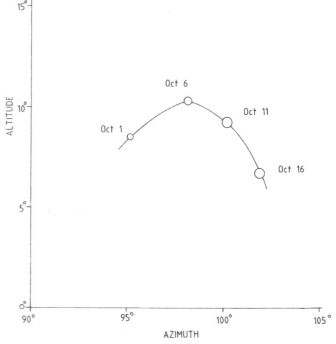

Figure 26. Morning apparition of Mercury, from latitude 52°N. The planet reaches greatest western elongation on 6 October. It will be at its brightest later in the month, after elongation.

changes in azimuth (true bearing from the north through east, south and west) and altitude of Mercury on successive mornings when the Sun is 6° below the horizon. This condition is known as the beginning of morning civil twilight and in this latitude and at this time of year occurs about 35 minutes before sunrise. The changes in the brightness of the planet are indicated by the relative sizes of the circles marking Mercury's position at five-day intervals. It will be noticed that Mercury is at its brightest after it reaches greatest western elongation of 18° on 6 October. During its period of visibility its magnitude brightens from +0.4 to −1.0. The diagram gives positions for a time at the beginning of morning civil twilight on the Greenwich meridian on the stated date. Observers in different longitudes should note that the actual positions of Mercury in azimuth and altitude will differ slightly from those shown in the diagram. This change will be much greater still for the Moon, if it is shown, as its motion is about 0.5° per hour. Mercury passes 0.3° south of Saturn on 8 October. This close approach could be a useful guide to locating Saturn, which will then be about five times fainter than Mercury.

VENUS, magnitude −3.9, remains visible as a brilliant object in the eastern sky in the early mornings. The period available for observation is now decreasing as the planet is gradually drawing closer to the Sun. Venus passes 0.5° south of Saturn on 13 October. This could serve as a useful aid to locating Saturn, though as it is about one hundred times fainter than Venus it may be a rather difficult observation to make in the pre-dawn twilight.

MARS is still a morning object, though it is now visible in the eastern sky before midnight. After passing about 6° south of Pollux early in October, its eastward motion carries it into Cancer shortly afterwards. At the very end of the month Mars starts to pass in front of Praesepe, the open cluster known as the 'Beehive'. During October the magnitude of the planet brightens from +0.8 to +0.5.

JUPITER, magnitude −2.6, continues to be visible as a conspicuous object in the western sky in the evenings. Jupiter is still well south of the Equator and even though observers in the southern hemisphere are more favourably placed than those further north, they will still lose it over the western horizon well before midnight. Jupiter reaches its second stationary point on 13 October and therefore recommences its eastward motion.

SATURN, magnitude +1.1, is slowly emerging from the morning twilight and becomes visible after the first week of the month to observers in northern and equatorial latitudes, and about a fortnight later for observers further south. It will be visible low above the eastern horizon for a short while before the morning twilight inhibits observation. Saturn is in the constellation of Virgo. On 8 October, Mercury, magnitude −0.7, passes 0.3° south of Saturn, and Venus, magnitude −3.9, passes 0.5° south of Saturn five days later.

The Eastern Sea. This is a very special anniversary year for lunar observers, and certainly for me. Half a century ago this month, in October 1959, the Russian spacecraft Lunik 3 flew round the Moon, and sent back the first pictures of the areas which are always turned away from the Earth and which therefore we can never see (Figure 27).

Like all major planetary satellites, the Moon has synchronous rotation, i.e. its orbital period is equal to its axial rotation period. There is no mystery about this; gravitational forces over the ages are responsible. However, while the rotational speed is constant, the orbital speed is not, and the result is that altogether, over time, we can see 59 per cent of the lunar surface; it is only the remaining 41 per cent which is permanently averted. The edges of the disc, brought in and out of view by what are called libration effects (as the Moon appears to rock very slightly back and forth and from side to side) are very foreshortened. I spent many years in trying to map them, and I produced charts which, I am proud to say, were found to be useful in the pre-Lunar-Orbiter days. But there is one case in which I must put the record straight.

In 1946, using my 12½-inch reflector, I came across something that I did not recognize. Under maximum eastern libration, I saw what looked like the edge of a lunar mare region. The more I looked the more certain I became. I notified the BAA Lunar Section, then directed by H. P. Wilkins, and photographs were taken; I saw it again later, when the libration was favourable, and suggested a name: Mare Orientalis, the Eastern Sea.

Then came Lunik 3, followed by the Lunar Orbiters. There was the Eastern Sea – but instead of being a minor feature, it turned out to be a vast ringed basin over 950 kilometres across, looking like a target ring

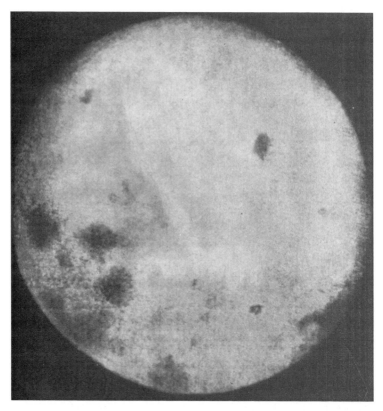

Figure 27. The Lunik 3 spacecraft returned the first views ever of the far side of the Moon. The first image was taken at 03:30 UT on 7 October 1959 at a distance of 63,500 kilometres, after Lunik 3 had passed the Moon and looked back at the sunlit far side. The last image was taken 40 minutes later from 66,700 kilometres. A total of 29 photographs were taken, covering 70 per cent of the far side. The photographs were very noisy and of low resolution, but many features could be recognized. This wide-angle view shows the far side comprising most of the image, with the near side making up about one-quarter of the disc at left. The dark patch at upper right is Mare Moscoviense and the dark areas at below and left of centre are Mare Marginus and Mare Smythii. These are on the border between the near and far sides. The small dark circle at lower right is the crater Tsiolkovsky. (Image courtesy of NASA/NSSDC/GSFC.)

bull's-eye. (Figure 28). The International Astronomical Union called it Mare Orientale, though subsequently east and west were reversed, so that as seen from Earth the 'Eastern Sea' is now on the western limb.

Then I discovered that the feature had been recorded as long ago as 1905 by a German observer, Julius Franz. I had never come across his account; it was never translated into English, and though I am fluent in French I speak no German at all. So I was not the first to record the Mare Orientale, as I had fondly believed. So – Dr Franz, a sincere though belated apology!

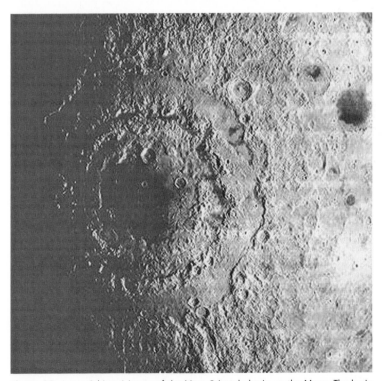

Figure 28. Lunar Orbiter 4 image of the Mare Orientale basin on the Moon. The basin forms a giant "bulls-eye" on the western limb of the Moon. Three distinct circular rings can be seen. The outermost is the Cordillera Mountain scarp, about 900 kilometres in diameter. The basin was formed by a giant impact early in the Moon's history. North is towards the top. (Image courtesy of NASA NSSDC.)

By now we have detailed maps of the entire Moon, and those Lunik 3 images seem very rudimentary, but they were the first, and to me they were immensely exciting.

Fomalhaut. This is the best time of the year for British observers to see Fomalhaut in Piscis Austrinus (the Southern Fish), southernmost of the first-magnitude stars ever visible from the latitudes of the British Isles. Fomalhaut is very low down in the south; locate it by using the two stars which form the right-hand side of the Square of Pegasus (Scheat and Markab) as guides. Do not confuse Fomalhaut with Diphda (Beta Ceti), which is well to the west, much higher up, and a magnitude fainter.

Fomalhaut is interesting because this white Main Sequence star is one of our nearer stellar neighbours, only 25 light years distant, and may well be the centre of a newly forming planetary system. Hubble Space Telescope observations have revealed that the star is surrounded by a dusty disc of debris, which probably contains planetary 'embryos' as large as Pluto that are now undergoing runaway growth into larger bodies. Further observations showed that the dusty disc is off-centre with respect to Fomalhaut itself, and has a very sharply defined inner edge, possibly due to the presence of a Neptune-sized planet in orbit just inside the disc.

We Britons never see Fomalhaut to advantage (from northern Scotland you will be lucky to see it at all), but go now to Australia or New Zealand; Fomalhaut will be nearly overhead, and you will appreciate what an imposing star it really is. It is very isolated; the Southern Fish contains no other star as bright as the fourth magnitude.

November

New Moon: 16 November   *Full Moon*: 2 November

MERCURY is unobservable at first as it passes through superior conjunction on 5 November, but during the last week of the month it becomes visible to observers in equatorial and southern latitudes as an evening object. It will be seen above the west-south-western horizon about the time of end of evening civil twilight. Its magnitude is +0.6.

VENUS continues to be visible as a brilliant object in the eastern sky before sunrise, magnitude −3.9. As Venus moves closer to the Sun the period available for observation is decreasing, particularly for those in the northern hemisphere, as the planet is also moving southwards in declination.

MARS, its magnitude brightening from +0.4 to 0.0 during November, is becoming a more prominent object in the eastern sky before midnight. The diagram shows the path of Mars among the stars during the later months of the year (Figure 29).

JUPITER, magnitude −2.3, continues to be visible in the western sky in the early part of the evening. The four Galilean satellites, which Galileo first saw in January 1610, are readily observable with a small telescope or even a good pair of binoculars, provided that they are held rigidly.

SATURN continues to be visible as a morning object in the southeastern quadrant of the sky, magnitude +1.1. Saturn is in the constellation of Virgo.

Farewell to the Beer Sea! Mars is now coming into view. It is still a long way away, and its disc is small, but enthusiastic observers will already be starting work; opposition is due late next January. Many spacecraft have now been sent there, and more will follow. Talk of a manned

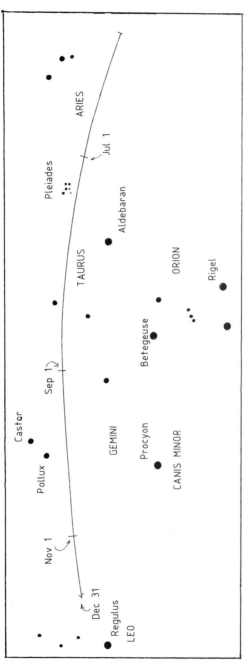

Figure 29. The path of Mars as it moves through the Zodiacal constellations from Aries to Leo between June and December 2009.

Martian base seems much less futuristic now than a journey to the Moon did in, say, 1950.

It seems strange now to reflect that as late as the nineteenth century it was still thought that there were extensive oceans on Mars. They were named accordingly, and it is fascinating to look back at the old charts. Those reproduced here were drawn by the well-known English astronomer, Richard Anthony Proctor, in 1867, and were based on the Reverend William Rutter Dawes' earlier drawings of 1865, then the best ones available. Many of the features are identifiable, even though they are curiously shaped. In 1877, Giovanni Schiaparelli introduced a completely new system of nomenclature, and this is the basis of the system we use today.

The main dark area is of course the V-shaped Syrtis Major, which is visible even when the planet's disc is small (look for it this month). Proctor's chart (Figure 30) shows it clearly; it leads off the Dawes Ocean and extends into the Kaiser Sea. Both these names honoured planetary observers; Dawes, nicknamed 'the Eagle-Eyed', was noted for his remarkable eyesight. Proctor's nomenclature never became popular overseas, mainly because so many of his names honoured

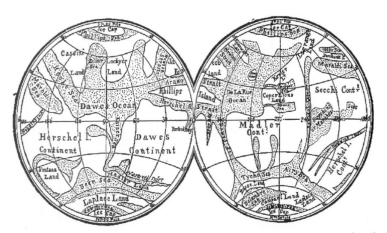

Figure 30. R.A. Proctor's 1867 map of Mars showing the Beer Sea. The map was based on drawings of Mars made by the keen-sighted observer William Rutter Dawes. It is worth noting that Proctor showed no canal-like features, although he did believe that he was seeing evidence for the presence of continents and oceans on Mars. Proctor's choice of the zero meridian for Mars is still currently accepted.

English astronomers, but also because he used many names more than once. Dawes appeared no fewer than six times (Dawes Ocean, Dawes Continent, Dawes Sea, Dawes Strait, Dawes Isle, and Dawes Forked Bay).

Above (south) of the Dawes Ocean we find Lockyer Land, named after Norman Lockyer. This feature can become so bright that it has been mistaken for an extra polar cap, and was assumed to be a snow-covered plateau. Schiaparelli renamed it 'Hellas' (Greece), and it is a huge impact basin, the deepest on Mars, which becomes brilliant when filled with clouds. Leading off the Dawes Ocean is Herschel II Strait (our Sinus Sabaeus), commemorating Sir John Herschel, son of Sir William; Dawes Continent is our Aeria and Arabia; Hooke Sea is Mare Tyrrhenum; Maraldi Sea is the Maria Cimmerium and Sirenum; De La Rue Ocean is Mare Erythraeum – and so on.

Inappropriate and inconvenient though they are, we have to admit that there is something attractive about these old names. One that I am very sad to lose is the Beer Sea, named after the German astronomer (Wilhelm Beer) who, with Johann Heinrich von Mädler, produced the most complete contemporary map of the Moon – *Mappa Selenographica* (1834–1836) – and the first systematic map of Mars ever made (1840). The Beer Sea seems to include the areas we now call Neith Regio, Meroe Insula and Umbra, but to future Mars colonists it would be a most significant address!

The Longest Star Name? Generally, proper names for stars are used only for stars of the first magnitude, plus a few special cases, such as Mizar and Algol. The rest have lapsed, though they are still on record. What is the longest? I searched some old records, and found Omicron Piscium in the Zodiacal constellation of the Fishes, which is of spectral type K and shines modestly at magnitude 4.3. It rejoices in the name of Torcularis Septentrionalis. I think I will continue to refer to it as Omicron Piscium.

Incidentally, in the same constellation Alpha Piscium (magnitude 3.8) can be called Al Rischa, Alrescha, Elrescha, Kaitaïn, or Okda. Take your pick!

December

New Moon: 16 December   *Full Moon*: 2 December

Solstice: 21 December

MERCURY reaches its greatest eastern elongation (20°) on 18 December and is visible as an evening object to observers in tropical and southern latitudes for all except the last few days of the year. Mercury can be seen in the west-south-western sky about the time of the end of evening civil twilight. During this apparition its magnitude fades from −0.5 to +1.1.

VENUS is still a morning object, low above the eastern horizon for a short while before dawn, magnitude −4.1. Observers in northern temperate latitudes will only be able to see it for about the first ten days of the month, those in the tropics for the first three weeks of the month, while observers further south will only see it for a few days longer than those in northern temperate latitudes.

MARS, its magnitude brightening from −0.1 to −0.7 during the month, continues to be a prominent object in the sky from the late evening onwards. Mars is now in Leo. Its easterly motion is slowing down appreciably as it reaches its first stationary point on 20 December and starts its retrograde motion. The year 2009 is unusual as far as Mars is concerned – there is neither a conjunction nor an opposition. There was a conjunction in December 2008 and the next opposition will not occur until January 2010.

JUPITER continues to be visible as a splendid early evening object in the western sky. There will be another good opportunity for locating Neptune on or near 20 December, when Jupiter passes only about 0.5° south of the fainter planet. Jupiter's magnitude is −2.2, while that of Neptune is +7.8, a difference in brightness of 10,000 times! Because of the glare from Jupiter it is advisable to use a telescope with as long a focal length as possible.

SATURN, magnitude +1.1, moving eastwards in Virgo, continues to be visible in the eastern sky in the mornings, and by the end of December becomes visible to observers in the northern hemisphere shortly after midnight.

Eclipses of the Moon. The year ends, very fittingly, with a partial eclipse of the Moon on 31 December. It is visible from Britain and the whole of mainland Europe; the eclipse begins at 18h 52m and ends at 21h 30m, but it will not be spectacular, since at maximum eclipse no more than 8 per cent of the Moon will be immersed in the Earth's shadow. Indeed, casual observers may not notice that an eclipse is in progress at all. Even a total lunar eclipse is not striking, though it has a quiet beauty. One eclipse, that of 29 February 1504, was used to advantage by Christopher Columbus. His ship was anchored off Jamaica, and the natives refused to supply his men with provisions. Knowing that a lunar eclipse was due, Columbus said firmly that unless they cooperated, he would 'extinguish the Moon'. When the eclipse started, the Jamaicans were so terrified that thereafter they did exactly what Columbus wanted.

It cannot be said that a lunar eclipse is important, but it was once thought to have effects upon certain features. William Henry Pickering, the last-century American astronomer who specialized in Solar System work, believed that ice could exist on the Moon's surface, and that frost could form in some areas; he cited Linné, on the Mare Serenitatis (Figure 31), which is a fresh young crater, only 2.4 kilometres across, surrounded by a bright patch. During a lunar eclipse, a wave of cold sweeps across the Moon, and Pickering believed that Linné would increase in size and brilliance. Very careful measurements were made, but with negative results. During a number of lunar eclipses I paid close attention to Linné, which is a completely normal, small-impact crater. But nothing unusual has ever been seen, and all ideas of lunar frost belong to the past. In any case this month's partial eclipse is so small that the shadow will not reach anywhere near the region of Linné.

Lunar eclipses can sometimes show beautiful colours; everything depends upon conditions in the Earth's upper atmosphere, through

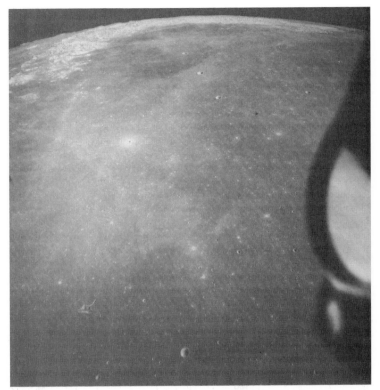

Figure 31. Apollo 15 view over the Mare Serenitatis, showing the Caucasus Mountains at the top left and the irregular Krishna depression at bottom. The small, bright crater Linné is clearly visible above centre. (Image courtesy of NASA.)

which all sunlight reaching the eclipsed Moon has to pass. I doubt whether any obvious colours will be seen at this month's eclipse – but one never knows.

The Brightest Variable Star. Excluding novae, what is the brightest variable star in the sky? If we limit this to stars which vary by more than a few-tenths of a magnitude, and also exclude the unique Eta Carinae, there can be only one answer; Betelgeux (or Betelgeuse), the semi-regular pulsating red supergiant in Orion (Figure 32).

Normally Betelgeux is of around magnitude 0.6 or 0.7, decidedly fainter than Rigel (Beta Orionis) but brighter than Aldebaran (Alpha

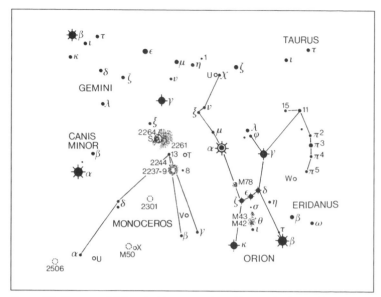

Figure 32. The stars of Orion, the Hunter, together with some bright neighbouring stars which may be used as comparisons when estimating the brightness of the semi-regular pulsating red supergiant star Betelgeux (Alpha Orionis).

Tauri). Betelgeux's variability was first noticed by Sir John Herschel in 1836. When at maximum, Betelgeux sometimes rises to magnitude 0.4, slightly fainter than Rigel, although the star probably reached magnitude 0.2 (near equality with Rigel) in 1933 and 1942. At minimum, as in 1927 and 1941, the magnitude may drop to 1.2, somewhat fainter than Aldebaran. Betelgeux is classed as a semi-regular star, having a main period of around 5.7 years, with shorter periods of 150 to 400 days superimposed, but these periods are decidedly rough.

Naked-eye estimates are not as easy as might be expected, for two reasons. First, there is a dearth of suitable comparison stars, and of these only Aldebaran is orange-red; the rest are of the earlier spectral type, and it is never easy to compare a red or orange star with a star which is white or bluish. Secondly, the comparison star will seldom or never be at the same altitude as Betelgeux, so that atmospheric extinction has to be taken into account. Yet it is always interesting trying to follow the slow changes of the red supergiant; use Procyon (magnitude 0.34), Aldebaran (0.85), and Pollux (1.14) – Pollux will almost certainly be too faint, while Rigel (0.12), and Capella (0.08) will be too bright.

Telescopically, Betelgeux is a lovely sight. It has even been called the most beautiful star in the whole of the night sky.

Eclipses in 2009

During 2009 there will be six eclipses, two of the Sun and four of the Moon.

1. *An annular eclipse of the Sun* on 26 January is visible as a partial eclipse from the southern Ocean, part of Antarctica, southern Africa, the Indian Ocean, Madagascar, southern and eastern India, part of south-west Asia, Indonesia, and Australia. The partial phase begins at 04h 57m and ends at 11h 01m. The track of annularity commences in the Southern Ocean, south of South Africa, at 06h 03m, crosses the Indian Ocean, southern Sumatra and Borneo before ending in the Celebes Sea at 09h 55m. The maximum duration of annularity is 7m 54s.

2. *A penumbral eclipse of the Moon* on 9 February lasts from 12h 37m to 16h 40m and is visible from north America, Australasia, Asia, eastern Europe, and eastern Africa.

3. *A penumbral eclipse of the Moon* on 7 July lasts from 08h 33m to 10h 44m, and is visible from the Americas and Australasia.

4. *A total eclipse of the Sun* on 21–22 July is visible as a partial eclipse from the eastern part of Africa, Madagascar, Asia, part of Indonesia, the extreme north-eastern tip of Australia, and the extreme northern part of North Island, New Zealand. The partial phase begins at 21d 23h 58m and ends at 22d 05h 12m. The path of totality starts just off the west coast of India, crosses India, the extreme north of Burma, China, passes south of Japan, and ends in the Pacific Ocean south of the Hawaiian Islands. Totality begins at 22d 00h 51m and ends at 22d 04h 19m. The maximum duration of totality is 6m 39s, but this occurs over the Pacific Ocean, several hundred kilometres north-east of Iwo Jima. This eclipse belongs to the famous 'Saros 136', which produced the longest duration total solar eclipses of the twentieth century. Sadly, Saros 136 is now past its best. The long duration total solar eclipses of

8 June 1937, 20 June 1955 and 30 June 1973 were all over seven minutes duration at their peak, but the 'six-minute plus' era of this Saros will end with the total solar eclipses of 2 August 2027 and 12 August 2045.

5. *A penumbral eclipse of the Moon* on 6–7 August lasts from 23h 01m to 02h 18m, and is visible from western Asia, Africa, Europe and the Americas, except north-west USA.

6. *A partial eclipse of the Moon* on 31 December is visible from Australasia, Asia, the Indian Ocean, Africa, Europe, Iceland, the Atlantic Ocean, Greenland, northern Canada, Alaska, and part of eastern Brazil. The eclipse begins at 18h 52m and ends at 21h 30m. At maximum eclipse only 8 per cent of the Moon's surface is obscured.

Occultations in 2009

In the course of its journey round the sky each month, the Moon passes in front of all the stars in its path, and the timing of these occultations is useful in fixing the position and motion of the Moon. The Moon's orbit is tilted at more than 5° to the ecliptic, but it is not fixed in space. It twists steadily westwards at a rate of about 20° a year, a complete revolution taking 18.6 years, during which time all the stars that lie within about 6.5° of the ecliptic will be occulted. The occultations of any one star continue month after month until the Moon's path has twisted away from the star, but only a few of these occultations will be visible from any one place during the hours of darkness.

There are nine lunar occultations of bright planets in 2009, two of Mercury, two of Venus, three of Mars, and two of Jupiter.

Only four first-magnitude stars are near enough to the ecliptic to be occulted by the Moon: these are Aldebaran, Regulus, Spica, and Antares. Only Antares is occulted during 2009.

Predictions of these occultations are made on a worldwide basis for all stars down to magnitude 7.5, and sometimes even fainter. The British Astronomical Association has produced a complete lunar-occultation-prediction package for personal computer users.

Occultations of stars by planets (including minor planets) and satellites have aroused considerable attention.

The exact timing of such events gives valuable information about positions, sizes, orbits, atmospheres, and sometimes of the presence of satellites. The discovery of the rings of Uranus in 1977 was the unexpected result of the observations made of a predicted occultation of a faint star by Uranus. The duration of an occultation by a satellite or minor planet is quite small (usually of the order of a minute or less). If observations are made from a number of stations it is possible to deduce the size of the planet.

The observations need to be made either photoelectrically or visually. The high accuracy of the method can readily be appreciated when one realizes that even a stopwatch timing accurate to a tenth of a second is, on average, equivalent to an accuracy of about 1 kilometre in the chord measured across the minor planet.

Comets in 2009

The appearance of a bright comet is a rare event which can never be predicted in advance, because this class of object travels round the Sun in enormous orbits with periods which may well be many thousands of years. There are therefore no records of the previous appearances of these bodies, and we are unable to follow their wanderings through space.

Comets of short period, on the other hand, return at regular intervals, and attract a good deal of attention from astronomers. Unfortunately they are all faint objects, and are recovered and followed by photographic methods using large telescopes. Most of these short-period comets travel in orbits of small inclination which reach out to the orbit of Jupiter, and it is this planet that is mainly responsible for the severe perturbations that many of these comets undergo. Unlike the planets, comets may be seen in any part of the sky, but since their distances from the Earth are similar to those of the planets, their apparent movements in the sky are also somewhat similar, and some of them may be followed for long periods of time.

The following periodic and three non-periodic comets are expected to reach perihelion in 2009, and to be brighter than magnitude +15.

Comet	Year of Discovery	Period (years)	Predicted Date of Perihelion 2009
P/Christensen (2003 K2)	2003	5.7	Jan 8
Lulin (2007 N3)	2007	–	Jan 10
68P/Klemola	1965	10.8	Jan 21
144P/Kushida	1994	7.6	Jan 26
67P/Churyumov-Gerasimenko	1969	6.5	Feb 28
22P/Kopff	1906	6.4	May 25
64P/Swift-Gehrels	1889	9.3	Jun 14
P/LINEAR (2003 A1)	2003	7.5	Jun 16
Christensen (2006 W3)	2006	–	Jul 6

Comet	Year of Discovery	Period (years)	Predicted Date of Perihelion 2009
116P/Wild 4	1990	6.5	Jul 19
24P/Shaumasse	1911	8.3	Aug 9
P/LINEAR (2004 X1)	2004	4.8	Sep 3
P/LINEAR (2001 MD$_7$)	2001	7.8	Sep 9
88P/Howell	1981	5.5	Oct 12
Siding Spring (2007 Q3)	2007	–	Oct 19
169P/NEAT	2002	4.2	Nov 30

Some ephemerides of comets which should be visible to observers with small telescopes in 2009 are given below.

Comet 85P/Boethin

(continued from the *2008 Yearbook of Astronomy*)

Date 2009 0^h		2000.0 RA		Dec.	Distance from Earth AU	Distance from Sun AU	Elong- ation from Sun °	Mag.
	h	m	°	'				
Jan 04	23	57.20	+05	34.0	0.883	1.177	78.0	7.6
Jan 09	00	18.86	+08	03.0	0.895	1.195	78.8	7.8
Jan 14	00	40.86	+10	28.2	0.912	1.216	79.7	8.0
Jan 19	01	03.07	+12	47.1	0.934	1.241	80.6	8.2
Jan 24	01	25.37	+14	57.4	0.962	1.268	81.3	8.5
Jan 29	01	47.60	+16	57.3	0.995	1.299	82.0	8.8
Feb 03	02	09.63	+18	45.3	1.034	1.332	82.5	9.1

Comet Lulin (2007 N3)

Date 2009 0ʰ	2000.0 RA h m	Dec. ° ′	Distance from Earth AU	Distance from Sun AU	Elong- ation from Sun °	Mag.
Jan 04	15 58.11	−19 36.2	1.751	1.217	42.2	8.6
Jan 09	15 54.39	−19 25.8	1.622	1.213	48.2	8.4
Jan 14	15 49.60	−19 11.7	1.485	1.213	54.4	8.2
Jan 19	15 43.30	−18 52.4	1.340	1.219	61.0	8.0
Jan 24	15 34.86	−18 24.9	1.190	1.230	68.2	7.8
Jan 29	15 23.22	−17 44.3	1.035	1.246	76.1	7.5
Feb 03	15 06.61	−16 41.3	0.879	1.266	85.3	7.2
Feb 08	14 42.01	−14 57.3	0.727	1.290	96.5	6.9
Feb 13	14 04.19	−11 54.8	0.586	1.318	111.3	6.5
Feb 18	13 05.32	−06 25.9	0.472	1.350	131.8	6.2
Feb 23	11 40.91	+02 15.2	0.414	1.385	159.7	6.0
Feb 28	10 06.97	+11 23.6	0.436	1.423	170.3	6.2
Mar 05	08 51.60	+17 09.1	0.531	1.463	146.2	6.8
Mar 10	08 01.81	+19 53.4	0.668	1.506	129.0	7.4
Mar 15	07 30.34	+21 08.6	0.825	1.551	116.6	8.0
Mar 20	07 10.15	+21 44.9	0.993	1.597	106. 9	8.5
Mar 25	06 56.90	+22 03.6	1.164	1.645	98.8	9.0
Mar 30	06 48.09	+22 13.6	1.337	1.694	91.8	9.4

Comet 22P/Kopff

Date 2009 0ʰ	2000.0 RA h m	Dec. ° ′	Distance from Earth AU	Distance from Sun AU	Elong- ation from Sun °	Mag.
Apr 19	20 05.72	−16 27.9	1.290	1.620	88.9	9.0
Apr 24	20 19.29	−15 53.3	1.248	1.609	90.4	8.9
Apr 29	20 32.63	−15 16.7	1.208	1.600	92.0	8.7
May 04	20 45.71	−14 38.7	1.170	1.592	93.7	8.6
May 09	20 58.48	−13 59.8	1.133	1.586	95.3	8.5
May 14	21 10.91	−13 20.5	1.099	1.582	97.1	8.4
May 19	21 22.94	−12 41.6	1.066	1.579	98.9	8.3

Comet 22P/Kopff – *cont.*

Date 2009 0h	RA h	m	Dec. °	′	Distance from Earth AU	Distance from Sun AU	Elong- ation from Sun °	Mag.
May 24	21	34.51	−12	03.9	1.034	1.578	100.8	8.2
May 29	21	45.59	−11	27.9	1.004	1.578	102.9	8.2
Jun 03	21	56.11	−10	54.4	0.976	1.580	105.1	8.1
Jun 08	22	06.03	−10	24.1	0.950	1.584	107.4	8.1
Jun 13	22	15.29	−09	57.6	0.924	1.589	109.9	8.1
Jun 18	22	23.83	−09	35.6	0.901	1.595	112.6	8.0
Jun 23	22	31.59	−09	18.9	0.878	1.604	115.4	8.1
Jun 28	22	38.51	−09	07.8	0.858	1.613	118.6	8.1
Jul 03	22	44.53	−09	02.9	0.839	1.625	121.9	8.1
Jul 08	22	49.62	−09	04.4	0.822	1.637	125.5	8.1
Jul 13	22	53.73	−09	12.6	0.807	1.651	129.4	8.2
Jul 18	22	56.83	−09	27.4	0.795	1.666	133.5	8.3

Minor Planets in 2009

Although many thousands of minor planets (asteroids) are known to exist, only a few thousand of them have well-determined orbits and are listed in the catalogues. Most of these orbits lie entirely between the orbits of Mars and Jupiter. All these bodies are quite small, and even the largest, Ceres, is only 913 km (567 miles) in diameter. Thus, they are necessarily faint objects, and although a number of them are within the reach of a small telescope few of them ever attain any considerable brightness. The first four that were discovered are named Ceres, Pallas, Juno, and Vesta. Actually the largest four minor planets are Ceres, Pallas, Vesta, and Hygeia. Vesta can occasionally be seen with the naked eye, and this is most likely to happen when an opposition occurs near June, since Vesta would then be at perihelion. Below are ephemerides for Ceres, Pallas, Juno, and Vesta in 2009.

1 Ceres

Date		RA (2000.0) h	m	Dec. °	′	Geo-centric Distance	Helio-centric Distance	Elong-ation °	Visual Magni-tude
Jan	4	11	18.56	+18	12.7	1.916	2.549	120	+7.8
Jan	14	11	20.98	+19	4.6	1.812	2.548	129	+7.6
Jan	24	11	20.60	+20	11.9	1.722	2.547	139	+7.4
Feb	3	11	17.39	+21	30.1	1.653	2.547	149	+7.2
Feb	13	11	11.58	+22	51.6	1.606	2.547	158	+7.0
Feb	23	11	3.81	+24	6.9	1.584	2.547	163	+6.9
Mar	5	10	55.06	+25	6.7	1.590	2.548	161	+6.9
Mar	15	10	46.56	+25	43.7	1.621	2.549	153	+7.1
Mar	25	10	39.40	+25	55.1	1.676	2.550	144	+7.3
Apr	4	10	34.44	+25	41.3	1.752	2.552	134	+7.5
Apr	14	10	32.12	+25	5.5	1.845	2.554	125	+7.7
Apr	24	10	32.49	+24	11.6	1.950	2.556	116	+7.9
May	4	10	35.41	+23	3.2	2.065	2.559	108	+8.1
May	14	10	40.59	+21	43.5	2.186	2.562	100	+8.2

1 Ceres – *cont.*

Date		RA		Dec.		Geo-centric Distance	Helio-centric Distance	Elong-ation	Visual Magni-tude
		h	m	°	′			°	
May	24	10	47.68	+20	14.7	2.310	2.566	93	+8.3
Jun	3	10	56.40	+18	38.8	2.436	2.569	86	+8.5
Jun	13	11	6.43	+16	57.0	2.562	2.573	79	+8.6
Jun	23	11	17.54	+15	10.5	2.685	2.578	73	+8.7
Jul	3	11	29.55	+13	20.1	2.805	2.582	67	+8.7
Jul	13	11	42.27	+11	26.8	2.920	2.587	61	+8.8
Jul	23	11	55.60	+ 9	31.2	3.030	2.593	55	+8.8
Aug	2	12	9.45	+ 7	34.1	3.133	2.598	50	+8.8
Aug	12	12	23.72	+ 5	36.1	3.229	2.604	44	+8.9
Aug	22	12	38.38	+ 3	38.1	3.317	2.610	39	+8.9
Sep	1	12	53.39	+ 1	40.6	3.395	2.616	34	+8.8

2 Pallas

Date		RA		Dec.		Geo-centric Distance	Helio-centric Distance	Elong-ation	Visual Magni-tude
		h	m	°	′			°	
Jan	4	4	49.80	−31	10.1	1.591	2.227	118	+8.0
Jan	14	4	45.88	−29	11.5	1.622	2.212	114	+8.1
Jan	24	4	45.05	−26	40.8	1.663	2.198	110	+8.2
Feb	3	4	47.45	−23	47.9	1.712	2.185	105	+8.2
Feb	13	4	52.92	−20	42.1	1.768	2.174	100	+8.3
Feb	23	5	1.18	−17	31.1	1.832	2.164	96	+8.4
Mar	5	5	11.90	−14	21.2	1.901	2.155	91	+8.5
Mar	15	5	24.76	−11	17.8	1.975	2.148	86	+8.6
Mar	25	5	39.43	− 8	24.5	2.053	2.142	81	+8.6
Apr	4	5	55.66	− 5	44.3	2.136	2.137	77	+8.7
Apr	14	6	13.17	− 3	19.5	2.221	2.134	72	+8.8
Apr	24	6	31.72	− 1	11.4	2.309	2.133	67	+8.8
May	4	6	51.12	+ 0	39.1	2.398	2.133	63	+8.9
May	14	7	11.15	+ 2	11.7	2.488	2.134	58	+8.9
May	24	7	31.65	+ 3	26.6	2.578	2.137	54	+9.0
Jun	3	7	52.48	+ 4	24.3	2.666	2.142	49	+9.0

2 Pallas – *cont.*

Date		RA		Dec.		Geo-centric Distance	Helio-centric Distance	Elong-ation	Visual Magni-tude
		h	m	°	′			°	
Jun	13	8	13.47	+ 5	5.6	2.752	2.147	44	+9.0
Jun	23	8	34.54	+ 5	31.8	2.835	2.155	40	+9.0
Jul	3	8	55.58	+ 5	43.9	2.914	2.164	35	+9.0

3 Juno

Date		RA		Dec.		Geo-centric Distance	Helio-centric Distance	Elong-ation	Visual Magni-tude
		h	m	°	′			°	
Aug	6	0	13.41	+ 3	26.5	1.550	2.327	129	+8.9
Aug	16	0	14.62	+ 2	34.0	1.440	2.300	139	+8.6
Aug	26	0	13.30	+ 1	15.1	1.346	2.274	149	+8.4
Sep	5	0	9.59	− 0	28.4	1.274	2.249	160	+8.1
Sep	15	0	3.94	− 2	30.5	1.224	2.224	172	+7.8
Sep	25	23	57.20	− 4	40.9	1.200	2.200	174	+7.7
Oct	5	23	50.51	− 6	46.1	1.202	2.177	163	+7.9
Oct	15	23	45.08	− 8	33.7	1.228	2.154	151	+8.1
Oct	25	23	41.84	− 9	54.8	1.275	2.133	140	+8.2
Nov	4	23	41.42	−10	45.2	1.339	2.113	129	+8.4
Nov	14	23	43.99	−11	5.3	1.417	2.094	120	+8.6
Nov	24	23	49.47	−10	57.3	1.504	2.076	111	+8.8
Dec	4	23	57.59	−10	24.8	1.597	2.060	103	+8.9

4 Vesta

Date		RA		Dec.		Geo-centric Distance	Helio-centric Distance	Elong-ation	Visual Magni-tude
		h	m	°	′			°	
Jan	4	2	3.75	+ 5	16.4	2.089	2.554	107	+7.7
Jan	14	2	8.74	+ 6	22.8	2.223	2.558	98	+7.8
Jan	24	2	15.78	+ 7	35.9	2.359	2.561	90	+8.0
Feb	3	2	24.61	+ 8	53.7	2.496	2.563	83	+8.1

4 Vesta – *cont.*

Date		RA		Dec.		Geo-centric Distance	Helio-centric Distance	Elong-ation	Visual Magni-tude
		h	m	°	′			°	
Feb	13	2	34.98	+10	14.1	2.630	2.566	75	+8.2
Feb	23	2	46.67	+11	35.5	2.760	2.568	68	+8.3
Mar	5	2	59.53	+12	56.4	2.884	2.569	62	+8.3
Mar	15	3	13.38	+14	15.4	3.000	2.571	55	+8.4
Mar	25	3	28.12	+15	31.4	3.108	2.571	49	+8.4
Apr	4	3	43.63	+16	43.2	3.206	2.572	43	+8.5
Apr	14	3	59.82	+17	50.0	3.293	2.572	38	+8.5
Apr	24	4	16.60	+18	50.8	3.370	2.571	32	+8.5
Sep	1	8	14.44	+20	11.5	3.259	2.530	37	+8.4
Sep	11	8	31.66	+19	28.4	3.168	2.525	43	+8.4
Sep	21	8	48.38	+18	41.7	3.067	2.519	49	+8.4
Oct	1	9	4.49	+17	52.9	2.958	2.512	55	+8.3
Oct	11	9	19.93	+17	3.3	2.840	2.506	61	+8.3
Oct	21	9	34.59	+16	14.7	2.715	2.499	67	+8.2
Oct	31	9	48.34	+15	28.9	2.584	2.491	74	+8.1
Nov	10	10	1.03	+14	47.9	2.448	2.484	80	+8.0
Nov	20	10	12.49	+14	14.2	2.310	2.476	88	+7.9
Nov	30	10	22.46	+13	50.3	2.171	2.468	95	+7.7
Dec	10	10	30.71	+13	38.8	2.034	2.459	104	+7.6
Dec	20	10	36.91	+13	42.5	1.902	2.451	112	+7.4
Dec	30	10	40.71	+14	3.8	1.777	2.442	122	+7.2

Meteors in 2009

Meteors ('shooting stars') may be seen on any clear moonless night, but on certain nights of the year their number increases noticeably. This occurs when the Earth chances to intersect a concentration of meteoric dust moving in an orbit around the Sun. If the dust is well spread out in space, the resulting shower of meteors may last for several days. The word 'shower' must not be misinterpreted – only on very rare occasions have the meteors been so numerous as to resemble snowflakes falling.

If the meteor tracks are marked on a star map and traced backwards, a number of them will be found to intersect in a point (or a small area of the sky) which marks the radiant of the shower. This gives the direction from which the meteors have come.

The following table gives some of the more easily observed showers with their radiants; interference by moonlight is shown by the letter M.

Limiting Dates	Shower	Maximum	RA		Dec.	
			h	m	°	
Jan 1–6	Quadrantids	Jan 3	15	28	+50	
April 19–25	Lyrids	Apr 22	18	08	+32	
May 1–8	Aquarids	May 4	22	20	−01	
June 17–26	Ophiuchids	June 19	17	20	−20	
July 29–Aug 6	Delta Aquarids	July 29	22	36	−17	M
July 15–Aug 20	Piscids Australids	July 31	22	40	−30	M
July 15–Aug 20	Capricornids	Aug 2	20	36	−10	M
July 23–Aug 20	Perseids	Aug 12	3	04	+58	M
Oct 16–27	Orionids	Oct 20	6	24	+15	
Oct 20–Nov 30	Taurids	Nov 3	3	44	+14	M
Nov 15–20	Leonids	Nov 17	10	08	+22	
Nov 27–Jan.	Puppids-Velids	Dec 9–26	9	00	−48	M
Dec 7–16	Geminids	Dec 13	7	32	+33	
Dec 17–25	Ursids	Dec 22	14	28	+78	

Some Events in 2010

ECLIPSES

There will be four eclipses, two of the Sun and two of the Moon.

15 January:	Annular eclipse of the Sun – Central Africa, Indian Ocean, Asia
26 June:	Partial eclipse of the Moon – Pacific Ocean, North America, Australasia, Asia
11 July:	Total eclipse of the Sun – Pacific Ocean, South America
21 December:	Total eclipse of the Moon – West Africa, Europe, The Americas, Australasia, Asia

THE PLANETS

Mercury may be seen more easily from northern latitudes in the evenings about the time of greatest eastern elongation (8 April) and in the mornings about the time of greatest western elongation (19 September). In the Southern Hemisphere the corresponding most favourable dates are 7 August (evenings) and 26 May (mornings).

Venus is visible from late February to October in the evenings, and in the mornings from November onwards.

Mars is at opposition on 29 January in Cancer.

Jupiter is at opposition on 21 September in Pisces.

Saturn is at opposition on 22 March in Virgo.

Uranus is at opposition on 21 September in Pisces.

Neptune is at opposition on 20 August in Capricornus.

Pluto is at opposition on 25 June in Sagittarius.

Part II

Article Section

Telescopes for Titans:
The GODs of the Future

CHRIS KITCHIN

The next two or three decades are going to be amongst the most exciting years ever witnessed by astronomers. We are at the starting post and the gun has just been fired to set off the fifth telescope race. The race will, in many peoples' lifetimes, see *optical* telescopes as large as the 250-foot (76-metre) Lovell *Radio* Telescope (Figure 1) probing the remotest depths of space for clues as to the origins of planets, stars, nebulae, galaxies, and of life and of the Universe itself. Giant Optical Devices (giving them the appropriate acronym of 'GODs') with sizes

Figure 1. The 250-foot Lovell Radio Telescope at Jodrell Bank. Some readers of this article could witness optical telescopes as large as this within their lifetimes. (Image courtesy of Ian Morison, University of Manchester.)

three to five times those of the largest existing telescopes could be operating within fifteen years and instruments two or three times larger than that within three decades.

EARLY TELESCOPE DESIGNS

But why should it be a race and why the fifth one? History tells us that every time a new development has occurred in the design of telescopes, astronomers and opticians have rapidly pushed that development to its practical limit by building ever larger and larger instruments. Thus Galileo's design for a telescope – which in modern terminology had first light four centuries ago this year – and its later improvement by Johannes Kepler to form the modern astronomical refractor, had within fifty years been enlarged to the point that Johannes Hevelius amongst others was using instruments 140 feet (43 metres) in length. That first telescope race ended at that point, since, being made largely of wood and string, the flimsy mountings for such long telescopes made them almost impossible to use.

The second and third telescope races took place more or less together from the end of the seventeenth to the end of the nineteenth centuries. The technological advances that underlay these races were: firstly, the invention of the various designs of reflecting telescope by James Gregory, Sir Isaac Newton, and Guillaume Cassegrain and, secondly, the invention of the achromatic lens by Chester Moor Hall and John Dollond. At the end of the races, just before the start of the twentieth century, reflecting telescopes using speculum-metal mirrors had culminated in Lord Rosse's 72-inch (1.8-metre) instrument and achromatic refractors in the 40-inch (1-metre) Yerkes Telescope. Larger telescopes than these were never made successfully because of the poor reflectivity (60 per cent at best) of speculum metal and the weight of huge lenses – which cause stress and distortion in the glass, because the lenses can only be supported around their edges.

THE FOURTH TELESCOPE RACE

The fourth telescope race occupied most of the twentieth century. The breakthrough in technology this time was the fabrication of metal-on-glass mirrors. These initially used silver and later aluminium (though silver is making a comeback today) as the reflecting layer, and reached 95 per cent or more reflectivity. When the metal layer tarnished, it could quickly be removed and replaced, leaving the mirror as good as new, whereas speculum-metal mirrors needed completely repolishing and perhaps refiguring every time. Opened in 1948, the 200-inch (5-metre) Hale Telescope on Mount Palomar (Figure 2) was the ultimate in such telescopes until the 1990s; the Russian 6-metre (236-inch) telescope, completed in 1976, is larger than the Hale Telescope, but the rather poor optics limit its usefulness. In 1993, the first of the Keck Observatory's two 10-metre (400-inch) telescopes started operations. However, these instruments belong to the fifth telescope race, not the fourth, and so we shall come back to them in a moment. The fourth telescope race thus came to an end (if indeed it has) with the Large Binocular Telescope (LBT) and its two honeycomb construction 8.4-metre (330-inch) mirrors.

Figure 2. The 200-inch (5-metre) Hale Reflecting Telescope on Mount Palomar, completed in 1948, which was the ultimate in its class until the 1990s. (Image courtesy of Palomar Observatory and California Institute of Technology.)

The forty-five year gap between the Hale and the Keck telescopes was not entirely due to our inability to make mirrors larger than 200 inches in size. It was also due to the fact that during that period, astronomers did not need larger telescopes. Over that time, the detectors used on telescopes changed from the human eye and the photographic plate to various electronic devices, culminating in the CCDs used today. Now photography detects light with only about 0.1 to 1 per cent of the efficiency of a CCD, so substituting a CCD for a photographic plate meant that an image that might take five hours' exposure on the latter could now be obtained in three minutes or less. Putting this another way – an amateur's 10-inch (0.25-metre) telescope with a CCD could now perform comparably to a professional's 100-inch (2.5-metre) telescope used photographically. Thus, fainter and more distant objects could be studied without needing to increase the size of the telescope.

THE NEED FOR LARGER TELESCOPES

However, by the late 1980s, CCDs were reaching 80% to 90% efficiency, so little further improvement could be expected from them. Astronomers wanting to see deeper and further into space thus once again had to turn to making bigger telescopes. Fortunately, the requisite technological development had occurred that permitted larger telescopes to be produced. That change was the increasing availability of computers cheap enough, fast enough, and powerful enough to be used to control the shape of telescope optics in real time. The surface of a telescope mirror must have its shape correct to within about 50 nanometres (about two-millionths of an inch) if the images that it produces are to be as good as possible. Until the 1990s, this was accomplished by making the mirrors rigid enough to keep their shapes whatever gravitational or other forces acted upon them. However, the thickness of the mirror needed to give this rigidity increases very rapidly as the diameter of the mirror increases. Thus, to reduce weight, mirrors such as those on the Hale and LBT instruments had much of their backs hollowed out, just leaving a few supporting ribs. Even so the Hale Telescope mirror weighs 14.7 tonnes, and those for the LBT, 15.6 tonnes each (Figure 3). All three mirrors and those in other large telescopes have to be supported at many points on their backs and their edges so that their weight does not distort the

Figure 3. The Large Binocular Telescope, with both of its 8.4-metre-diameter primary mirrors installed on the telescope structure and aluminized. The telescope is pointing at the horizon in this view. (Image courtesy of Ray Bertram and the Large Binocular Telescope Observatory.)

mirrors. The LBT mirrors, for example, each have 158 supporting positions.

The thirty-six supports for the Hale Telescope mirror are pivoted and have counterweights so that the forces that they apply to the mirror change as the telescope slews around the sky. Such 'active supports' soon became the norm, but with hydraulic jacks replacing the pivoted counterweights. Even the small computers of the 1960s and 1970s were able speedily to control and adjust the hydraulic jacks so that they provided the correct support wherever the telescope might point – and that brings us to the heart of the development needed for the fifth telescope race – the active support of the telescope mirror under computer control with sufficient speed and accuracy to maintain the mirror's correct shape at all times. Despite their active mirror supports, though, both the Hale and LBT telescopes remain as fourth-race instruments since their surface shapes are primarily maintained by the intrinsic rigidity of the thick mirrors.

Figure 4. Easy does it! Protected by its shipping container, the second 8.4-metre mirror of the Large Binocular Telescope ascends the road up to the summit of Mount Graham. (Image courtesy of R. Smallwood, W. Boltinghouse and the Large Binocular Telescope Observatory.)

It is probable that single rigid mirrors larger than 8.4 metres or so could now be made, but it is unlikely that any will ever be produced. Quite apart from the different approaches now taken to producing telescope mirrors, which we will discuss in a moment, the logistics of transporting huge monolithic mirrors to their sites on remote mountain tops (Figure 4) is becoming prohibitively expensive. Thus, roads would need to be constructed from scratch or existing roads widened, hills flattened, bridges strengthened, and bends straightened, etc. simply in order to get the mirror to its observatory, and these unproductive costs could soon become greater than the cost of the telescope. Also large rigid monolithic mirrors inevitably weigh many tens of tonnes and that means stronger, larger and much more expensive mountings are needed.

ACTIVE MIRROR SUPPORTS

An early attempt to get around the problems caused by large individual telescope mirrors was the Multi-Mirror Telescope (MMT). Sited on Mount Hopkins, Arizona, and opened in 1979, the MMT used six 1.8-metre (70-inch) monolithic mirrors arranged in a hexagonal array on a single mounting and feeding a common focus. Together the mirrors had a collecting area equivalent to that of a single 4.4-metre (173-inch) mirror, with just a small fraction of the latter's weight and cost. The positions of the mirrors were monitored by a laser system and the secondary mirrors adjusted under computer control to maintain all the light paths in alignment. Unfortunately the MMT did not perform to expectations and the six mirrors have now been replaced by a single 6.5-metre (256-inch) mirror.

Despite their limitations, the active supports for rigid monolithic mirrors and the MMT were the first indicators of the way ahead. The route to larger telescopes lay through abandoning the attempt to make the mirror intrinsically rigid enough to preserve the correct shape for its surface. Computer-controlled active supports would be relied upon to maintain that shape instead. The mirror itself would now be in the form of either a monolithic but thin slab of material, or made up from many smaller segments. The European Southern Observatory's (ESO) Very Large Telescope (VLT) and the two Gemini telescopes are examples of the first approach. The VLT's four 8.2-metre (323-inch) and Gemini's two 8.1-metre (320-inch) mirrors are 0.175 metres (7 inches) and 0.2 metres (8 inches) thick respectively. Had they been designed to be intrinsically rigid like the 200-inch (5-metre) mirror for the Hale Telescope, they would have needed a thickness of around 4 metres (160 inches). The VLT and Gemini mirrors sag under their own weight, so the active supports which apply carefully calculated forces to the backs and sides of the mirrors are essential to keep the shapes of their surfaces correct to within the required 50 nm (Figure 5). While both these instruments have been (and continue to be) extremely successful, their mirrors represent a developmental dead-end. Since the mirrors are monolithic, although they are considerably lighter in weight than rigid mirrors of similar sizes, they are still the same physical size – and pose the same logistical problems in their transport to their observing sites.

Figure 5. The primary mirrors of the four Unit Telescopes of ESO's Very Large Telescope (VLT) each weigh 22 tonnes and measure 8.2 metres across, but are only 17 centimetres thick. Each of them rests on 150 computer-controlled supports (shown here) that are installed in an exceedingly rigid mirror cell that weighs about 11 tonnes. The supports are an integral part of the VLT active optics system which ensures that the large mirrors always have the optimal shape. (Image courtesy of ESO.)

SEGMENTED-MIRROR TELESCOPES

Thus the second alternative is the route now being followed towards the GODs – that of fabricating a large mirror from many smaller, independently positioned and controlled segments. The fifth telescope race really started, therefore, in 1992 when first light was achieved using the 10-metre (400-inch) Keck I Telescope.

The mirror for the Keck I Telescope (and also for its twin, Keck II, completed four years later) is no longer circular in shape but is roughly hexagonal and is built up from thirty-six 1.8-metre hexagonal segments (Figure 6). The optical design of the telescopes is a modification of the Cassegrain system known as the Ritchey-Chrétien and this uses a hyperboloid shape for the main mirror. The segments thus have to be off-axis slices of that hyperbola. Producing a surface with this shape is difficult, but the opticians making the mirror used a new technique – stress polishing. Each segment was loaded down with weights until it was deformed in the opposite sense to the finally required profile. A spherical shape (easy to make) was then polished on to the surface of the segment. When the weights were removed, the segment sprang back to become the desired off-axis hyperboloid. Unfortunately when these circular segments were sawn into their final hexagonal forms, they warped. The warping was slight, but sufficient to ruin the images that the telescope would finally produce. Each segment has therefore had to be stressed again, this time by some thirty springs attached to the back surfaces, to try to correct the warping. The result is not perfect, so the Keck Telescope, which has a theoretical angular resolution of about 0.01 seconds of arc, can only achieve about 0.25 seconds of arc resolution in the visible part of the spectrum. This is not as disastrous as it may appear, though, since – even using adaptive optics to correct for the distortions caused by the Earth's atmosphere – the visible resolution would not be very much better than this. The segments of

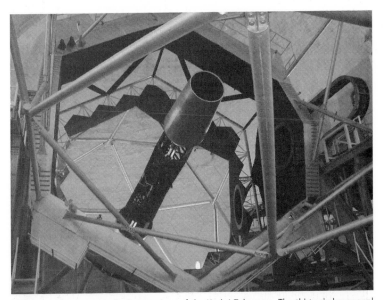

Figure 6. The segmented primary mirror of the Keck I Telescope. The thirty-six hexagonal mirror segments are arranged in the form of a honeycomb and kept in perfect alignment by a computer-operated active control system. Each mirror segment is 1.8 metres wide, 7.5 centimetres (about 3 inches) thick, and weighs about half a tonne. (Image courtesy of W. M. Keck Observatory.)

the Keck mirrors are just 75 mm (3 inches) thick and are formed from the low-expansion ceramic, Zerodur. In total the mirror weighs only 14.6 tonnes – a rigid mirror like that of the Hale Telescope with a similar diameter would weigh close to 900 tons. The thirty-six segments of the mirror are mounted on pivoted supports called 'whiffle-trees' (from their similarity to the cross-bars employed in harnessing a horse to a cart) that allow the thirty-six supports for each segment the freedom to move up and down but not from side to side. Additionally the positions of the segments are monitored twice a second to an accuracy of about 25 nm (one-millionth of an inch) by 168 electronic sensors. One hundred and eight position actuators then adjust the segments' positions as needed to maintain their correct mutual alignment.

Several other segmented-mirror telescopes are now in operation. The Hobby-Eberly Telescope (HET) at the McDonald Observatory in

Figure 7. The primary mirror array of the Hobby-Eberly Telescope (HET) is made up of ninety-one segments, and has an effective aperture of 9.2 metres. The HET sits at a fixed elevation angle of 55°, and rotates in azimuth to access 70 per cent of the sky visible from the McDonald Observatory. (Image courtesy of Marty Harris, McDonald Observatory, and the University of Texas at Austin.)

Figure 8. The 11.3-metre Gran Telescopio Canarias – currently the largest telescope in the world. (Image courtesy of Natalia Zelmanovitch, Instituto de Astrofísica de Canarias.)

Texas (Figure 7) has ninety-one 1-metre (40-inch) segments making up an 11 × 10 metre (430 × 400 inch) main mirror. The mirror is spherical in shape and so uses correcting optics to produce acceptable images. The telescope can rotate in azimuth, but points to a fixed altitude of 55° – it can therefore only observe objects for short intervals and between the declinations of −11° to +71°, but the resulting simplification in the mirror supports and the mounting reduces the instrument's cost to a fifth of that of a fully manoeuvrable telescope. The Southern African Large Telescope (SALT) in Sutherland, South Africa, is closely modelled on the HET. The currently largest telescope in the world, the Gran Telescopio Canarias (GTC), sited on La Palma in the Canary Isles (Figure 8) saw first light in July 2007 using twelve of its mirror segments. Its main mirror is composed of thirty-six 1.9-metre (75-inch) segments each 80 mm (3.1 inches) thick and weighing 470 kg – making a mirror with a final diameter of 11.3 metres (445 inches – equivalent in area to a closely packed mirror, 10.4 metres (410 inches) across) and having a total weight of just over 17 tonnes.

EXTREMELY LARGE TELESCOPES

The GTC has just eight years to reign as the world's foremost optical telescope, for in 2016 a new instrument with twice its diameter and four times its collecting area is scheduled to start working. The Giant Magellan Telescope (GMT) is currently under construction, but has more in common with the MMT than the Keck and Hobby-Eberly-type telescopes. It will use seven 8.4-metre (330-inch) monolithic circular mirrors (Figure 9), with a combined resolving power equivalent to that of a single 24.5-metre mirror. It will be sited in the Chilean Andes at Cerro Las Campanas. Six of the mirrors will be off-axis and encircle the seventh, central mirror (Figure 10).

The last decade has also seen a proliferation of preliminary studies for even bigger GODs. These have included:

- California Extremely Large Telescope (CELT) – 30-metre (1,180-inch) segmented mirror, with 1080 segments and a completion date (now superseded) of around 2018
- Maximum Aperture Telescope (MAXAT – 30–50-metres (1,180–1,970-inch) aperture (very early design study)
- Very Large Optical Telescope (VLOT) – 20-metre (790-inch) aperture
- Giant Segmented Mirror Telescope (GSMT) – 20–30-metre (790–1,180-inch) instrument(s) – now subsumed into the GMT and the TMT
- Euro50 – 50-metre (1,970-inch) diameter, segmented mirror and the granddaddy of them all:
- Overwhelmingly Large Telescope (OWL) – 100-metre (3,940-inch) diameter, segmented mirrors (Figure 11).

These somewhat wild and speculative suggestions have now been refined down to two serious proposals. The first four have been combined into the Thirty-Metre Telescope (TMT) project, while the last two have given rise to the European Extremely Large Telescope (E-ELT) plan.

The TMT (Figure 12) has so far been funded (to the tune of $17.5 million) for a detailed design study by a US–Canadian team. Initial concepts for the telescope suggest a thirty-metre (1,180-inch) primary mirror formed from 738 1.2-metre (47-inch) segments. It would have an adaptive optics system using up to nine laser guide stars, allowing its

Figure 9. Members of the Steward Observatory Mirror Laboratory's casting team check the surface of the first 8.4-metre mirror for the Giant Magellan Telescope. (Image courtesy of Lori Stiles and the University of Arizona.)

Figure 10. An artist's impression of the Giant Magellan Telescope in its enclosure. The completed GMT will include seven 8.4-metre-diameter mirrors. (Image courtesy of Giant Magellan Telescope–Carnegie Observatories. Artwork by Todd Mason, Mason Productions.)

Figure 11. An artist's concept of how the 100-metre Overwhelmingly Large Telescope (OWL) might have appeared when completed. The baseline design was similar to that of the Hobby-Eberly Telescope, the main difference being a secondary, segmented, flat-folding mirror allowing a shorter structure. The 100-metre primary mirror was to be made of 3048 identical hexagonal segments, each 1.6 metres in size. The 25.6-metre secondary mirror was to be made of 216 flat segments, also 1.6 metres across. (Image courtesy of ESO.)

Figure 12. An artist's concept of the Thirty-Metre Telescope, shown inside a cutaway of the dome. The huge telescope will contain more than 700 hexagonal-shaped mirrors that span 30 metres across. (Image courtesy of Thirty-Metre Telescope Project.)

angular resolution to reach its diffraction limit in the near infrared (around 0.01 seconds of arc, or close to it). The adaptive optics system might use a deformable secondary mirror rather than a dedicated, but separate, system like those in current use. A total of $200 million has now been raised towards the expected $300 million cost of the project. Various dates are suggested for the start of operations of the TMT, ranging from an incredibly optimistic 2012, through the possible 2016, to the probably achievable 2018 to 2020.

ESO has recently approved funding for the phase-B design study of the E-ELT (Figure 13). Beyond a decision to go for a 42-metre (1,650-inch) primary mirror made up from 900 or more segments, much of the design remains to be firmed up. A Gregorian configuration is one possibility under consideration, with a novel five-mirror design as a possible alternative. Adaptive optics would be essential, but whether to

Figure 13. This artist's impression of the European Extremely Large Telescope (E-ELT) shows a 42-metre-diameter mirror made from 906 individual segments. (Image courtesy of ESO.)

use a flexible secondary or tertiary mirror for this or a separate system remains to be decided; either way, an angular resolution of around 0.005 seconds of arc should be achievable (equivalent to detecting a double-decker bus on the Moon – in the unlikely event that one should ever travel that far!). No dates for first light on the E-ELT have yet surfaced, but if there are no delays due to funding or other outside factors, the instrument could be completed around 2016 to 2020.

THE WAY FORWARD

But even the E-ELT will not be the end of the fifth telescope race – though it might perhaps be about the halfway point. With segmented mirrors, there is nothing technical to stop ambitious astronomers using more and more segments to make bigger and bigger mirrors. The limits are thus largely financial. Scaling up the costs of a conventional telescope suggests that a 100-metre (3,940-inch) telescope might cost £10,000 million to £30,000 million. These are staggering sums, but perhaps not totally impossible – the International Space Station is now costing in excess of £100,000 million, and the Apollo Moon missions, in today's money, cost about £30,000 million. Thus what would be needed is the political will to spend the required amount of money. Fortunately for the politicians, a scaling-up of the costs of a conventional telescope is a gross overestimate of the cost of a segmented-mirror telescope. The savings due to the mass production of the segments, their enormously lighter weight compared with a monolithic mirror, and the resulting reductions in the construction costs of the mounting, dome etc., mean that a more realistic estimate for the price tag of a 100-metre segmented-mirror telescope would be £500 million to £1,000 million. For comparison, the James Webb Space Telescope is currently projected to cost around £500 million – so it seems likely that we could see a 100-metre-class instrument operating by 2025 to 2040. If such an instrument achieved its diffraction limit in the visible, then its angular resolution would be 0.001 seconds of arc – a hundred times better than the Hubble Space Telescope and the angular size of an astronaut walking on the surface of the Moon.

What of the future beyond three decades or so from now? One-hundred-metre telescopes may well represent the finishing post of the fifth telescope race. The 250-foot (76-metre) Lovell Radio Telescope at

Jodrell Bank was completed in 1957. In the subsequent half century the size of fully steerable dish-type radio telescopes has only grown to 110 metres (360 feet). Thus it may be that this is the largest practicable, or at least affordable, size for an individual telescope. Thereafter it seems likely that optical astronomers will have to follow radio astronomers and combine the outputs from several large telescopes separated by tens, hundreds or thousands of kilometres to synthesize telescopes with equivalent sizes. Such aperture-synthesis systems are already starting to be used on smaller scales – the VLT, for example, can already act as the equivalent in resolution, if not in sensitivity, of a 250-metre (9,800-inch) telescope. However, aperture synthesis at optical wavelengths seems likely to be the development that triggers the start of the sixth telescope race – so I shall leave speculating about its outcome until the *Yearbook of Astronomy* which appears sometime around 2025.

The Longest Total Solar Eclipses and Saros 136

MARTIN MOBBERLEY

Every 18 years, throughout the last century, astronomers have travelled to see the super-long total solar eclipses of 'Saros 136'. On 22 July 2009, the first total solar eclipse of this famous series in the twenty-first century will cross India, China, the East China Sea, and the Pacific Ocean. Many astronomers, amateur and professional, are heading to that eclipse track and dreaming they will avoid the cloud and see up to 6 minutes, 39 seconds of totality. But what causes the longest total solar eclipses and why has this particular series become so renowned?

A FACTOR OF 400

It is a truly remarkable fact that our Sun and Moon appear almost the same size in the sky, namely, roughly half a degree in diameter. *Of course, you should NEVER look directly at the Sun to verify this! Even staring at the Sun for a few seconds will permanently scar your retina and damage your eyesight for life.* Roughly speaking, the blindingly bright Sun is 400 times further away, and 400 times larger in diameter, than our absurdly large Moon. I say 'absurdly large' because our Moon would look more at home orbiting Jupiter, rather than a planet less than four times its own diameter. It appears that a chance collision with a small planet, aeons ago, created our Moon, rather than the Earth's rather weak gravity ensnaring it. Regardless of the capture method, the Earth has ended up with an outsized Moon, and only the Pluto–Charon system is more extreme in our Solar System. A big moon is one thing, but one that looks pretty much the same size as the Sun in our sky really is a gift from the gods. The system could have been precisely designed for eclipse-chasers! When the Moon covers the Sun (Figure 1) you want the blindingly bright surface to be totally eclipsed,

Figure 1. A total solar eclipse is the most spectacular astronomical event that can be witnessed. This image composite shows the intricate structure of the solar corona seen during the total eclipse of 29 March 2006 from a site near Göreme, Cappadocia, Turkey. (Image courtesy of Miloslav Druckmüller and Hana Druckmüllerová.)

but you also want to see all of the ghostly corona too; so you don't want the Moon to appear, say, 100 per cent larger than the Sun. You want the Moon to appear significantly larger, to give you a few minutes to savour the view before the Sun re-emerges, but you don't want it to be that much larger. A great compromise would be a total solar eclipse (TSE) where you get maybe six or seven minutes of totality, with the Moon about 7 or 8 per cent larger than the Sun. Remarkably, that is exactly what you do get, in the ultimate TSEs. The longest theoretical TSE offers 7 minutes and 31 seconds under the Moon's shadow.

APHELION AND PERIGEE

The apparent sizes of the Sun and Moon are not fixed at exactly half a degree. (Half a degree is equal to 30 arcminutes (30′) and each arcminute is made up of 60 arcseconds (60″)). For the longest total solar eclipses you want the Sun to be at its smallest and furthest (aphelion) and the Moon to be at its largest and nearest (perigee). The orbit of the Earth around the Sun is relatively simple in this regard. We are furthest from the Sun around 4–5 July, when we are 152.1 million kilometres away. Six months later, around 3–4 January, we are at our closest, i.e. 147.1 million kilometres away. This elliptical orbit causes the apparent size of the Sun's disc to vary between 31′ 28″ and 32′ 32″ or 32′ 00″ ± 1.7 per cent. So, for a small Sun the first ingredient is to have an eclipse that is as close as possible to the 4–5 July date. With the Moon, things are rather more complicated and the size variation is much greater (Figure 2). Our distance from the Moon (measured from the Earth's centre) can range between 406,697 and 356,410 kilometres, and this variation causes the apparent size of the Moon's disc (as seen

Figure 2. This composite, by the author, illustrates well how important the apparent size of the Moon is for producing the longest total solar eclipses. The average size of the Sun is shown sandwiched between the smallest possible and largest possible Moons.

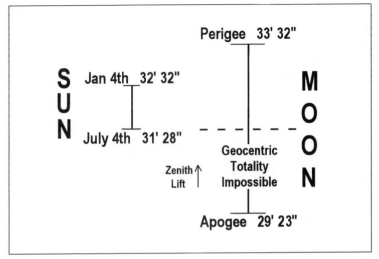

Figure 3. This diagram shows the relative range of sizes of Sun and Moon between solar aphelion and perihelion (left) and lunar apogee and perigee (right). A total solar eclipse can only occur when the Moon is above (larger than) the dotted line, as viewed by an observer level with the Earth's centre (geocentre). Away from this rather pessimistic viewpoint the 'zenith lift' arrow indicates the maximum 'Moon-enlarging' effect of the observer being on the Equator, at noon, relative to the situation at moonrise/moonset.

from the Earth's core, or, in practice, the moonrise/moonset points) to vary between 29' 23" and 33' 32" or 31' 23" ±6.8 per cent. Only New Moons where we are nearer to lunar perigee (closest distance) than we are to lunar apogee (greatest distance) produce total solar eclipses. This is because even the smallest Sun (near 4–5 July) appears as big as the average Moon (Figure 3). To put it another way, although the Sun is 400 times bigger than the Moon, on average it is only 390 times further away. On average the umbral shadow doesn't quite reach the Earth's surface (Figure 4). So there are more annular eclipses than total solar eclipses, and quite a few borderline hybrid (annular–total) cases where the Sun and Moon have virtually the same apparent diameter. An annular eclipse is interesting, but is just a special type of partial eclipse. The sky does not get dark and a blazing (and blinding) ring of light around the Moon prevents you from seeing the corona, or looking at it without special solar filters. Obviously we want a Moon that is close to its largest to guarantee a lengthy eclipse: a small Sun will stay behind a

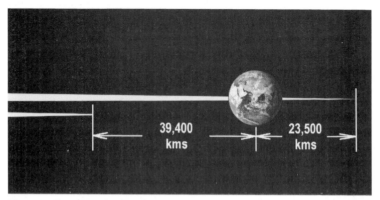

Figure 4. The extreme lengths of the lunar shadow. When the Sun is closest and the Moon furthest the lunar umbra falls 39,400 km short of the Earth's centre. With the optimum situation, i.e. the Sun furthest and the Moon closest, the lunar umbra can (theoretically) travel 23,500 kilometres past the Earth's centre, and a 7-minute totality can be witnessed from the tropics.

large Moon for far longer, all other things being equal. So we want one of those Moons that is nearly 7 per cent larger than average for the best possible TSE.

The *anomalistic* month is the term used for the interval between successive closest or furthest lunar approaches; in other words, the perigee-to-perigee, or apogee-to-apogee interval. This *anomalistic* month has an average length of 27.554 550 days (27d 13h 18min 33.2s), or about 27½ days. So every 27½ days the Moon is at its biggest, but the phase at that time can be anything from New to Full and back again. For a maximum-length eclipse we need a Moon at perigee, and admittedly, every anomalistic month that situation does arise, but, sadly, it rarely occurs at precisely New Moon. So now we have worked out the solar and lunar diameter requirements for a great eclipse; but how often does a total solar eclipse occur around May/June/July/August at the time of lunar perigee? Before we can resolve that there is one other orbital criterion to be satisfied.

ORBITAL NODES AND THE EARTH'S RADIUS

For solar (and lunar) eclipses Sun, Earth, and Moon have to line up. At first glance it might seem that some sort of eclipse would take place every month. After all, the Moon orbits the Sun every 29.5 days or so (from New Moon to New Moon) so surely every month it will pass in front of the Sun? If only this were the case! Although if it was, flying to all the total, hybrid, and annular solar eclipses would become a hobby reserved for multimillionaires! In fact, the plane of the lunar orbit is tilted with respect to the Earth's orbit around the Sun by roughly 5°. The average tilt is 5° 9′, and it ranges from 4° 59′ to 5°18′. This means that the shadow of the Moon, when it is long enough, usually passes way above or way below the Earth at New Moon. In fact, if the Earth had a diameter of 90,000 kilometres, rather than its actual (equatorial) diameter of 12,756 kilometres we would catch all of the total, annular, or hybrid solar eclipses as the Moon's shadow axis would always cross the Earth's surface at New Moon. The positions where Earth's orbital plane and the Moon's orbital plane intersect are called the nodes, and for an eclipse to occur the Sun has to be passing through a node at New Moon (it takes between 30 and 37 days to complete a nodal crossing). If this were not complicated enough to visualize in 3D, the nodes do not quite line up every six months, as you might expect. The lunar orbital plane itself regresses westward in space at a rate of 19 degrees every year, so that node crossings occur rather more frequently than every six months. In fact, they occur every 173.3 days. The time between the Sun crossing the same node twice is also shorter than a year, it is 346.6 days, in fact. This period is known as *the eclipse year*.

There is just one other factor to consider now we have dealt with solar aphelion, lunar perigee, and the Sun passing through a node. For a maximum duration TSE the Moon's shadow should pass close to the central equatorial bulge of the Earth. There are two reasons for this. The speed of the Moon's shadow across the Earth (Figure 5) is largely down to the Moon's speed in orbit (61 kilometres per minute) minus the speed of the Earth's rotation (28 kilometres per minute on the Equator). At the Equator, the relatively leisurely 33 kilometres per minute (roughly 2,000 kilometres per hour) shadow speed makes for a long eclipse and at a velocity which the late lamented Concorde aircraft could actually keep pace with! Away from the Equator, the extreme

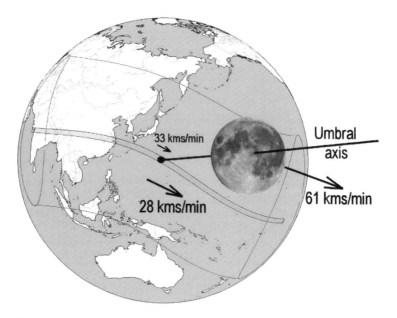

Figure 5. Looking from behind the Moon at the Earth during the total solar eclipse of 22 July 2009. The Moon speeds along at 61 kilometres per minute in its orbit, while the ground at Earth's Equator moves along at 28 kilometres per minute. Essentially, and without delving into precise maths, the speed of the umbra along the ground is largely determined by these two factors, i.e. 61 − 28 = 33 kilometres per minute or roughly 2,000 kilometres per hour. (Earth globe and track generated by Heinz Scsibrany's WinEclipse.)

cases being the polar regions, the ground is moving much more slowly and so the Moon's shadow will race across the ground at a higher speed, making the eclipse shorter. In addition, being sited on the Equator, or at least, on a point where the eclipsed Sun is near the zenith, you are raised up by the Earth's full radius, so the Moon appears bigger and its shadow appears larger. This may seem trivial, but it can add another 1.6 to 1.8 per cent to the apparent diameter of the Moon (at apogee and perigee, respectively), increasing its apparent diameter to 34′ 9″ in the extreme case (with the Moon at your zenith at precise lunar perigee). If the Moon is at the zenith and you are on the Equator too, that is even better, as the Earth's diameter is greatest at the Equator.

6,585 DAYS, OR THEREABOUTS . . .

Let's just have a recap on what we have learned so far. For an optimum solar eclipse we need the date to be as close to 4–5 July as possible, as close to lunar perigee as possible, and with the Sun well inside a node and the Moon close to the zenith. Also, quite obviously, it has to be New Moon for a total solar eclipse to occur at all. We now have enough numbers to invoke a bit of coincidence-hunting maths, which, hopefully, anyone with a pocket calculator can verify. We have seen that an eclipse-year interval is 346.6 days long. In fact, to be super accurate, it is 346.620077 days. We also know that a synodic month, the average interval between New Moons, is 29.5 days, or 29.530589, to be precise, and that an anomalistic month, the average time between successive lunar perigees, is 27.554550 days. Maybe, if we are very lucky, we can find a period in days after which all these cycles coincide? What if we try 6,585 days? (It's so easy if you know the answer before you start looking!!) Well, 19 eclipse years gives us 19×346.620077 days = 6,585.78 days; 223 lunar (synodic) months gives us 223×29.530589 days = 6585.32 days; and, finally, 239 anomalistic months (perigee to perigee) gives us $239 \times 27.554550 = 6585.54$ days. That looks like a pretty good tie-up to me; within a span of half a day we have a near-perfect coincidence of eclipse year, New Moon, and lunar perigee cycles. As many of you will have guessed, 6,585.32 days is the basis of the so-called Saros Cycle. It is better known as 18 calendar years, 11 days, and 8 hours (or 18 years, 10 days, and 8 hours if there have been five, not four leap years in that period). Eclipses of a similar type occur after a Saros interval, i.e. at a similar time of year (just 11 days later), and, remarkably, with the Moon at a similar size too. The main difference between consecutive TSEs 18 years, 11 days, and 8 hours apart is that the 8 hours shifts the track by 120 degrees west on the Earth's surface, but if you wait for three Saros periods (54 years, and 34-ish days, but no hours) even the ground track is very similar, just one month later and slightly further north or south.

SAROS 136

Throughout the twentieth century, Saros Cycle no. 136 produced some wonderful total solar eclipses (Figures 6 and 7). They were all more than six minutes in duration, at least, on the track centre, and they all occurred with the Sun near aphelion (May to July) and the Moon near lunar perigee. In addition their tracks all crossed through the tropics so the Moon was largely overhead. This latter fact was mainly because Saros 136 was in the middle of its lifetime. Table 1 shows the 31st through 39th eclipses of this 71-eclipse cycle. An entire Saros Cycle only lasts about 1,300 years from the first shadows striking one pole of the Earth to the last ones leaving the opposite pole. A typical Saros produces about 75 solar eclipses, of which 50 are total, hybrid, or annular.

Figure 6. After three Saros intervals, of 54 calendar years, 32 days and 0 hours, the ground track of the Saros 136 eclipse on 20 June 1955 (lower track) and that of this year's Saros 136 eclipse on 22 July 2009 are seen to be very similar. (Diagram generated by Heinz Scsibrany's WinEclipse.)

Figure 7. For consecutive total solar eclipses in the same Saros series the ground track is shifted eight hours westward. The two Saros 136 tracks that occurred between those in Figure 6 are shown here, i.e. those of 30 June 1973 (right) and 11 July 1991 (left). (Diagram generated by Heinz Scsibrany's WinEclipse.)

The best years of any Saros are in the middle, i.e. when the lunar shadow passes across the tropics. When this occurs near June/July, a seven-minute eclipse is on the cards, lunar perigee, New Moon, and orbital nodes willing!

Sadly the peak years of Saros 136 are now behind us. The super-long TSEs of 8 June 1937, 20 June 1955, and 30 June 1973 were all over seven minutes in duration at their peak, and the 'six minute plus' era of this Saros is confined to the period from 1901 to 2045. Before and beyond this golden period the eclipses occur away from the months of solar aphelion and, of course, the three periods of 6,585.32, 6,585.54 and 6,585.78 days start to slip as the years go by. New Moons, lunar perigees, and eclipse years go out of synch and ruin the perfect eclipse situation. After 600 years, the Saros may just be able to produce lesser eclipses around that critical June/July date again, but only if its umbral shadows still hit the Earth's surface at all. At best they will probably graze the polar regions. The potential six- and seven-minute heyday of a great Saros cycle is pretty much confined to a 150-year period.

SAROS 139

But, before we all get too misty-eyed at the demise of Saros 136, is there anything coming along to replace this Saros' monster eclipses? The answer is yes, but not for a long while! Long totalities are currently getting shorter, and the era when Saros 136 is still king bottoms out on 24 August 2063 with the last dominant TSE of that series; only 5 minutes, 49 seconds in length. Fifteen years later the era of the long eclipses of Saros 139 begins; modestly at first, with a 5-minute, 40-second totality on 11 May 2078, but it will produce some real 'stonkers' in the twenty-second century. The next eclipse that is longer than that of July 2009 will be from Saros 139: a 6-minute, 55-second totality on 13 June 2132. Saros 139 totalities will peak with three absolute monsters: a 7-minute, 26-second TSE on 5 July 2168, a 7-minute, 29-second TSE on 16 July 2186 and a 7-minute, 22-second TSE on 27 July 2204. Of course, whether the inhabitants of Earth in that era are still human, part human, immortals, or just robots is a matter for conjecture . . .

Table 1. The nine longest eclipses of Saros 136, numbers 31 to 39 (of 71) in that cycle, from 1901 to 2045.

Date	Duration		Umbral Track Across the Earth
	m	s	
18 May 1901	6	29	Indian Ocean/Indonesia
29 May 1919	6	51	Bolivia/Brazil/Atlantic Ocean/Africa
8 June 1937	7	04	Pacific Ocean/Peru
20 June 1955	7	08	Sri Lanka/S. Asia/Phillipines/W. Pacific Ocean
30 June 1973	7	04	Guyana/Atlantic Ocean/Africa/Indian Ocean
11 July 1991	6	53.2	Hawaii/Baja/Mexico/Central & South America
22 July 2009	6	38.9	India/China/East China Sea/W. Pacific Ocean
2 August 2027	6	22.7	Atlantic Ocean/Mediterranean/North Africa/Indian Ocean
12 August 2045	6	06.0	USA/Venezuela/Brazil

FURTHER READING

For further information on Saros 136, including a listing of all 71 eclipses in this Saros Series, see the NASA Eclipse website at: http://eclipse.gsfc.nasa.gov/SEsaros/SEsaros136.html.

The Unexpected Comet

PETE LAWRENCE

As it happened, 2007 turned out to be something of a good year for comets. At the very start of the year our skies were graced with C/2006 P1 McNaught, a wonderful example of the genre, being bright and displaying a fantastically intricate dust tail (Figure 1, *Left*). Unfortunately for UK observers, as C/2006 P1 McNaught just started to get interesting, it disappeared below our horizon and at its best the comet was only visible from the Southern Hemisphere (see article by Martin Mobberley in the *2008 Yearbook of Astronomy*).

At the opposite end of the year we had a revisit from periodic comet 8P/Tuttle. With a period of around 13.6 years, observations of 8P/Tuttle aren't all that rare. In fact this particular comet has been observed on all but one of its returns since it was first discovered on 5 January 1953. The missed one occurred in 1953 when the circumstances of the comet made picking it up particularly unfavourable. What made the 2007–8 return special was the fact that 8P/Tuttle, passing perihelion when it was close to the Earth. Consequently, it was expected to become just visible to the naked eye in early January 2008, making it the brightest return on record. Typically, the UK's weather over the period when the comet was supposed to be at its brightest was poor, but tenacious observers did manage to catch this small green object together with its thin, faint ion tail (Figure 1, *Right*).

In between the appearances of C/2006 P1 McNaught and 8P/Tuttle there was something of a surprise. As anyone who has ever tried to make a prediction of the brightness of a comet will know only too well, comets can be highly unpredictable. Those that are predicted to be bright often pass by a magnitude or more fainter than estimated. This isn't always the case though, and like stocks and shares, the observed brightness of comets can go up as well as down. Experienced comet observers are well aware of this fact and tend to be prepared for the unexpected. The surprise comet of 2007, however, caught even the experienced observers unaware.

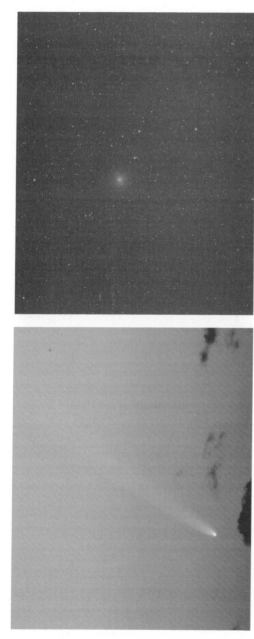

Figure 1. (*Left*) UK observers got an all too brief opportunity to spot the magnificent comet C/2006 P1 McNaught at the start of 2007. (*Right*) At the other end of the year, periodic Comet 8P/Tuttle faintly graced our skies with a rare naked-eye appearance. (Images by the author.)

Just after midnight on 23 October 2007, in the early hours of the 24th, astronomer J. A. Henriquez Santana observing from Tenerife in the Canaries recorded that periodic comet 17P/Holmes was visible at magnitude +7.1. After confirming the observation (Oct 23.17), Bob King in Minnesota, USA, made a second observation several hours later (Oct 24.47) noting that the comet had brightened further and was now at magnitude +4.0 – an easy naked-eye object. What made this remarkable was that comet 17P/Holmes should, at this time, have been around magnitude +17, in other words 13 magnitudes, or 150,000 times fainter! More remarkable still was the fact that the comet continued to brighten. By the end of October, 17P/Holmes was just shy of magnitude +2.5, making it the third brightest object in its host constellation of Perseus. Only Mirphak (Alpha Persei) and the variable star Algol (Beta Persei) were brighter. This was quite impressive for an object that should have passed through our night skies virtually unnoticed some half a million times fainter.

With the efficiency of modern communications, the astronomical world was soon buzzing with news of the comet's incredible outburst and understandably many amateur astronomers were keen to get their first look. For many of us in the UK, the late October 2007 weather wasn't terribly kind and we had to wait patiently for several days before getting our first opportunity to view. This happened on 26 October when gaps in thinning cloud provided all too brief glimpses of this amazing object. Lying fairly close to Mirphak (Alpha Persei), the +2.5 magnitude comet was very easy to locate, even with a bright Full Moon lying just 30° to the east. In binoculars, Holmes appeared just like a planet – a resemblance that many observers subsequently commented on. At this time the comet's apparent angular diameter was around four arcminutes and visually it appeared golden-yellow in colour. The poor visibility at this time meant that imaging the comet was something of a challenge, and my only shots captured on 26 October were taken through cloud. Even so, something interesting became evident; the inner yellow disc appeared surrounded by a faint green outer envelope. The following night the cloud came back with a vengeance and it was not until 28 October that UK observers got their first proper look at 17P/Holmes under cloud-free skies (Figure 2).

The positioning of the comet was fortuitous. Being located in the constellation of Perseus during the latter months of the year meant that it was possible to see Holmes immediately after the evening twilight

Figure 2. Comet Holmes as imaged by the author on 28 October 2007. Extended photographs revealed the green-hued outer envelope that had been glimpsed on the 26th. Many comets exhibit such a green colouration, which is caused by resonant fluorescence, a process that occurs, in this case, when molecules of diatomic carbon (C_2) and cyanogen (CN) are bathed in sunlight.

had faded. Better still, its location meant that it was visible for the entire night, passing virtually overhead from mid-northern latitudes shortly after midnight. There are considerable advantages when viewing delicate astronomical objects, like comets, at high altitudes, because the thickness of the Earth's atmosphere in these directions is at its thinnest, reducing any atmospheric interference to a minimum.

Visual observations made on 28 October once again confirmed the pseudo-planetary appearance of Holmes and extended photographs similarly revealed the green-hued outer envelope seen on the 26th. Many comets exhibit a green colouration. Comet 8P/Tuttle that just made it to naked-eye visibility at the start of 2008 was seen to be intensely green. This colour is caused by resonant fluorescence, a process that occurs, in this case, when molecules of diatomic carbon (C_2) and cyanogen (CN) are bathed in sunlight.

Comets are ancient leftovers from the formation of the Solar System. They are often likened to dirty snowballs, only becoming active

when their orbits bring them close enough to the Sun for their constituent materials to sublimate, i.e. change from a solid to a gas without
passing through the liquid phase. The 'snowball' representing the heart
of a comet is called the nucleus and is typically fairly small. In the case
of Comet Holmes, it is estimated that the nucleus is 3 to 4 kilometres
across. As the rotating nucleus moves to a distance from the Sun where
sublimation can occur, so gas and dust are ejected from its surface. As
this occurs, a cocoon of tenuous particles envelops the nucleus and it
is these particles that form the 'head' of the comet, also known as the
coma.

In the case of Comet Holmes, the term 'outer-coma' was coined to
describe the green halo of fluorescing diatomic carbon and cyanogen
that surrounded the main coma. In the very core of the main, or inner,
coma lay a small, star-like point marking the position of the comet's
nucleus. Despite often being called the nucleus, this point of light
within the head of a comet actually represents a tight inner region of
material freshly ejected from the nucleus itself. Typically, the nucleus of
a comet is hidden within this 'pseudo-nucleus' and cannot be seen
directly. Even if the pseudo-nucleus were not there, the real nucleus
would be too small to be seen even in the largest of Earth-based
telescopes.

As well as its unexpected brightness, another interesting aspect of
Comet Holmes over this period was the apparent increase in the size of
its coma over just a few days. On the night of 28 October, the main
coma measured approximately eight arcminutes across – a doubling of
size from what had been seen just 48 hours earlier, on the 26th.

As the end of October approached, the ever-expanding bright disc
of the coma started to show definite structure. There was a marked
asymmetry visible with the pseudo-nucleus which now appeared
slightly off-centre with respect to the main coma. With long exposures
the green envelope surrounding the inner coma could still be seen, but
it was getting more difficult to pick up.

The Full Moon which had considerably brightened the sky close to
the start of the outburst was starting to wane by the end of October, and
this allowed imagers to extend the length of their exposures without
over-exposing the bright moonlit background. Due to the distance of
17P/Holmes from the Sun at the time of outburst it was generally
thought that the comet would be unlikely to generate much of a tail. To
compound this, the comet was almost at opposition in the sky, meaning

that it was located in approximately the opposite part of the sky to the Sun. Comet tails always point away from the Sun, which meant in this case that if one did form, we would only see it as a very foreshortened and stubby affair. Incidentally, this geometry was also responsible for the odd, slightly planet-like initial appearance of Holmes.

Despite predictions, long exposures of several minutes duration at high sensitivity settings did start to reveal something heading off in a south-westerly direction. Once alerted, those who were equipped to take long guided exposures were soon revealing a considerable amount of structure in yet another unexpected twist to Comet Holmes – its tail. Then, without warning, on 8 November, this tenuous and rather beautiful feature of the unexpected comet broke off in what's known as a disconnection event (Figure 3).

Figure 3. Ever the unpredictable, despite predictions to the contrary, long-exposure images of comet 17P/Holmes revealed beautiful tail structures had formed by the start of November 2007. This image was acquired by Paolo Candy on 5 November. The camera was a Zen Baker-Schmidt 8-inch f/2 with a STL 6303E for a total of 36 minutes of exposure. Then, on 8 November, the comet's tail broke off, never to reform. (Image courtesy of Paolo Candy.)

Everything within the Solar System effectively exists within the extended outer atmosphere of the Sun. Here, a constant stream of charged particles known as the solar wind carries the Sun's influence out to the outermost regions of its kingdom; a Sun-driven bubble within the vast island of stars in space known as the Milky Way galaxy. When these particles leave the immediate vicinity of the Sun, they carry with them a record of the state of the Sun's magnetic field at the time of departure. This frozen magnetic field, known as the Interplanetary Magnetic Field or IMF, varies in intensity and polarity over time, and is also influenced by the rotation of the Sun. The common analogy is to think of the Sun as a circular rotating lawn sprinkler. Looking from an overhead vantage point, as the sprinkler rotates it causes the water droplets to create a spiral pattern over the lawn. As the Sun rotates, so the frozen-in state of the IMF appears to paint a similar spiral pattern which expands throughout the Solar System. Known as the Parker Spiral, this pattern has regions within it which have a certain magnetic polarity, and other regions which have the opposite polarity.

The tail that formed downwind (i.e. the solar wind) from the head of Comet Holmes had an accumulated charge and was reliant on the magnetic polarity of the IMF at the time it formed. As the solar wind flowed and a new region of opposite polarity passed the comet, so the tail detached and moved off with the region in which it had originally grown. From Earth we saw the delicate tail structure become detached from the comet's head and move off into space. This is what is termed a disconnection event. In major, bright tail-bearing comets close to the Sun such events often cause a section of tail to disconnect or become heavily distorted. Where we have a good 'sideways' vantage point we can see these features literally flow down the entire length of a comet's tail. For active comets which lose their tails, a new one will often form, of opposite polarity to the one that's just been disconnected. However, in the case of Holmes the detachment was final, and no further tail – not that could be detected from Earth anyway – was seen to form.

Something else strange started happening to the head of Comet Holmes at the start of November 2007. Where it had originally appeared like a regular, circular disc moving against the background stars, it suddenly developed what's best described as a fuzzy edge. In the nights that ensued, this fuzziness, again directed to the south-west – the direction of the now detached tail – became more noticeable from one night to the next. Where once the comet had appeared circular, it

Figure 4. Early into November 2007, 17P/Holmes became lopsided, appearing distinctly fuzzy around its south-western edge. (Image by the author.)

now started to take on a more comet-like 'tear-drop' appearance (Figure 4).

Over the past few years, astronomical photography has undergone a radical change due mainly to the introduction of digital imaging equipment. Desperate to capture anything that looks interesting in the night sky, amateur astrophotographers from all over the world maintained an almost constant vigil on Comet Holmes. For the most part, these imagers were using DSLR (digital single lens reflex) cameras or dedicated CCD imaging equipment. However, Holmes was also bright enough to catch the attention of the planetary imagers.

Astrophotographers can be subdivided into two main groups: those who photograph Solar System objects (the Moon, Sun, and brighter planets) and those who enjoy everything outside the Solar System (stars, nebulae, galaxies, etc.) in a realm known as the deep sky. The distinction between the two camps does overlap somewhat and the techniques employed for imaging fainter Solar System bodies, such as comets, are borrowed from the deep-sky imagers. However, the bright main coma of Holmes was bright enough for the planetary purists to get excited.

The bane of the lunar- and planetary-imager's life is the Earth's atmosphere. Being in a constant state of turbulence, it has a tendency to blur fine details on the major planets and the Moon, making it hard to record such detail. Planetary imagers are a tenacious lot, however, and with a fair amount of trial and error, techniques were developed to reduce the distorting effects of atmospheric seeing. One of the most successful techniques employed involves the use of high frame-rate cameras. These are inserted at the eyepiece end of a conventional tele-scope, taking the place of the observer's eye. Once everything is focused and framed as required, the camera is set to record a sequence of image stills (anything from hundreds to thousands of frames in a single capture) of the constantly distorting subject. In amongst the many distorted frames there will typically be a small percentage that are relatively distortion-free. When you look at the planets or the Moon through a telescope your eye is remarkably good at picking out and remembering the detail you can see in the fleeting moments when the seeing is good. Well, this is essentially what the high-frame-rate camera is trying to do, only along the way it has little choice but to capture the blurry bits as well.

Once captured, the resulting movie file has to be sifted and the best frames extracted. After this has been done, they are further processed (stacked) to reduce the image noise and improve the quality of the signal captured. Fortunately, these somewhat tedious processes can be done, with a fair degree of accuracy and relatively quickly, using a computer. It is particularly amazing that the software to perform this arduous task, Registax, is available for free.

What brought the attention of Comet Holmes to the interest of a number of planetary imagers was the fact that the head of the comet was bright enough to be recorded with certain high-end planetary cameras. This meant that it was possible to apply the same techniques that are used to pull out fine detail of the surface of, say, Mars or Jupiter, to reveal the delicate inner structure of the coma of Comet Holmes. When this was done, a 'plume' feature pointing to the south-west of the pseudo-nucleus revealed itself to be made up of numerous straight jets or streamers. It's not uncommon for large active comets to exhibit such inner structures, but it's worth remembering that Holmes is not, under the normal terms of the description, an active comet, and to be able to apply these processing techniques to such a normally dim and distant object was a fascinating treat (Figure 5).

In many ways this was a comet of the people. Like Hale-Bopp and Hyakutake, which graced our skies back in 1997 and 1996, respectively, bright comets are relatively easy to see and image. With the current popularity in astronomical imaging and the immediacy of the Internet for distributing such images, pictures of Comet Holmes started filling astronomical forums and bulletin boards. Despite being highly

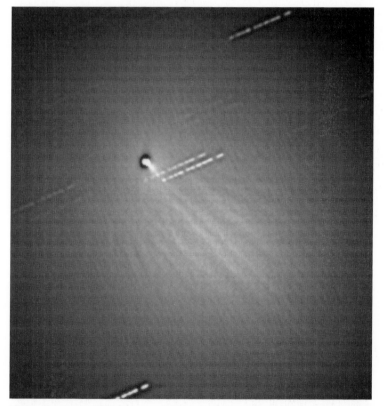

Figure 5. Comet 17P/Holmes was bright enough to apply registration and stacking imaging techniques, normally used for lunar, solar, and planetary imaging. When these were applied to the inner coma of the comet, multiple jets were revealed. (Images by the author.)

photogenic, as the days passed, Comet Holmes presented astrophotographers with an interesting problem – it was starting to get too big for many cameras attached to telescopes to cope with. This was, of course, the apparent size of the comet (the projection of its physical size on the distant background stars, taking into account its distance). In many respects, its physical size was just as remarkable, and, by 9 November, the actual diameter of the comet's head had actually grown larger than the physical diameter of the Sun's photosphere (Figure 6). At this time Holmes was about 242 million kilometres away, its distance from Earth slowly increasing with time.

By the middle of November, Comet 17P/Holmes had become a disembodied head of a comet, drifting slowly through the northern regions of the constellation of Perseus. As it tracked towards the main star of the constellation, Mirphak (magnitude +1.8) and the cluster of stars that surround it, known as the Alpha Persei Moving Cluster or Melotte 20, the comet took on a decidedly lopsided appearance. In many ways it was quite reminiscent of the ghosts that appear in

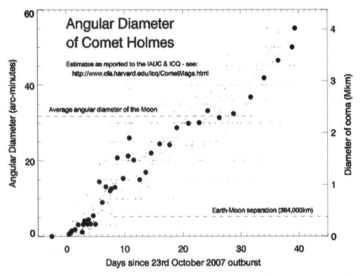

Figure 6. The amazing growing comet. The apparent and actual diameters of 17P/Holmes plotted over time reveal just how rapidly the coma grew. Approximately 15 days post flare-up, the diameter of the comet's coma was the same as the Sun, i.e. 1.4 million kilometres (Mkm). (Graphic courtesy of Dr Darren Baskill.)

Figure 7. Sequence of images by the author showing the apparent motion of Comet Holmes against the background stars of Perseus.

the now rather ageing Pac-Man video game, although a slightly more classical description had it looking like an ancient trilobite.

At this time the comet was still easily visible to the naked eye as a misty blob. As November passed it became too large for many telescopes, and binoculars took over as the instrument of choice. Since Comet Holmes remained bright, easy to pick out and relatively slow-moving, the initial excitement with its outburst began to wane. It was almost as if it became difficult to know what to do with this now huge and rather persistent comet.

Heading into December, the comet's coma continued to grow and remained remarkably visible to the naked eye. At the start of 2008, the comet had begun to fade but it was still visible from really dark sites without optical assistance. Photographically Holmes now appeared very faint, the surface brightness of its coma now quite low. The once bright tear-drop had now become a faint, translucent mist still wandering through the stars of Perseus (Figure 7). As the last week of January 2008 approached, some two months after Holmes had engulfed the constellation's brightest star, Holmes repeated the trick by passing over Beta Persei, the famous eclipsing variable star Algol. The comet's path then took it back through Perseus, fading rapidly as it passed between the Greek hero's legs during February 2008. Despite a fairly high visual magnitude ranking at this time, the huge apparent size of the coma and extremely low surface brightness meant that few amateurs were now taking much notice of this remarkable comet.

Although we still don't know what caused Comet Holmes to outburst like this, there is perhaps a strong clue in the fact that it has done it before. It was originally discovered by the English astronomer Edwin Holmes on 6 November 1892 (see Table 1). At the time of its discovery the comet had undergone a brightening to magnitude +4.5, making it easily visible to the naked eye. Like the 2007−8 outburst, the comet was then seen to slowly fade from view, until, several weeks later on 16 January 1893, 71 days following discovery, it underwent a second outburst which once again restored it to naked-eye visibility. The most probable cause of the outbursts is a rich seam of material in the nucleus of the comet that happens to be optimally exposed to sunlight. As the warmth of the Sun hits this material, it rapidly sublimates, as in the explosive outbursts witnessed in 1892 and 2007. An alternative theory suggesting an impact event now seems unlikely due to the duplicity of the outbursts.

Table 1. Periodic Comet 17P/Holmes

Designation: 17P/Holmes
Discovery: 6 November 1892, Edwin Holmes
Pre-discovery perihelion date: 13 June 1892
Orbital period: 6.88 years
Aphelion distance: 5.2 AU (Jupiter = 5.2 AU)
Perihelion distance: 2.1 AU (Mars =1.5 AU)
Orbital eccentricity: 0.43
Orbital inclination: 19.11°
2007 outburst date: 24 October 2007
2007 perihelion: 4 May 2007
1892/93 peak brightness: +4.0 (approximately)
2007/08 peak brightness: +2.5
Next perihelion (predicted): 22 March 2014

Comet 17P/Holmes has an orbital period of around 6.9 years subject to perturbations from the giant gas planet Jupiter. Following discovery it was subsequently seen in 1899 and 1906 before being lost. The next successful recovery was in 1964 and it has been recorded on every return ever since. No doubt following the amazing and spectacular out-burst of the 2007/08 apparition, all eyes will be trained towards Comet Holmes following its next perihelion which occurs in the spring of 2014.

Titan: The Giant Moon With an Atmosphere

RALPH D. LORENZ

Saturn's giant moon, Titan, is larger than the planet Mercury and, were it not orbiting Saturn, would surely be called a planet rather than a moon, as its thick atmosphere gives it a range of phenomena and processes that rival the Earth in complexity. Titan is accordingly a principal target of the NASA-ESA-ASI Cassini-Huygens mission, now in its fourth year in the Saturnian System (Figure 1).

Figure 1. View of Titan beyond the rings. Cassini shows Titan looming in the background beyond the small irregular moon Epimetheus, with Saturn's A and F rings stretching across the scene. Epimetheus is 116 kilometres (72 miles) across and giant Titan is 5,150 kilometres (3,200 miles) across. The view was acquired with the Cassini spacecraft narrow-angle camera on 28 April 2006, at a distance of approximately 667,000 kilometres (415,000 miles) from Epimetheus and 1.8 million kilometres (1.1 million miles) from Titan. Titan's north polar region (just behind Epimetheus) is slightly darker than the rest – a real colouring, not just the winter shadow. (Image courtesy of NASA/JPL/Space Science Institute.)

Cassini made seventeen close fly-bys of Titan in 2007, racking up several new discoveries – meanwhile, results from earlier Cassini encounters, and the dramatic descent of the Huygens probe to Titan's surface in 2005, continue to be analysed. Titan is a complex and dynamic place, and clues to its many mysteries are emerging from various directions, some new findings prompting re-examination of older data. Accordingly, for this review of Titan System Science, we will start at the top and work our way down.

IONOSPHERE AND HAZE

The origin and evolution of Titan's thick atmosphere, mostly nitrogen, with a few per cent of methane and traces of literally dozens of other organic molecules, is a major topic of enquiry, since no other planetary satellite has anything like it. The methane (and to a lesser extent) the nitrogen is converted by ultraviolet light from the Sun and energetic electrons in the Saturnian magnetosphere into molecular fragments which recombine to form the heavier organics (although some traces of gas escape into space).

The Titan ionosphere is dynamic because these energy sources (electrons and sunlight, as well as a few positive ions) come from directions that are always changing their relative geometry. Plasma is swept along by Saturn's magnetic field, which rotates in the same direction as Titan's orbital motion. This motion changes both diurnally (a Titan orbit around Saturn, its day, is 15.945 Earth days), and seasonally, with respect to the direction of the Sun. A further complication is that as the solar wind fluctuates in strength, the magnetopause can be pushed inside Titan's orbit, so that Titan is temporarily outside the magnetosphere.

Unsurprisingly this dynamic environment leads to complex structures that are being revealed by Cassini's fleeting encounters (it spends only an hour below about 10,000 kilometres altitude on each fly-by, with fly-bys occurring typically two to six weeks apart). The ionosphere has multiple layers, and data seem to show two separate loss mechanisms from the upper atmosphere: light ions get pulled radially away from Titan by an electric field, while heavier ions are swept downstream by the plasma rotating with Saturn's magnetic field.

Cassini's in-situ results gave new clues into the ways in which these organics are formed. The Ion and Neutral Mass Spectrometer (INMS) counts molecules that fly into a forward-pointing aperture as Cassini skims through the tenuous upper atmosphere: Cassini flies through no lower than 950 kilometres above the surface, but even at that high altitude, the INMS detects organic molecules such as Benzene (C_6H_6, mass 78 daltons).[1] When INMS discovered these in 2004, it was a complete surprise that such large molecules were so abundant so high above the surface. Although INMS is not equipped to measure ions heavier than 100 daltons, indirect data from the Cassini Plasma Spectrometer (CAPS) analysed in 2006 and 2007 showed that ions with mass-charge ratios up to 10,000 were present. These large macro-molecules (Figure 2) are presumably precursors to haze particles and suggest that the haze-formation process may rely on the chemistry of charged ions rather than neutral gas species, and proceeds much more quickly than had been anticipated. Some of these molecules are lost to space (perhaps being deposited on Iapetus?), but most are ultimately deposited on the surface.

On their way down, the organics form the optically opaque haze that hid Titan's surface for the first few decades of the space age. This haze interacts with the gas composition (both affecting how heat and light are transmitted and absorbed, and gases can condense on to the haze in cold regions) as well as the latitudinally varying winds and temperatures. As a result, the haze has a different density in the Southern and Northern Hemispheres, an asymmetry which was observed to change with season by the Hubble Space Telescope in the 1990s. However, changes while Cassini has been at Saturn have not been dramatic – the pace is expected to pick up in the next couple of years, however. Over the winter pole, there is an accumulation of darker haze called the 'polar hood' (in some ways analogous to the noctilucent clouds on Earth that form over its winter pole and lead to the formation of the ozone hole). The hood connects to a higher 'detached haze' layer (Figure 3) – which Cassini observed, curiously, to be at a higher altitude than when Voyager observed it back in 1981.

1. The dalton (Da), or unified atomic mass unit (u), is a small unit of mass used to express atomic and molecular masses. It is defined to be one-twelfth of the mass of an unbound atom of ^{12}C at rest and in its ground state.

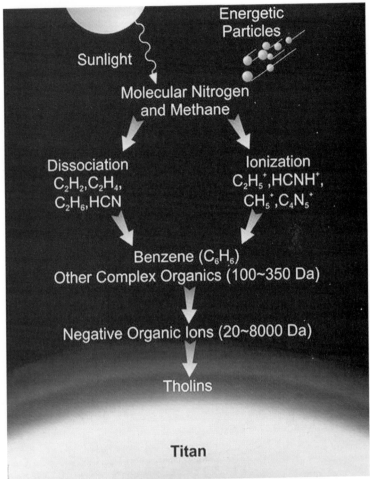

Figure 2. Tholin synthesis. This diagram shows that the heavy organic molecules that make up Titan's haze, and perhaps ultimately its sands, are synthesized in Titan's upper atmosphere, as revealed by Cassini. Solar ultraviolet light and energetic electrons in the Saturnian magnetosphere break up methane and nitrogen molecules (requiring, by the way, a source to replenish the atmospheric methane) to form heavier molecules, such as benzene, which was detected by Cassini's Ion and Neutral Mass Spectrometer. The presence of much larger molecules is indicated by the presence of heavy (up to 2000 daltons) negative ions, and these ions are presumably the precursors of tholin haze particles. (Image courtesy of South-West Research Institute.)

Figure 3. Backlit haze showing polar structure. The intriguing structure of Titan's north polar 'hood' can be seen at upper left. A thin, detached, high-altitude global haze layer encircles the moon, above its main haze layer. North on Titan (5,150 kilometres, 3,200 miles across) is up and rotated 23 degrees to the left. The image was taken in visible blue light with the Cassini spacecraft wide-angle camera on 29 June 2007. The view was obtained at a distance of approximately 210,000 kilometres (131,000 miles) from Titan, with the Sun essentially behind Titan: the Sun-Titan-spacecraft angle ('phase angle') was 167 degrees. (Image courtesy of NASA/JPL/Space Science Institute.)

CLOUDS AND RAIN

Although large methane storm clouds were observed around Titan's south pole in 2004 by Cassini upon its arrival at Saturn (and for several years prior to that from Earth), those clouds disappeared soon thereafter. Only smaller, sporadic clouds have been seen since, often around 40° south latitude. These changing cloud patterns are evidently a feature of Titan's seasons – Titan is inclined by about 26° to Saturn's

29.5-year orbit around the Sun, and so it experiences seasons similar to, but longer than, those of Earth or Mars. Late 2002 was southern midsummer, where the strongest solar heating occurs at the south pole, and so the clouds seen there are believed to be like summertime cumulus clouds on Earth, triggered by updraughts caused by solar heating. Whether the mid-latitude clouds are similarly driven by sunshine, or perhaps are somehow influenced by the supply of methane moisture in damp ground or perhaps cryovolcanic vents, is not yet known.

Further analysis of the Huygens results suggested that the probe had descended through a thin layer of cloud about 20 kilometres above the surface. Not only was the air close to saturation (as would be expected in a cloud, otherwise the cloud droplets or ice crystals would evaporate) but measurements of the probe's buffeting motion under its parachute showed characteristics similar to those observed in the turbulence associated with freezing clouds on Earth.

In 2007, observations from the giant Keck and Gemini telescopes suggested that there might be a widespread low-latitude, low-altitude cloud – and perhaps even drizzle. To what extent this cloud may vary with time of day, or location, remains to be fully explored.

As the seasons march on, and the subsolar point climbs back towards the Equator (in 2002 the Sun hovered at 26° south, and so high northern latitudes were in winter darkness; by the end of 2005 the Sun was at 20° south, and at the end of 2007 it had climbed to just 9° south) the northern pole is becoming illuminated. Cassini's VIMS (Visual and Infrared Mapping Spectrometer) showed a large cloud complex – possibly of small ethane droplets – around the north pole (Figure 4). This may be related to down-welling air over the north which brings many organic compounds down into the lower stratosphere, which is cold enough for them to condense in wide cloud decks.

Early research (by this author in 1993!) suggested that Titan's raindrops would fall so slowly that they would have time to evaporate before they reach the ground, which can happen in dry areas of the Earth such as Arizona where the process is called 'virga'. (It is much less common in damp places like the UK!) However, the fact that Huygens found rounded cobbles and gullies at the landing site (Figure 5), indicating erosion by rainfall and transport of sediment by running liquid on the surface, shows that at least sometimes rain can get to the ground. Huygens did not observe pooled or flowing surface liquids, but

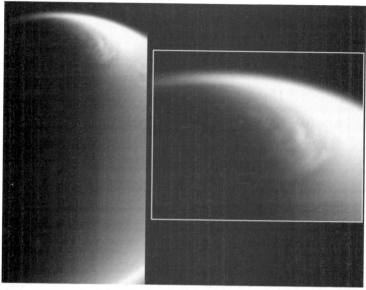

Figure 4. Ethane cloud. Cassini's visual and infrared mapping spectrometer imaged this huge cloud system covering the north pole of Titan. This composite image shows the cloud, imaged at a distance of 90,000 kilometres (54,000 miles) during a 29 December 2006 fly-by designed to observe the limb of the moon. Cassini's visual and infrared mapping spectro-meter scanned the limb, revealing this spectacular cloud system, perhaps laden with condensates, which ultimately are deposited as liquids to fill Titan's polar lakes. It covers the north pole down to a latitude of 62 degrees north and at all observed longitudes. The original image was colour-coded, with blue, green, and red at 2 microns, 2.7 microns, and 5 microns, respectively. (Image courtesy of NASA/JPL/University of Arizona.)

indications from the mechanical and thermal properties of the ground suggested it was damp with liquid methane, which was sweated out and detected by the heated inlet of the probe's Gas Chromatograph Mass Spectrometer (GCMS).

One possibility is that when methane storms occur, they do so with sufficient intensity that the first drops do indeed evaporate before reaching the ground, but in so doing moisten the lower atmosphere to form a humid channel ('rainshaft') along which subsequent drops can fall intact. Another, more subtle effect that has now been modelled, is that the raindrops are out of thermal equilibrium with their surround-ings – they fall from higher, cooler altitudes and are cooled further by

Figure 5. An artist's impression of Huygens on the surface of Titan. The view is approximately correct, based on data from the probe's descent imager, and the size and texture of the rounded, perhaps icy, cobbles around the probe is based on the images obtained from the surface. The exact location of the parachute is not known. The probe itself is 1.3 metres across. (Image courtesy of ESA.)

any initial evaporation, and subsequent evaporation is therefore slower because of the lower temperature. This evaporative cooling effect is not substantial in humid conditions (which is why the rain is often warm in Houston, for example), but, again, can be noticed in the dry southwestern USA. The same effect determines why outdoor swimming pools are cold after windy days – regardless of how much sunshine there has been.

Whichever of these effects (or indeed of other effects not yet determined) is the main factor allowing rain to the surface, the key point is that there are meteorological phenomena which are profoundly important to us here on Earth that can be studied in instructively different circumstances on Titan. Titan is like a giant laboratory to understand Earth-system processes.

In a sense, Titan is to the Earth's hydrological cycle what Venus is to the Earth's greenhouse effect – a terrestrial situation taken to extremes.

The reasoning for this is as follows: heating by sunlight causes surface moisture to evaporate, and so the atmosphere becomes progressively more saturated. If we divide the moisture content of the Earth's atmosphere (equivalent to a couple of centimetres of liquid water) by the rate at which it evaporates or rains (in a steady state over the long term, the two rates must be the same) of about one metre per year, then it follows that the moisture in the atmosphere turns over in a week or two. And while there is a spectrum of rain rates and storm sizes and so on, to a first approximation, a rainstorm empties out the atmospheric moisture locally – perhaps incompletely or perhaps even concentrating the moisture in updraughts. So, terrestrial weather is characterized by a few centimetres of rain every few weeks. Now, as the atmosphere becomes warmer, it can hold more moisture. This means individual storms can dump more rainfall, but it takes longer to re-saturate the atmosphere afterwards, because the evaporation rate is limited by the amount of sunshine, which has not appreciably changed. The uncomfortable result, then, of a warmer and moister atmosphere is more heavy rain and flooding, interspersed by longer droughts.

It seems Titan takes this situation to extremes. The amount of sunlight reaching its surface is enough to evaporate only about 1 centimetre per (Earth) year of methane moisture. However, the atmosphere holds methane equivalent to several metres of liquid. So the characteristic recharge time of the atmospheric moisture, and thus the typical recurrence interval (on a global average basis) of rainstorms is perhaps a thousand years. This explains the rather heavy erosion implied by the gullies – despite what must be on average a weak rainfall rate – and the fact that clouds typically cover only one per cent or so of Titan's area (instead of the roughly 30 per cent on Earth).

LAKES AND SEAS

Late 2006 and 2007 saw extensive coverage of Titan's north polar regions by radar, which mapped out hundreds of hydrocarbon lakes (Figure 6). Indeed, some bodies were so large – hundreds of kilometres across – that they have earned the designation *maria*, or seas.

The presence of channels draining into the lakes, islands, and coastlines indicate a flooded landscape, and the microwave properties of the features (some are literally pitch-black to radar, returning no

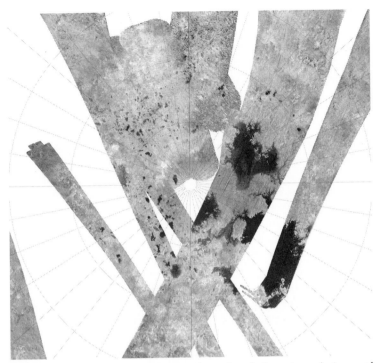

Figure 6. Lakes mosaic. This Cassini mosaic shows all synthetic-aperture radar images of Titan's north polar region up to October 2007. Approximately 60 per cent of Titan's north polar region, above 60 degrees north latitude, is now mapped with radar. About 14 per cent of the mapped region is covered by what are interpreted as liquid hydrocarbon lakes. Features appearing darkest to the radar are thought to be liquid, and the radar-bright areas are likely to be solid surface. The terrain in the top centre of this mosaic is imaged at lower resolution than the remainder of the image. Most of the many lakes and seas seen so far are contained in this image, including the largest known body of liquid on Titan. These seas are most likely filled with liquid ethane, methane, and dissolved nitrogen. Many bays, islands, and presumed tributary networks are associated with the seas. The large feature (now named Ligeia Mare) in the upper right centre of this image is at least 100,000 square kilometres (40,000 square miles) in area, greater in extent than Lake Superior (82,000 square kilometres or 32,000 square miles), one of Earth's largest lakes. This Titan feature covers a greater fraction of the surface, at least 0.12 per cent, than the Black Sea does on Earth, our largest terrestrial inland sea, at 0.085 per cent. Larger seas may exist, as it is probable that some of these bodies are connected, either in areas unmapped by radar or under the surface. (Image courtesy of NASA/JPL/USGS.)

measurable echo) all suggest that most of these features are currently filled with liquid. This will be a mixture of ethane and methane (both are the dominant components of liquefied natural gas on Earth) with some dissolved nitrogen and propane.

Estimates of the total volume of liquid in the lakes exceed the total amount of oil and gas reserves on Earth by a factor of a hundred or more. However, this amount – perhaps a third of a million cubic kilometres – is still less than the total amount of methane in the atmosphere, and so the observable lakes do not make a viable reservoir to buffer the atmospheric methane for geological time against photolysis. This process (by which solar ultraviolet breaks down methane and converts it into heavier molecules like ethane and the tholin haze) would destroy the atmospheric methane inventory in about ten million years. Unless we are looking at an unusual episode in Titan's history, there must be a subsurface reservoir and/or episodic delivery of methane by cryovolcanoes. Unless exquisitely finely tuned, such delivery would lead to wide fluctuations in the amount of methane in the hydrosphere and thus (since methane is the dominant contributor to the greenhouse effect on Titan, which keeps Titan some 20K warmer than it would otherwise be) dramatic changes in climate.

There have not yet been radar images of the south pole, so whether there are lakes there, and/or whether they are systematically different from their counterparts in the north, is not yet known. However, early in the mission, Cassini's ISS did observe a lake-shaped dark feature, now named Lacus Ontario, near the south pole.

DUNES AND MOUNTAINS

While Cassini has shown that Titan is remarkably Earth-like in having bodies of liquid on its surface (Figure 7), it also found that Titan is not always damp. In fact, large tracts of its surface resemble the Arabian or Saharan deserts in that they are covered in giant dunes of sandy material. Radar images showed that dark sand dunes cover a remarkable 20 per cent or so of Titan's surface, essentially all within 30° of the Equator (Figure 8, *Top*). Under good conditions, the VIMS and ISS data could detect individual dunes as well. The dunes form massive sand seas, that are in fact the dark regions observed in near-infrared images from the Hubble Space Telescope and large ground-based

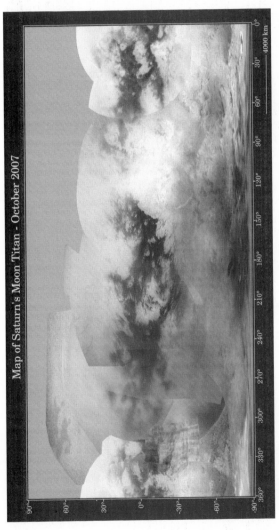

Figure 7. This near-global map of Titan was created using near-infrared images (938 nanometres wavelength – about the same as a TV remote control) taken by the Cassini spacecraft Imaging Science Subsystem (ISS) showing the pattern of bright and dark materials on the surface. The resolution of the map varies, being rather poor on the trailing hemisphere (270 degrees west longitude), but shows just a few kilometres per pixel near the centre and edges of the map. There is presently very little coverage of high northern latitudes, which have been in winter shadow since Cassini's arrival, but the coming years will show these areas (including the lakes seen by radar in Figure 6) as the polar lighting improves with the changing seasons. (Image courtesy of NASA/JPL/Space Science Institute.)

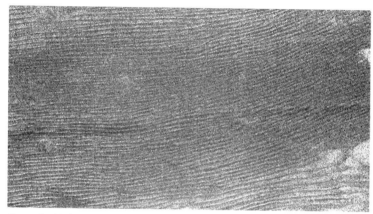

Figure 8. (*Top*). Giant linear dunes on Titan. The radar image of the Belet region of Titan's trailing hemisphere (just south of the equator) is about 200 kilometres from top to bottom. The bright patches are mountains poking up through the sea of organic-rich sand – these bright 'islands' trail off to the upper right, indicating that the dunes are longitudinal and that the winds run predominantly towards the east-north-east. The individual dunes are over a hundred metres high in many cases and a few kilometres apart. (Image courtesy of NASA/JPL/University of Arizona.)

Figure 8. (*Bottom*). Giant linear dunes on Earth. This image shows the coast of Namibia, as imaged with a digital camera on board the space shuttle. The dunes there are the same size as those on Titan (Figure 8, top), formed in the same way, but of different material from the Titan dunes. (Image courtesy of NASA/JSC/EOL.)

telescopes like Keck, Gemini and the Very Large Telescope (VLT), even since the mid to late 1990s, although their nature as dunefields came as a total surprise, it being originally thought that the dark regions might be seas of liquid!

Dunes were seen as dark streaks in radar images acquired north of Xanadu by Cassini in February 2005, on T3, the next Titan fly-by after the one that delivered the probe. The origin of the streaks was not certain at that point, but became strikingly obvious when much more extensive dunes were observed near the Equator on T8, in August of that year. These dunes were seen broadside-on by the radar, allowing their heights to be estimated at some 150 metres, comparable with the largest dunes on Earth. The dunes had a typical width of one kilometre or so, and were many tens of kilometres long (hundreds in some cases) and a few kilometres apart.

The T8 radar image that revealed the dunes also covered the Huygens landing site. This proved remarkably tricky to find in the image, because the radar image displays different surface properties to optical imaging (the radar reflectivity indicating roughness and texture at scales above the wavelength of two centimetres), which indicates the near-infrared reflectivity which is dominated by the composition of the uppermost microns of material. The key turned out to be a pair of dunes, seen off near the horizon as two vague streaks in the images taken by the Huygens probe during its descent. These matched up with two dunes in the radar image and allowed the ground-truth local data from the probe to be tied into the global picture being developed remotely from Cassini's fly-bys.

The material that makes up the dunes is sand in the sense of its particle size – grains a quarter of a millimetre in size are easiest to blow across the surface by wind on both Earth and Titan. However, on Titan the sand material is not silicate rock as on Earth, but probably organic solids produced high in the atmosphere. How such sand grains are formed from the much smaller haze particles (about a micron across) is not known – perhaps they clump together in the lakes which periodically dry out? At present no one knows. The dune sands may also include a small amount of icy material from impact craters or river channels, but the bulk appears to be organic, as evidenced by its optically dark appearance.

Another striking feature of the dunes is that they flow around mountains, and through gaps between them. In other words, the dunes line up along the sand-transport direction (so-called linear or longitudinal dunes). This implies the winds flip around, typically between two converging directions, and the dune lines up along the long-term average wind. This happens in the Namib Desert on Earth (Figure 8, *Bottom*), and also in the Sahara, Arabian, and some Australian deserts, although this type of dune is less common in the Americas, where winds tend to be either very irregular (forming star-shaped dunes) or in a constant direction (forming transverse dunes with the dune crests orthogonal to the wind, like waves at sea). It has been calculated that, in Titan's low gravity (about the same as the Earth's moon, 1.35 ms^{-2}, or a seventh of that of Earth) and in its thick atmosphere, winds of only 1 ms^{-1} would be enough to move sand. While the weak sunlight reaching Titan's surface is not easily able to stir up such winds, it may be that the large gravitational tides caused by Saturn generate tidal winds, like the tidal currents in the Earth's oceans. That tidal winds may be so significant is unique to Titan in our Solar System, although such winds may be prominent on some extra-solar planets.

Although there are local variations, notably a divergence around Xanadu, the dunes are aligned in such a way as to indicate predominantly eastwards winds ('westerlies' in meteorological parlance). This is in fact quite surprising, as models show (in contrast to high altitude eastwards winds) that near-surface winds near the Equator should in fact be predominantly easterlies. The reason for this discrepancy is not currently understood.

Although parts of Titan such as the sand seas are flat on a large scale – there are height variations of just a few tens of metres over hundreds of kilometres (apart from the local height variation due to the dunes themselves!) – there are also mountains over a kilometre high. Some of these form mountain ranges about a hundred kilometres long or more. How they form is not known.

SPIN AND INTERIOR

The growing coverage of Titan's surface by radar opened up surprising new insights into both the atmosphere and the interior. The Cassini radar team announced that by comparing the positions of landmarks spotted in multiple radar images taken at different times, they deduced that Titan's rotational pole was about 0.3° away from the normal to its orbit around Saturn. Further, the mismatched positions (in some cases by 20 to 30 kilometres) indicated that Titan was rotating slightly faster than synchronous, and that the rotation was accelerating. This change in rotation had been anticipated theoretically a couple of years before – the zonal winds in Titan's massive atmosphere would change season-ally, and in slowing down would deposit angular momentum into the surface. The amount by which the surface rotation would change would depend on whether Titan was a solid body, or if the surface was attached to only a thin icy crust overlying a liquid water ocean which decouples it from a rocky core. The large asynchroneity and its rapid change showed that Titan had to have an internal ocean, much like that of Europa. Future radar observations may be able to identify further changes in the rotation, and thereby deduce how much the zonal winds change with the seasons.

Precision Doppler-tracking of Cassini to infer Titan's tidally changing gravity field may yield independent insights into how thick Titan's ice crust might be, although this measurement is much more challenging to achieve from fly-bys than it would be from a Titan orbiter. Similarly, the magnetic field that might be induced in a con-ductive ocean is quite small on Titan (since, unlike Jupiter, Saturn's magnetic field is barely tilted relative to its satellites' orbits, and so the field seen at Titan does not change much) and the complications of Titan's ionosphere have so far prevented any definitive statement on its interior.

However, geomorphological indications are that at least parts of Titan's interior are molten, at least sometimes. Several cryovolcanic features have been identified separately in radar and VIMS data – although there is so far no evidence of present-day eruptions (Figure 9). As VIMS and radar coverage build up, the overlapping areas where coverage from both instruments is available is growing fast and this correlative analysis will likely be a major feature of future work. One early example shows that what had been identified in radar data morphologically as a cryovolcanic lava flow appears to be spectrally quite distinct from its surrounds, indicating an anomalous com-position.

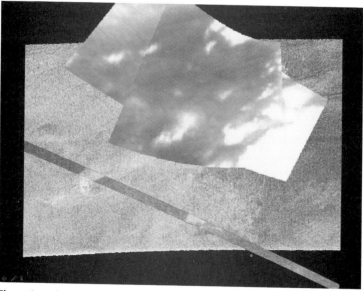

Figure 9. Radar-VIMS combination: a cryovolcano? This image composite contains a radar image taken during a February 2005 (T3) fly-by, and overlaid are images from the visual and infrared mapping spectrometers taken on 7 September 2006, (T17) and 25 October 2006 (T20). The thin strip is the infrared image taken on the inbound leg of the T20 fly-by and crosses the radar image near an area with a small, crater-like feature. In the radar image a faint fan of material seems to originate at the crater, and the portion of the infrared image that crosses the faint fan shows both a large contrast in brightness and very sharp boundaries. The fan-like deposit has such sharp boundaries and strong contrast with its surroundings that it supports the idea that the deposit seen in the radar images is a flow of material erupted from the small crater. This may be the strongest evidence yet of cryovolcanism on Titan. The infrared image was taken at a distance of 1,100 kilometres (680 miles) from the surface of Titan and shows distinct features as small as 400 metres (1,300 feet) in size. The infrared images were taken at wavelengths of 1.3 microns, 2 microns, and 5 microns. (Image courtesy of NASA/JPL/University of Arizona.)

FUTURE OUTLOOK

Cassini's four-year nominal mission (with 44 Titan fly-bys in total) ended on 30 June 2008. The spacecraft was in good health and had plenty of fuel, however, and a two-year extended mission, with 26 more Titan flybys, known as the Cassini Equinox Mission, was proposed and approved by NASA headquarters. This will run until 30 June 2010, and will take Cassini through the northern spring equinox in May 2009, after which Titan's atmospheric circulation and perhaps its weather patterns are expected to change dramatically. Initial plans are being drawn up for a possible extension of the mission beyond that.

The year 2007 also saw a concerted build-up of studies for potential future Titan missions. In Europe, a concept named TANDEM (Titan AND Enceladus Mission) was proposed successfully for further study under ESA's Cosmic Visions programme. In the USA, a Titan mission was one of four outer Solar System 'Flagship Mission' studies (the others being Enceladus, Europa, and the Jupiter System). These million-dollar studies, of missions to cost between two to four billion dollars, ran from January to August of 2007. In late December 2007, NASA announced that it would pursue studies of Titan mission concepts (as well as Europa/Jupiter-System mission ideas) further in 2008, with the studies being coordinated with their European counterparts.

Titan's thick atmosphere opens it up to many possible exploration architectures. The atmosphere allows an orbiter to arrive by aerocapture (braking in the atmosphere, like the Leonov in Arthur C. Clarke's *2010*) – essentially providing four kilometres per second of velocity change without rocket propulsion. This very efficient mode of arrival (dispensing with massive propulsion capability, but requiring a modest heat shield around the orbiter) allows large and capable payloads to be delivered affordably. The atmosphere also makes it easy to deliver instrumentation to the surface – instead of large retro rockets, a lander simply needs a parachute. Finally, the thick, cold atmosphere lends itself to all kinds of aircraft – not just light gas balloons filled with hydrogen or helium, but aeroplanes and hot-air balloons (Figure 10). The latter is an attractive option not only because it is mass-efficient (not requiring hydrogen tanks – its buoyancy comes from local Titan air, heated by the waste heat from the RTG that

Figure 10. Titan Balloon. A future Titan mission might include a Montgolfière (a hot-air balloon), with the air kept warm, not by a propane burner as on Earth, but with the 'waste' heat from a radioisotope thermoelectric generator that also provides electrical power. Hot-air balloons can last for years (since small leaks do not matter) and can descend from a cruising altitude of perhaps ten kilometres down to the surface using a vent valve. (Image courtesy of Tibor Balint/JPL/NASA.)

provides electrical power to the balloon gondola) but also because hot-air balloons are relatively insensitive to leaks, and by opening a vent valve, the balloon's altitude can be controlled to exploit different wind speeds at different altitudes. In addition to an orbiter and balloon, the NASA Flagship study (led by the Johns Hopkins University Applied Physics Lab, with participation from JPL and NASA Langley) also proposed a lander able to make surface-chemistry and long-term meteorological and seismic measurements. Exactly which of the portfolio of many options NASA and ESA pursue together – if any – remains to be seen.

FURTHER READING

Harland, D. M., *Cassini at Saturn: Huygens Results* (Springer-Praxis, 2007).

Lorenz, R. D. and Mitton, J. M., *Lifting Titan's Veil* (Cambridge University Press, 2002).

Lorenz, R. D. and Mitton, J. M., *Titan Unveiled* (Princeton University Press, 2008).

WEB RESOURCES

The excellent JPL Cassini web page is http://saturn.jpl.nasa.gov/. Its European counterpart is http://sci.esa.int/huygens.

New discoveries are often covered well and in depth by The Planetary Society: http://www.planetary.org. There are detailed discussions of new findings (and many excellent amateur image products) at http://www.unmannedspaceflight.com.

Plans for future Titan missions and related topics can be found at the website of the Outer Planets Assessment Group (OPAG): http://www.lpi.usra.edu/opag/.

Deep-Sky Imaging With a Small Refractor

GREG PARKER

Is it possible to take reasonable-looking deep-sky images with just a small-aperture refracting telescope?

Well, if you take a look at the images acquired at the New Forest Observatory, Hampshire, UK[1] by the author of this article, and duly processed by Noel Carboni in Florida, USA, you might be surprised to learn that the wide-field images you see there, and in Figure 1 here, were all taken using a 90-mm-aperture refractor! So maybe the answer to the above question is 'Yes', you can take nice deep-sky images with just a small refractor, but there are a few provisos.

Although the instrument used to capture the image of M31 shown in Figure 1 was of small (90 mm) aperture, you also need some means of tracking the sky with your telescope, and some means of photographing the deep-sky object captured in the telescope's field of view.

In order to track deep-sky objects for astrophotography, your imaging telescope needs to be equatorially mounted and polar-aligned so that it can track the stars for up to an hour at a time without any 'star trailing' effects. For a telescope on an altazimuth mounting, it takes only a few seconds of exposure before you notice star trailing caused by field rotation. If you are lucky, you may manage exposures of up to nearly 30 seconds, depending on the area of sky you are imaging, but for serious astrophotography and longer exposure times, you simply cannot get away from an equatorial mounting and good polar alignment.

In Figure 2 you can see how I have equatorially mounted the little Takahashi Sky 90 refractor.[2] I have been using it to take wide-field

1. http://newforestobservatory.com/
2. http://selltelescopes.com/product.asp?pid=1980

Figure 1. M31 – the Great Galaxy in Andromeda. Image taken using a Takahashi Sky 90 refractor and SXVF-M25C one-shot colour camera. (All images courtesy of the author.)

images of deep-sky objects. I have 'cheated' by piggy-backing the little refractor on a large wedge-mounted Celestron Nexstar 11 GPS reflecting telescope.[3] The wedge allows me to equatorially mount the big reflector, which comes on an altazimuth mounting. You could also buy

3. http://www.celestron.uk.com/catalogues/view_item.asp?ItemID=30675&CatalogueID=272&CategoryID=3822

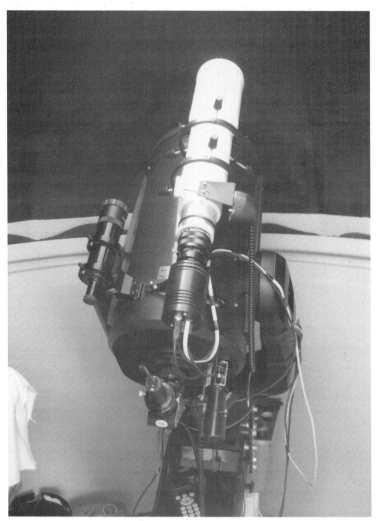

Figure 2. The author's Takahashi Sky 90 refractor piggy-backed on a wedge-mounted Celestron Nexstar 11-inch GPS reflecting telescope. The big reflector is used as a guide scope, and the autoguiding CCD can be seen fitted at the eyepiece position of the reflector.

a purpose-built equatorial mount, such as the Celestron CGE mount, or the several Losmandy mounts which are available,[4] and fix your small refractor to one of these. It doesn't matter which option you choose, provided your system allows you to accurately follow the stars.

Unfortunately, with the exception of all but the most expensive mounts available, such as the Paramount ME,[5] you are unable to accurately track the apparent movement of the stars for extended periods of time without the addition of an autoguider. An autoguider is a subsystem that 'locks' your imaging telescope on to an appropriate 'guide star' that lies in the field of view you are attempting to image. By locking on to a star it ensures that the mount, and the imaging telescope, accurately follows the apparent movement of the stars across the sky and does not rely on highly accurate mount drives to do the entire job for you. Autoguiding can be achieved in several ways, but the easiest and most flexible approach is to use a second (cheaper) refractor with an autoguiding CCD camera attached.[6] In Figure 2, I was using the big reflector as a guide scope (this is not a cheap option!) and the little autoguiding CCD can be seen fitted at the eyepiece position of the reflector. The signal from this autoguiding CCD-camera is analysed by specialist software – I use Maxim DL for this purpose[7] – and a guide star is chosen by mouse-clicking on a suitable-looking star as seen on the read-out monitor. The software takes care of the rest and will do its best to keep the guide star centrally positioned by moving the mount to within very tight accuracy, typically just one pixel!

So you now have three of the four necessary parts of your imaging system, the imaging telescope, the equatorial mount, and the auto-guiding subsystem. The last piece of the jigsaw is the imaging camera itself, the camera you will fit to your small refractor to acquire the deep-sky images.

My main interest is to just take 'pretty pictures' of deep-sky objects. I am not concerned with carrying out scientific research – I get enough of that with the day job; I am only interested in pretty images. To this end I have chosen to work with a one-shot colour CCD-camera that takes a full colour image per frame – so you don't need to work through red, green and blue filters as you do with a monochrome

4. http://www.telescopesales.co.uk/mounts-01.htm
5. http://www.bisque.com/Products/Paramount/
6. http://www.starlight-xpress.co.uk/SXVguider.htm
7. http://www.cyanogen.com/products/maxim_main.htm

camera. As a bonus, the camera I currently use, a Starlight Xpress SXVF-M25C[8] also works well with narrow-band filters too, so I actually get the best of both worlds. If you are plagued with light pollution, you may need to work with narrow-band filters for all your work, in which case you may as well use a monochrome camera. In my case, the light pollution, although not good by any means, isn't too bad, and I can get away with one-shot colour camera imaging if I use a Hutech IDAS light pollution filter[9] in the imaging train. The IDAS filter takes out the mercury and sodium emission lines typically found in street lighting and other commercial lighting systems, but allows all other wavelengths to get through to the CCD-camera. I find these filters incredibly effective, and the added bonus is that you don't seem to need to alter the colour balance when processing the colour image either.

The SXVF-M25C camera is quite a large format at 23.4 × 15.6 mm and boasts six megapixel resolution. Fitted to a Sky 90 working at f/4.5 (a reducer-corrector lens inserted into the optical train is needed for this), the SXVF-M25C gives a massive 3.33 × 2.22° field of view at a very acceptable 3.96 arcseconds per pixel sampling. I don't want to get into the details of sampling other than to say that for deep-sky imaging sampling between two and four arcseconds per pixel should be used for best results. If the sampling goes much above four arcseconds per pixel, then your images will tend to look a little 'soft'.

So with regard to the components for imaging, I think we're pretty much there. However, rather than carry this lot of heavy and expensive equipment in and out of doors each time you want to image, it is a very good idea – if you have the space and the finances available – to create a permanent set-up, i.e. an observatory.

The New Forest Observatory is based around a very neat and highly effective 7-foot-diameter fibreglass dome supplied by Pulsar Optical[10] as shown in Figure 3.

The dome sits on wooden decking and there is a central concrete pillar (mechanically isolated from the decking) that carries the custom-built all-aluminium pier and the telescope systems. The pier is all aluminium so that it doesn't interfere with the Celestron's GPS system. I can warrant that the observatory is completely weatherproof and

8. http://www.starlight-xpress.co.uk/SXV-M25.htm
9. http://www.scsastro.co.uk/it050024.htm
10. http://www.pulsar-optical.co.uk/cat/observatory/dome/glassfibre.html

Figure 3. The author's New Forest Observatory, which is based around a highly effective 7-foot-diameter fibreglass dome supplied by Pulsar Optical. The dome sits on wooden decking and there is a central concrete pillar (mechanically isolated from the decking) that carries the custom-built all-aluminium pier and the telescope systems.

that the telescope's GPS system works through the fibreglass shell (although it doesn't seem to work indoors). It doesn't stop there, of course. You also need to get mains power to the dome for your computer (unless you use a laptop for this purpose) and you may need to invest in a dehumidifier[11] and a small greenhouse heater[12] for those

11. http://www.amazon.co.uk/exec/obidos/ASIN/B000BHLRTK/ref=nosim/coffeeuk21288-21
12. http://www.garden4less.co.uk/proddetail.asp?prod=TR-2000/GB

bitterly cold winter evenings. I run the Celestron Nexstar 11 GPS reflecting telescope from a 'Power Tank',[13] which is basically a 12-volt rechargeable battery. The observatory computer is a home-built mini-ATX system,[14] which is absolutely perfect for this application, having a tiny footprint and very low noise and power consumption. The mini-ATX is connected to the mains via an uninterruptible power supply (UPS),[15] since in deepest Hampshire we do seem to get more than our fair share of power cuts. Finally, all mains-driven equipment is fed from Belkin SurgeMaster, a surge-protected distribution box,[16] because I have had the extremely unpleasant experience of a power glitch taking out two computers and a motor control board for the telescope!

That pretty much completes the hardware requirements, so now it's down to the hard work of acquiring the images.

Start off by doing your normal alignment procedure and then moving to the object you wish to image. Take a few short sub-exposures to frame the object correctly and then focus the telescope using the software-based focusing routine. I use Maxim DL for this purpose, and on a night of good 'seeing' I will obtain FWHM readings on a reasonably bright star of 1.4–1.5 pixels. You also need to check your CCD is flat to the focal plane if you are using a large format CCD. For this purpose I use another piece of software called CCD Inspector,[17] which is purpose-built for the job. Although a little on the expensive side for astronomical software, CCD Inspector is invaluable for checking chip flatness and system collimation and I simply couldn't carry out my work without it.

With your object framed, the telescope focused, and the CCD chip flattened, it is finally time to start acquiring the image. Set the auto-guider going and prepare to take your first set of sub-exposures. When you start imaging for the first time you will find that even an hour on one subject seems like an inordinate amount of time, especially when there are so many other objects you want to image. The bad news is that unless you have a 'fast' imaging system like those based on the

13. http://www.celestron.uk.com/catalogues/view_item.asp?CatalogueID=272&CategoryID=3874&ItemID=30965
14. http://www.mini-itx.com/store/?c=2#p1649
15. http://www.novatech.co.uk/novatech/specpage.html?APC-500VAE
16. http://www.novatech.co.uk/novatech/specpage.html?BEL-100657
17. http://www.ccdware.com/products/ccdinspector/

HyperStar unit,[18] your total imaging times are typically going to be very much longer than an hour.

By taking lots of sub-exposures (subs) and stacking them together, your image quality (the signal-to-noise ratio) improves by a factor equivalent to the square root of the number of subs. I find you will end up with a nice smooth image if you can manage to acquire more than 80 subs on an object; 100 subs is near ideal. The question then becomes, how much time do I spend per sub? This depends a lot on your local sky glow, and the good news is that star clusters, and single star shots (see Figure 4) require a lot less time than galaxies and nebulae. So for my f/4.5 system, I can use subs as short as three to four minutes for star clusters or for very bright objects such as M42 (the Great Nebula in Orion) or even M31 (the Andromeda Galaxy). For virtually all other objects we are talking of sub-exposure times in excess of five minutes. For most deep-sky objects I will use sub-exposure

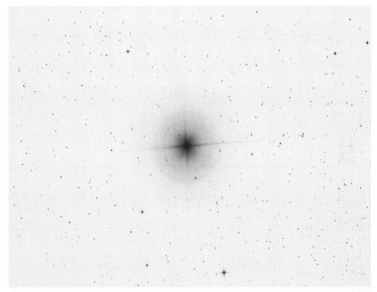

Figure 4. A negative black and white image of the first magnitude star Aldebaran (Alpha Tauri). The imaging of single stars and of star clusters requires a lot less time than galaxies and nebulae.

18. http://starizona.com/acb/hyperstar/index.aspx

times of around nine to ten minutes at f/4.5, but remember this all depends on your local sky-glow conditions and on the speed (f-number) of your imaging system. The *number* of subs will dictate the final signal-to-noise ratio of your image and the *duration* of the individual subs will dictate how deep your image will go in terms of magnitude.

As with most things in life, there is a trade-off situation that we find ourselves in. We have a limited amount of good imaging time, and we have to maximize the quality of the data we collect during that limited time period. If we collect 100 sub-exposures of ten minutes per sub, we will have invested over 16.5 hours in imaging just one object. This is likely to take up three or four nights' good imaging time, so you'd better be sure you *really* want a high-quality image of this particular object. It's true you can get away with quite a lot less time than this (especially if you have equipment of larger aperture), but you will see from the published images that the very best examples all have total exposure times exceeding ten hours or so. The image of the Sword of Orion in Figure 5 represents over 12 hours of imaging time, including over four hours of H-alpha data, as well as over 12 hours' image-processing time by Noel Carboni!

Figure 5. This image of the magnificent Sword of Orion represents over 12 hours of imaging time, including over four hours of H-alpha data, as well as over 12 hours' image-processing time by Noel Carboni.

The only significant difference if you are taking narrow-band data using filters such as H-alpha, SII, OIII, or H-beta[19] is that your sub-exposure times will typically be a lot longer. I normally use sub-exposure times of 20 to 30 minutes with narrow-band filters, but if your local sky-glow conditions allow you to go to even longer sub-exposure times, then do so. The only really negative thing to go along with long sub-exposure times is the pain you suffer over a lost sub. This might be due to a plane or helicopter entering the field, or a bumped 'scope, or anything else that spoils your long sub-exposure. The other thing you need to keep in mind is the longer your sub-exposure, the better your mount and autoguiding needs to be.

From the above you can see that there are a lot of parameters to keep in mind at any one time when deep-sky imaging. That's why it is a very good idea, when you have a nicely tuned system that you understand quite well, that you stick with it and don't change anything unless you really have to.

For me, the current set-up I have is pretty much optimized for the wide-field imaging work I want to carry out. There are, however, always ways to improve things and these invariably mean more expense!

My next system upgrade will be to move into 'parallel imaging', which you can consider to be the optical analogue of parallel processing. From the above discussion we have seen that a lot of time commitment is required just to image a single object. To make matters worse, here in the UK we don't get many clear nights, let alone clear moonless nights with good seeing – and we need several of these to get sufficient data to create a nice image. At first sight this looks like an insurmountable problem, until we see a possible solution in arrangements like the SuperWASP array.[20] In the SuperWASP concept we have a number of independent imagers used in parallel to cover a large area of sky. Alternatively, you could use a number of independent imagers to image *the same area of sky*! In this way you can multiply the hours of data collected on the one object by the number of independent imagers, making it entirely feasible to take very high-quality images of deep-sky objects in a single evening's imaging session. This is the basic idea behind the miniWASP array currently under construction at the New Forest Observatory.

19. http://www.iankingimaging.com/show_products.php?category=18
20. http://www.superwasp.org/

I have just made a start on designing the NFO miniWASP array with the help of my good friend Eric Kennedy of NTE Poole Ltd.[21] Eric is currently constructing the telescope framework out of aluminium plate. The framework will be able to accommodate up to four separate telescopes and their associated CCD-cameras. It will also be possible to drill and tap the outside top of the frame at a later date if I want to accommodate another two telescopes.

Initially I propose using the four internal slots to take:

1) Sky 90 + SXVF M25C one-shot colour camera
2) Sky 90 + SXVF M25C one-shot colour camera
3) FSQ-106 ED + H36 large-format mono camera
4) William Optics 80-mm refractor and SXV guide camera

The two Sky 90s and their colour cameras will be set up to take a two-frame mosaic in one go with a total field of view of 4.1 × 3.33 degrees. The FSQ-106 will be used at its native f/5 (i.e. no field reducer/corrector), which when combined with the H36 large-format mono camera will give a field of view of 3.9 × 2.6 degrees. The mono camera will be used with a True Technology slimline filter-wheel[22] to take narrowband images of the same area that the M25C cameras are imaging.

The H36 mono camera is 16 megapixel, and the colour cameras are each 6 megapixel. Each sub-exposure taken is therefore the equivalent of a single 28-megapixel camera, so you can see that the data (computational) handling implications are going to be non-trivial, just as in the actual SuperWASP array.

Please view http://www.newforestobservatory.com regularly to keep up to date on the progress with this unique amateur imaging array.

21. http://www.ntepoole.co.uk/
22. http://www.trutek-uk.com/cwss/ss3.htm

When the Stones Speak: An Archaeoastronomy Tour of Peru

FRED WATSON

'They're eyes,' said Iván Ghezzi. And, indeed, they were – quite unmistakably. Out of the upright slab of carved stone in front of us peered row upon row of stylized eyes.

Symbols of a great culture of ancient sky-watchers? I wondered, thinking of the extraordinary solar observatory a few kilometres from here that we had visited yesterday. There was no doubt that the astronomical knowledge needed by its builders to place their thirteen square towers in exactly the right position along a barren hilltop would have taken decades – maybe centuries – to accumulate. Iván himself had nailed down the construction of those towers to the fourth century BC using carbon-14 dating, but this orderly array of staring eyes was known to be at least a thousand years older.

As if hearing my question, Iván pointed out another upright panel of stone in the wall, a few metres from the peering eyes. A dozen faces, all uniformly glum, were carved, one above the other, into the surface of the slab. All of them seemed to have their eyes closed. Could they be sleeping astronomers?

Evidently not. Between the two slabs, a third stone revealed the true meaning of these intriguing symbols. It carried the unmistakable figure of an armed warrior, proud in victory, wearing an elaborate headdress. 'Those aren't faces,' said Iván. 'They're heads, stacked on top of one another. With their eyes gouged out.'

Now, as we looked with new enlightenment in either direction along this hundred-metre mural wall, we could discern a horrific celebration of slaughter and dismemberment. Severed heads by the dozen trailed blood from their eyes and mouths. Detached arms and legs vied with stylized human backbones to shock the onlooker. A warrior, cut in half, his entrails hanging from the stump of his torso, gazed blindly skywards. And, in a carving described by the doctor in our party as 'amazingly accurate', a complete digestive tract from gullet to intestine trailed down the face of another slab. For the ancient craftsmen who had sculpted these stones, such confronting of the remnants of a vanquished foe was evidently nothing less than commonplace.

ASTRONOMY AND RITUAL

Iván Ghezzi is an archaeologist. In fact, as the former Archaeology Director of Peru's Instituto Nacional de Cultura, he is a leader in his field. It was a great privilege to have him accompany us to this coastal desert region some 370 kilometres north of the nation's capital, Lima. Only a few months earlier, he and his collaborator, Clive Ruggles of Leicester University, had made worldwide headlines with their announcement that the mysterious Thirteen Towers of Chankillo constituted a previously unrecognized solar observatory some 2,300 years old. And only a few days ago, I had written to these two high-profile professors from my home in Coonabarabran, explaining that I was about to bring a party of interested Australians on a study tour of the ancient astronomical sites of Peru – and that we would be starting with Chankillo.

To be honest, my email was intended mainly as a courtesy. The most I expected in reply was a polite welcome, which I could proudly read out to my little band of enthusiasts to demonstrate that we had the imprimatur of the masters. What I actually received amazed me. In fact, to borrow the word Clive Ruggles himself famously used when the significance of Chankillo dawned on him – I was gobsmacked. A friendly message from Iván told me that not only was he willing to meet us when we arrived in Lima, but that he would be delighted to accompany us to the site when we visited it. This was beyond my wildest expectations, but I soon discovered that such generosity is typical of the man.

So it was that, having seen for ourselves the Thirteen Towers – of which more later – the seventeen members of the study tour were gathered at the nearby temple of Sechín, listening to Iván's account of the gruesome mural art that stretched before us on its outer wall (Figure 1). He described what we know of the cultural background underpinning the scene, and how it relates to the astronomical significance of the towers. Though the builders of the temple and the

Figure 1. Looking decidedly unwell, a 3,300-year-old participant in ritual warfare decorates the mural wall at Sechín. Note his long thumbnails, which are handy for gouging out the eyes of enemies. (Image courtesy of the author.)

towers were separated widely in time, their main stock-in-trade seems to have been the same. Ritual warfare.

Perhaps more than most folk in today's world, astronomers are tuned in to the idea that primitive people attributed great significance to the things they saw in the sky. You have only to think of our familiar constellations and the stories attached to them. They are based on the star patterns of the ancient Greeks, which, in turn, owe their origins to earlier Sumerian constellations. But many ancient peoples identified their own star patterns, and evolved legends to go with them. Often, as in the case of the indigenous people of Australia, those legends had a practical purpose. For example, they defined seasons when it was worthwhile hunting for a particular food – berries or insect larvae – and, in other cultures, when it was the right time to plant crops.

In the coastal deserts of Peru, human settlement clung to the flood plains of the Andean rivers, which even today cut a green swathe through the pale grey-brown of the desert soil. Water meant everything, and the ebb and flow of the rivers – which in reality is determined by distant snow-melt – was believed to be controlled by supernatural beings. Perhaps these were the ancestor-gods, or *huacas*, who were considered by many ancient Peruvian cultures to intervene directly in everyday affairs, and who were closely linked with the phenomena of the sky.

What happened when these gods disagreed among themselves? They would fight battles, and maybe the outcomes of those battles would determine who in the human world got water, and who didn't. But in the belief system of many ancient Andean people, a supernatural battle would have its parallel on earth, in the form of a ritual battle founded on religious belief – a holy war. Today, anthropologists distinguish between such sacred wars, with their specific religious aims, and true warfare, in which there are wider socio-political goals. The ultimate aim of true warfare is the total destruction of the enemy, while in a ritual war, the loss of life might be quite limited. On the other hand, the ritual butchery of the vanquished in early religious warfare could assume barbaric proportions.

To initiate a ritual war, so the theory went, the *huacas* would speak to the leaders of their respective communities in dreams, or through astronomical phenomena. Thus, a belief in such messages was fundamental to the process, and clearly astronomical observations could have serious consequences in initiating battles with rival communities. Fortunately, today's astronomers don't have to worry about such outcomes, except in the mildest possible way.

It is Iván Ghezzi's thesis that many of the most spectacular archaeological sites of the Casma valley – where both Sechín and Chankillo lie – are ceremonial settings for such ritual battles. He has good reasons for believing this. Set high on a hilltop overlooking the Chankillo archaeological complex (Figure 2) – which itself covers an area of several square kilometres – is its most substantial and prominent feature. This imposing construction consists of two roofless circular buildings some 40 metres in diameter with a third rectangular building of similar size close by. The three structures are all erected on an earthwork platform and surrounded by two rough stone walls, approximately triangular in plan, and massively built – up to 8 metres high and 6.5 metres thick (Figure 3).

It is principally from the wooden lintels in doorways piercing these walls that the accurate carbon-14 dating of the structure has been made. Carbon dating from other contemporary plant samples (such as seeds and fibres) is in good agreement with the 2,300-year estimate of

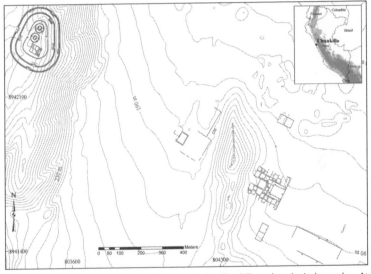

Figure 2. A map showing the principal sites in the Chankillo archaeological complex. At upper left is the hilltop temple-fortress, containing the rectangular Temple of the Pillars. Running north–south at centre right are the thirteen towers on their prominent ridge, with the eastern and western observation points about 300 metres away on either side. They are, respectively, the small structure on the 185-metre contour, and the open end of a corridor in the rectangular structure to the left of the towers. (Map courtesy of Iván Ghezzi, Proyecto Chankillo, Proyecto Líneas de Nasca, Universidad Católica del Perú, Yale University.)

Figure 3. The two outer walls of the hilltop temple-fortress at Chankillo follow the local topography. Built 2,300 years ago, the walls are 8 metres high in places. (Image courtesy of the author.)

its age. The whole site also shows evidence of damage due to seismic activity, which produces characteristic triangular breaks in the masonry. Peru, of course, is no stranger to earthquakes.

The question that plagues archaeologists when they examine this structure at Chankillo is: what exactly was it for? It is frequently referred to as a fort, and it certainly looks like one, with its massive defensive walls. However, if that is the case, what was its strategic purpose? As well as being 180 metres above the valley floor, it is more than two kilometres from the fields and water sources that it might be expected to have defended. It has no water-storage facilities of its own, so it would be quite unable to endure a siege. And strangely for a fort, the stonework reveals that the wooden bars that would have latched its gates firmly shut are on the *outside* of the main walls, rather than the inside. Could it be possible that enemies wanting to gain entry would have simply been able to let themselves in, without even having to knock?

To many archaeologists, this strongly suggests a ceremonial rather than a defensive purpose. Perhaps this was a seat of power, symbolizing the holy place of a particular community. In that regard it has more in common with a temple than a fort. But there is other evidence, uncovered by a team of archaeologists led by Iván Ghezzi, that points to its importance in ritual conflict. Remnants of parapets have been found surmounting the inner platform on which the three buildings stand. They prove that this place was genuinely intended to be defended against an attacker. Moreover, thousands of round stones of a uniform size are scattered on the hillside and the plain below it. These are sling stones, which would have been gathered from the riverbed two kilometres away. In the hands of warriors, they would be lethal weapons. And many fragments of ceramic figurines depicting such warriors with a variety of weapons have recently been found.

There is other evidence too. That rectangular building within the main complex aligns with the summer-solstice sunrise, and this alignment is maintained in the remnants of other buildings that stretch away two kilometres and more to the east. Of these, we will hear more later. But the uniform alignment tends to suggest that the rectangular building on the hill was of great importance for the whole site – a focal point for the activities carried out there. Indeed, it can be seen from almost anywhere in the district.

What was in this building? It contained several rooms. Raised platforms in two of the rooms suggest that ceremonial rituals were carried out there. The remains of decorated pillars in these two rooms have given the building a name – the Temple of the Pillars – for their function seems to have been primarily ceremonial rather than merely holding up the fabric or wooden roof (Figure 4).

Remarkably, however, one room in particular – a kind of 'inner sanctum' – shows evidence of having been systematically destroyed. A thick layer of dirt and stone has been piled into this room in a manner quite different from the damage caused naturally by earthquakes. Indeed most of the stony material is of a type not found at Chankillo, and it must have been transported from elsewhere. It is as if the intention was to annihilate this room completely. Along with whatever gods and altars it had housed, it was meant to be eradicated from memory altogether.

These pieces of evidence lead Iván to conclude that the Chankillo structure is neither a fortress nor a temple, but an amalgamation of both. During its period of occupation, it had enormous religious

Figure 4. The shattered remains of the Temple of the Pillars at Chankillo. The long axis of the building (across the photo) aligns with the summer-solstice sunrise. (Image courtesy of the author.)

significance to the people of the Casma valley, but the systematic destruction of the Temple of the Pillars marked the end of its era of dominance. And from this he draws broader conclusions:

> At least for the construction of the Chankillo fort, settlements and their populations had lesser priority than ceremonial spaces in the assignment of public labour for defensive works; it suggests that a major goal of warfare may have been to attack the seats of religious power ... The threat of total destruction may have been key to justifying leadership [together with] the mobilisation of public labour to erect massive fortifications to protect gods and their temples from the dangers of a world in which holy wars were fought to destroy them.

For the astronomers of Chankillo, that threat, too, was the motivation for their careful observations. And the thirteen towers remain today as spectacular evidence of this.

CHARIOTS OF THE GODS AND ALL THAT

Think of ancient civilizations in Peru and it's a fair bet that your mind will go first to the Incas. The amazingly precise stonework of Inca buildings speaks of a culture that was highly accomplished in both the theory and practice of architecture. Its characteristic trapezoidal doorways, windows and niches bears testimony to a deep understanding of the kind of civil engineering necessary to withstand frequent earthquakes, and it is clear that such knowledge – like that of the ancient astronomers of Chankillo – did not come overnight. Moreover, recent research by Andean history specialist Juan Carlos Machicado Figueroa suggests that even the basic design of Inca stonework embodies ritual symbolism of a most sophisticated kind.

How surprising, then, that this extraordinary culture lasted little more than a hundred years, from the expansion period of King Pachacutec in the 1430s to the capture of the last Inca monarch, Atahualpa, by Spanish conquistadors in 1532. Most of the Inca structures that remain today date from this period, and the associated ceramics and textiles that are preserved in Peru's museums tell of a creative and artistic civilization. Perhaps it was that very accomplishment that goaded a few hundred power-hungry conquistadors to wipe out some 12 million Incas after Atahualpa's capture and execution the following year. The technological prowess of the Spanish made that task as easy as pulling the trigger of a flintlock.

The principal god in Inca religion was the Sun, followed by the creator god, Wiracocha – and then the Moon, and various other deities. It is therefore no surprise to find that many Inca buildings and complexes align with the direction of sunrise or sunset at the winter or summer solstice. Such an alignment is found at one of the Incas' principal religious sites, the Temple of Wiracocha at Raqchi in southern Peru (Figure 5). This vast, cathedral-like structure would have been awe-inspiring in its heyday, with a central roof-bearing wall 12 metres high, and a total extent of 92 metres × 25 metres. Streets of smaller buildings lay to the south – also aligned with the winter-solstice sunrise, and the whole is still surrounded by a wall some 5 kilometres long. An artificial lagoon within the wall is fed by waterways built in stone by Inca hydraulic engineers, and one suggestion for the purpose

Figure 5. Remains of the central roof-bearing wall of the Temple of Wiracocha at Raqchi. This amazing 12-metre high structure was built during the Inca period (c. AD 1430–1532), and, like other buildings at the site, aligns with the winter-solstice sunrise. (Image courtesy of the author.)

of the lagoon is that it might have been used to observe a reflected image of the Sun in worship.

Raqchi is about 100 kilometres south-east of Cusco, the principal city of the Incas, and today the hub of archaeological and tourist activities in this area of the country. Founded around the year 1250, Cusco lies at the head of the so-called 'Sacred Valley' of the Urubamba River, which cuts through lofty mountains to the north-west of the city. Prominent among the Inca villages that line the valley floor is Ollantaytambo, site of a royal palace and associated barracks which housed large numbers of soldiers. Once again, the winter-solstice sunrise played an important ceremonial role in Ollantaytambo, but this time its position was marked, not by an alignment of streets, but by a prominent feature on the near-vertical wall of a sacred mountain viewed from the terraced hillside behind the town. It is thought that the rising of the Pleiades also had religious significance, and another feature on the same sacred mountain appears to mark the place where the asterism comes into view.

The jewel of the Sacred Valley – and perhaps the jewel of all Peru – is the astonishing mountain-top Inca settlement of Machu Picchu, further down the Urubamba River (Figure 6). Known to science only since 1911, when it was rediscovered by Hiram Bingham of Yale University, this extraordinary city in the clouds escaped destruction by the Spanish, perhaps because it was abandoned unfinished by its Inca builders at the time of the conquest. Now recognized as one of the New Seven Wonders of the World, Machu Picchu has become a Mecca for tourists, although archaeological research on the site still continues.

Of interest to astronomers is the so-called Temple of the Sun, which is sometimes described as an observatory – though it is not one in the modern sense of the word. A clue to the temple's significance comes from the fact that its stonework is among the finest on the site, and it was the standard practice of Inca stonemasons to grade the finish of their work according to the importance of the structure. In plan, the temple is D-shaped, with the upper and right-hand walls of the 'D' being perforated by small trapezoidal windows (Figure 7). In the centre lies a natural slab of unworked rock, which forms the top of the outcrop on which the temple stands.

You will probably not be surprised to hear that at sunrise on the winter and summer solstices the rock slab is illuminated by one or the other of the small windows, giving the building its name. The

Figure 6. The incredible mountain-top Inca citadel of Machu Picchu, one of the New Seven Wonders of the World. (Image courtesy of the author.)

alignments are precise, and suggest some ritual significance in the Sun's light falling on the rocky surface at the solstices. Quite what ceremony took place on those occasions is a mystery that is compounded by a third, larger window in the left-hand wall of the 'D'. This window has strange holes in the complex stonework around its lower edge, which

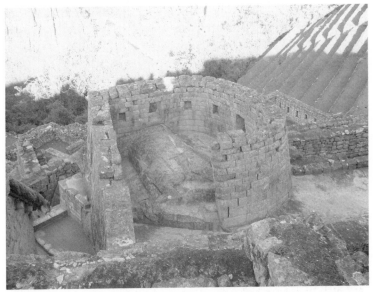

Figure 7. Shaped like a letter 'D', the Temple of the Sun at Machu Picchu has trapezoidal niches and windows. The windows in the rear and right-hand walls allow the winter and summer-solstice sunrise to illuminate the central rock slab, which may have had offerings placed upon it. (Image courtesy of the author.)

are thought to have been used for introducing snakes into the room. *Snakes?* That might suggest notions of human sacrifice, but it's unlikely, as the Incas were not too big on that particular pastime. Nevertheless, the idea of snakes in a temple dedicated to sun worship is somewhat mind-boggling . . . I have to say, though, that my mind was boggled much more by the amazing precision with which the lower courses of stonework blended into the rock on which the temple stands, giving the impression of a human-made structure simply growing out of the Earth. The subtlety of those Inca architects was simply awe-inspiring.

As we have seen, the expertise that went into the design of such fantastic structures was gained over many centuries, and nowhere is that more apparent than at the other iconic site of Peru's spectacular past – Nazca. Down in the southern half of Peru, on the coastal desert strip some 60 kilometres from the Pacific Ocean, lies the Nazca Plateau. Like the splendour of Machu Picchu, its secrets are a twentieth-century discovery, for it was only when commercial aircraft began flying over the region in the 1920s that reports of strange lines and trapezoids criss-crossing the plateau began to emerge.

It was the nature of the desert surface in this part of Peru that allowed the Nazca people of the so-called Early Intermediate Period (AD 250–600) to leave their indelible mark for posterity. The desert is covered with a layer of brownish pebbles, which can be removed to reveal the lighter-coloured soil beneath, and that is how most of the lines were made. The fragile construction has been preserved by the dry, almost windless climate of the region, allowing modern archaeologists to gain unique insights into the rituals of these early Peruvians – for we now know that ritual is what the lines are all about.

In fact, there are thousands of lines – some running for tens of kilometres – traversing the plateau between the towns of Nazca and Palpa, in many different directions. Moreover, since the work of the American archaeologist Paul Kosok and his famous protégé Maria Reiche in the 1940s and 1950s, we have known that there are also gigantic figures of living creatures – birds, fish, and land animals – scattered across the desert (Figure 8). Their scale beggars belief, with the largest ranging over almost half a kilometre, although many are only a fraction of this size. It is the fact that these figures can only be seen properly from the air that has given rise to many wild speculations about how and why they were built, most famously by the Swiss author Erich von Däniken in his 1968 book *Chariots of the Gods: Unsolved Mysteries of the Past*. Von Däniken decided that the lines, and their wider, trapezoidal counterparts, were evidence of terrestrial landings by alien spacecraft, and that the figures were designed by said aliens to be viewed from above. Great stuff – but it's a fantasy story that wholly undervalues the abilities of the Nazca people themselves.

Modern research has demonstrated clearly that far from requiring alien supervision, the lines and geoglyphs (figures) could be easily made by primitive people using the technology available to them, by scaling up the pictures from smaller versions, using sticks and ropes. Evidence of this has been found in the form of wooden marker pegs left behind by the builders. The Nazca people were clearly expert surveyors, marking out the desert with ruler-straight precision, and if they were a little forgetful in leaving behind their marker pegs, it has worked to our advantage. Carbon-dating of these samples gives us an accurate estimate of the age of the lines.

Figure 8. Almost 100 metres long, the hummingbird is one of the most iconic of the Nazca figures. A wholly astronomical interpretation of the thousands of straight lines and trapezoids like those at left is not now accepted by archaeologists. (Image courtesy of the author.)

The question of why the lines and figures were made remains under discussion, but a wholly astronomical interpretation now seems improbable. It was Paul Kosok who discovered solsticial alignments among the lines in 1941, leading him to declare that Nazca was 'the largest astronomical calendar in the world'. Maria Reiche followed that interpretation, discovering alignments with the rising and setting points of bright stars (corrected back in time to the Nazca period), as well as with the Sun. But the problem with this approach is that there are so many lines – and so many bright stars – that one can interpret them in almost any way one chooses. Why should those that seem to align with celestial objects mean any more than those that don't? As Clive Ruggles said, when he was first invited to investigate the astronomical alignments of the site at Chankillo, 'Inside I was thinking, "Yeah, yeah, yeah" – people are always saying this to me.' In archaeoastronomy, it pays to be sceptical.

Perhaps the best explanation of the significance of the Nazca lines comes from the fact that many of them seem to align with small hills on the plateau. It is suggested that these hills are somehow representative of the larger mountains in the region (including a giant 2200-metre-high sand dune, Cerro Blanco), which were known to be reservoirs of water. Once again, the supply of water was the key parameter in the lives of the Nazca people – and once again they were faithful custodians of that precious resource, designing underground aqueducts to protect it against evaporation. Did the Nazca lines form a gigantic map of the region, with ceremonial significance in the supply of water by the gods? And were the figures part and parcel of this – animals and birds lovingly drawn in the desert to please their heavenly masters?

Recent research on shamanistic rituals still practised today in parts of South America suggests that shamans (holy men) of the Nazca period used hallucinogenic drugs to create the illusion that they were flying over the desert, interceding with the gods on behalf of their human congregation. Perhaps the figures were intended for the spirit eyes of the shamans, to encourage and support them during their flight? Other research suggests that the figures may have had a processional significance, allowing worshippers to walk along their outlines

Figure 9. Lines ancient and modern. The Pan American Highway was built over the Nazca desert in 1937, before the lines were recognized. The lines and figures are up to 2,000 years old. (Image courtesy of the author.)

in an act of gratitude to the gods for the continuing supply of water –
and a hint that it would be really nice if the supply kept on coming.
This idea seems particularly attractive, given that most of the figures
are depicted by means of a single continuous line that would allow
a 'there and back' procession, without the walkers having to retrace
their steps.

The mystique of the Nazca lines remains undiminished for today's
visitors, herded as they are into the succession of half-hour flights
over the region (Figure 9). Seeing these extraordinary markings for
oneself from the cabin of a small aircraft brings a direct link with a
culture whose ideals and aspirations were wholly different from ours –
but which one can't help but respect deeply.

THIRTEEN TOWERS

No archaeoastronomy tour of Peru worth its salt would miss any of
the places that have featured so far in this article – and ours didn't.
Moreover, we threw in a few more for good measure. There is no space
here to describe the floating Uros islands of Lake Titicaca, for example,
nor the extraordinary funeral chambers of Sillustani, built over a span
of 2,000 years. The archaeological sites of Sacsayhuaman in Cusco, and
of Lima itself, must likewise go uncelebrated.

For many of us on the tour, however, that wealth of first-hand
archaeological exploration was eclipsed by the epic journey we had
made at the start of our sojourn in Peru. In our small way, we
had made history by becoming the first study group from Australia –
and among the first in the world – to see the extraordinary Thirteen
Towers of Chankillo for ourselves. And our pilgrimage to this largely
unvisited area of northern Peru left an indelible mark on us all.

Encouraged by our expert guide, Iván Ghezzi, our goal was to
witness the Sun setting behind the towers in a re-enactment of the way
they would have been used in their heyday. That turned into a race
against time as our coach sped up the Pan American Highway from
Lima north to Chankillo – and then struggled to negotiate a couple of
dozen kilometres of impossibly narrow farm track to reach the site
itself.

I think we probably would have made it, had it not been for the
attentions of the police. No, the coach driver wasn't speeding, or

drunk, or driving dangerously. The cops weren't interested in any of those misdemeanours, nor in the roadworthiness of our vehicle – or even the behaviour of its passengers. All they wanted to know was whether the driver's paperwork was in order. Fine – but they seemed to want to know that every twenty kilometres or so. That made the 370-kilometre trip from Lima very slow, and it took a lot longer than we had expected.

When we arrived at the Thirteen Towers, the Sun was already low in the sky, and, unusually for the afternoon, was setting behind banks of cloud. So we didn't see any breathtaking astronomical alignments. But what we did see in the fading light left us all with a spine-tingling impression of the utterly amazing place that is Chankillo (Figure 10).

What are these Thirteen Towers? Why are they so significant – and what is it about them that made Iván Ghezzi and Clive Ruggles household names in the world of archaeology after they announced their discoveries in March 2007?

In the desert to the east of the hilltop temple-fortress described earlier are many archaeological remains. Foundations of gigantic

Figure 10. The Thirteen Towers of Chankillo run along a narrow north-south ridge. Despite the effect of earthquakes throughout their 2,300-year history, each tower still has two stair-cases like the one seen here at the northern end of the row. (Image courtesy of the author.)

rectangular structures, clearly visible on satellite imagery, litter the desert floor. These are the remnants of buildings and plazas, the main fabric of the ceremonial complex of Chankillo. Running northwards through the middle of the complex is a line of low hills, and the north-ernmost one – a prominent ridge rising some tens of metres above its surroundings – is surmounted by a row of thirteen square towers. Their solid stonework construction and regular spacing (of about five metres from one tower to the next), together with the provision of a pair of staircases running up each tower, speak of an important purpose whose identity has, until now, remained a mystery.

The 200-metre-long line of towers runs almost exactly north–south, although there is a well-defined bend in the alignment of the three southernmost towers. They twist around to the south-west, following the line of the ridge. From points to the east or west of the towers, observers are presented with the extraordinary spectacle of a skyline punctuated by a series of regularly spaced notches formed by the gaps between the towers. This suggested to Ghezzi and Ruggles that the towers had some astronomical significance, and their subsequent research has borne this out.

What these scientists have done is to identify two significant points among the low-lying ruins of the complex where observations of the rising and setting Sun could be made. On the western side of the towers (where sunrises would be observed), this is the open end of a long corridor, the walls of which would originally have been more than 2 metres high. Thus a doorway at the end of the corridor would have faced the line of towers some 235 metres away. On the eastern side (corresponding to sunset observations), there are the remains of a small building some 6 metres square, which also seems to have an open doorway.

These two doorways define an east-west line that bisects the line of towers. Ghezzi and Ruggles note that viewed from either of them, the row of towers corresponds in length to the range of azimuths (bearing) that the rising and setting Sun would adopt throughout the year, calculated for 300 BC. Thus, at any time of the year, the rising or setting Sun could be observed and its alignment measured in relation to the series of artificial notches along the hilltop (Figure 11). This would give an estimate of the time of year which was accurate to just a few days. It contrasts strongly with the other Peruvian sites, in which only the sunrise and sunset positions at the solstices are marked.

Figure 11. Although only eleven of the thirteen towers are visible from the eastern observation point identified by Iván Ghezzi and Clive Ruggles, their purpose is clear. They provide an artificial skyline graduated to mark the position of the setting Sun. (Image courtesy of Rob Hollow.)

The purpose of the line of towers was therefore to serve as a giant calendar, allowing the high priests of the community to dictate with certainty when crops should be planted, or when religious ceremonies should be enacted – or perhaps even when ritual wars should be initiated. Iván Ghezzi also notes that the structure of the observing points on the east and west sides of the towers is quite different, the western one being restricted in its accessibility, while the eastern one is in an open space overlooking a large, flat area. This suggests that perhaps observations of sunrise were made by a small number of high-ranking officials with an element of privacy, while sunset observations could have had an audience of thousands.

Notwithstanding Ghezzi's and Ruggles' careful reconstruction, there are still mysteries surrounding the thirteen towers. One is that their height varies systematically along the hilltop. We know from their structure that despite significant earthquake damage, the towers are the same height today as they were when they were built, so there is a strong impression that the varying height of the towers is quite deliberate. But why should that be the case?

Since the height of the towers increases towards the northern end of the row, they combine to effectively reduce the inclination of the artificial skyline compared with the natural line of the hilltop itself. Perhaps this means the tops of the towers follow a meridian-of-hour angle more closely, meaning that the Sun would always cross them at the same time of day throughout the year (solar time, not mean time). Or is this an over-interpretation that would make Clive Ruggles thinks 'Yeah, yeah, yeah' once again? Clearly, further research is required.

Another mystery concerns the visibility of the towers themselves. Because of the westerly bend in the line of towers at its southern end, only eleven of them are seen from the eastern observation point. The other two are either on or below the local horizon. From the western side, all thirteen towers are visible (Figure 12). But there's a subtlety. If Ghezzi's and Ruggles' identifications of the two observing points are correct, the eastern point is slightly closer to the line of towers than the western point, meaning that the towers still cover the full range of azimuths displayed by the setting Sun, even though two of them aren't visible.

Perhaps this was a natural way of compensating for the twist in the

Figure 12. From the hilltop temple-fortress a kilometre to the west, all thirteen towers can be seen. The sunrise observation point identified by Ghezzi and Ruggles is at the further end of the narrow corridor whose remains are in the lower right corner of the photo. (Image courtesy of Marnie Ogg.)

hilltop that hid the southernmost towers from view at sunset, but the builders could equally well have dealt with it by making the southernmost towers higher, keeping the eastern observation point at the same distance from the line as the western one. Is it too fanciful to suggest that having the two observation points at different distances from the line provides additional information to an observer who watches both sunrise and sunset on the same day? Potentially, it would allow the astronomical calendar to be calibrated more finely, perhaps even allowing the exact day of the year to be determined – at least near the equinoxes, when the Sun is moving most rapidly.

At the time of writing (January 2008), Ghezzi and Ruggles are planning further investigations of the eastern and western observation points at Chankillo. By the time this *Yearbook* article appears in print, it's possible that we will have new insights into the functionality and use of the thirteen towers (Figure 13). Whatever the outcomes, there will certainly be no diminution of the almost magical aura that surrounds these remarkable structures.

Figure 13. Participants in the archaeoastronomy tour reconstruct the Thirteen Towers of Chankillo in a local restaurant after the visit. (Image courtesy of Rob Hollow.)

For me, the memory of my first sight of Chankillo will always stay with me. Approaching the line of towers nearly end-on in the weak late-afternoon sunshine with my companions, I became aware that the desert country we were walking over was littered with broken ceramic fragments. They were everywhere, and were readily recognizable as parts of earthenware vessels. Many of them would have been broken in ritual ceremonies, and Iván assured us that they dated from the main occupation period of Chankillo some 2,300 years ago. We could have picked up handfuls of them – though of course, since this was an archaeological site, we didn't. But there was no more poignant reminder of the fact that the haunting structures in the empty desert before us were once the focus of a thriving population, who lived, breathed, ate, and drank – and were, in essence, just like us.

ACKNOWLEDGMENTS

I am indebted to Iván Ghezzi for his generosity in welcoming a group of rank amateur archaeoastronomers into his world, and for giving us many valuable insights into the archaeology of Peru. It is also a great pleasure to thank Juan Carlos Machicado Figueroa, who not only freely shared his knowledge of Inca tradition, but allowed me to borrow the title of his book for this article. I should like to thank my fellow members of the Peru expedition most warmly for their stimulating company on the trip, and Helen Sim of the Anglo-Australian Observatory for useful input during the planning stage. Finally, it was Marnie Ogg of Thrive Australia who proposed, arranged, and ran the tour. Her consummate professionalism facilitated a stunning trip that all the participants will remember with gratitude for the rest of their lives.

FURTHER READING

Ghezzi, Iván, 'Religious Warfare at Chankillo', *Andean Archaeology III: North and South* (ed. W. Isbell and H. Silverman) (Springer, 2006), pp. 67–84.

Ghezzi, Iván and Ruggles, Clive, 'Chankillo: A 2300-Year-Old Solar Observatory in Coastal Peru', *Science*, vol. 315 (2007), pp. 1,239–1,243.

Machicado Figueroa, Juan Carlos, *When the Stones Speak: Inka Architecture and Spirituality in the Andes* (Inka 2000 Productions, 2002).

Reiche, Maria, *Mystery on the Desert* (published privately by the author, 1968).

The Voyager Interstellar Mission

DAVID M. HARLAND

The heliosphere is a vast bubble inflated in the interstellar medium by the high-energy electrically charged particles that flow outwards from the Sun. After finishing their planetary encounters, the two Voyager spacecraft set off in search of the boundary of the heliosphere, as a prelude to investigating interstellar space.

THE INTERSTELLAR MEDIUM

The interstellar medium is dominated by clouds of gas, and of its mass roughly three-quarters is in the form of hydrogen (either atomic or molecular), with the remaining one quarter as helium. This interstellar gas is composed both of neutral atoms and molecules as well as electrically charged particles such as electrons and ions. The gas is extremely rarefied, having an average density of about one atom per cubic centimetre.

Supernova explosions create low-density holes or cavities in the interstellar medium. Radio and X-ray observations show that the Sun is within an ultra-low-density and high-temperature shell known as the 'Local Bubble' (Figure 1). This region is thought to be roughly peanut-shaped and in the order of 300 light years in extent. The gas within the bubble is extremely tenuous (about 0.001 atoms per cubic centimetre) and very hot (about one million degrees) – that is, 1,000 times less dense and 100 to 100,000 times hotter than ordinary interstellar gas. During the past five to ten million years, the Sun and its system of planets have been moving through the lower-density interstellar gas of the Local Bubble. However, astronomers have discovered a denser cloud of interstellar gas, about 25 light years across, dubbed

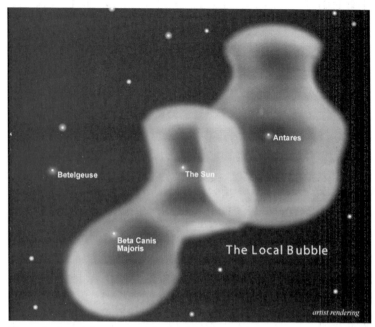

Figure 1. An artist's concept of the Local Bubble containing the Sun and Beta Canis Majoris. It is thought that the Local Bubble was formed as a result of the shock wave from a supernova explosion several million years ago. Beyond the Local Bubble, there are several similar bubbles, known simply as Loop 1, Loop 2, and Loop 3, which are expanding and intruding upon the Local Bubble. One of these, the Loop 1 Bubble containing the star Antares (Alpha Scorpii), is shown here. (Image courtesy of NASA.)

the Local Interstellar Cloud (LIC) or 'Local Fluff' that is moving towards the Sun (Figure 2). Stretched out towards the constellation of Cygnus, the Swan, the powerful stellar winds from young stars in the star-forming region known as the Scorpius-Centaurus Association near the Aquila Rift (a high-density molecular cloud) have been blowing the Local Fluff so that its denser parts may reach the Sun's heliosphere in about 50,000 years' time.

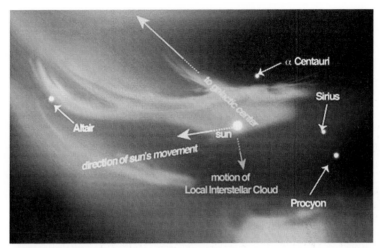

Figure 2. A schematic diagram of the local interstellar medium within ten light years of the Sun. Recent observations indicate that our sun is moving through a Local Interstellar Cloud (also known as the 'Local Fluff') as this cloud flows outwards from the Scorpius-Centaurus Association star-forming region. Much remains unknown about the local interstellar medium, including details of its distribution, its origin, and how it affects the Sun and the Earth. (Image courtesy of Priscilla Frisch, University of Chicago.)

THE SOLAR WIND AND THE HELIOSPHERE

In the 1950s, the German scientist Ludwig Biermann suggested that because the tail of a comet points away from the Sun, irrespective of the comet's direction of motion, the Sun must emit a steady stream of particles which 'blow' the comet's tail directly away from the Sun. In 1958, Eugene Parker in America, having studied the physics of the ionized gas (plasma) in the solar corona (the outer 'atmosphere' of the Sun), postulated that there was a supersonic flow of high-energy charged particles, mainly protons and electrons, streaming from the corona. This prediction of a 'solar wind' was received with some scepticism, since it was believed that space was a vacuum. However, the Soviet probe Lunik 1, which flew past the Moon on 4 January 1959, confirmed the existence of magnetic fields and charged particles in this region, and when NASA's Mariner 2 was launched on 27 August 1962, it not only characterized the solar wind all the way inwards to the orbit of Venus, but it also noted 'gusts' caused by solar flares.

At some heliocentric distance, the solar wind must meet the interstellar medium and its outward flow be halted. The region in which the solar wind predominates is called the heliosphere. However, the heliosphere will be compressed in the direction towards which the Sun is travelling in its orbit around the centre of the Galaxy, and drawn out into a 'tail' on the opposite side. Furthermore, the size of the heliosphere will vary in response to the density of the interstellar medium. It is possible that when the Sun is in a dense cloud of gas and dust the heliosphere is compressed in very close around the Sun.

At the distance at which the pressure of the increasingly rarefied supersonic solar wind decreases to that of the interstellar medium, it will slow to subsonic speed in a shock wave named the termination shock. The supersonic interstellar wind will also be slowed, and become subsonic in the bow shock. In between, the solar and the interstellar winds will mix in a region of turbulent plasma called the heliosheath. The outer surface of this mixing zone is known as the heliopause. It marks the limit of the Sun's influence.

The heliosheath is important because it helps protect the Earth and its life forms from galactic cosmic rays. These are subatomic particles accelerated to almost the speed of light by extremely energetic processes associated with supernovae and black holes. Astronauts out in space are exposed to such particles – and that can be a problem, in that cosmic rays can penetrate flesh and damage DNA. Fortunately, magnetic turbulence in the plasma of the heliosheath can scatter cosmic-ray particles harmlessly away. The heliosheath deflects about 90 per cent of such galactic cosmic rays; only the most powerful 10 per cent penetrate this 'shield' to reach the inner Solar System. Although we have many shields against cosmic rays, ranging from the thin walls of spaceships to the atmospheres of the planets, the heliosheath may be considered as our first, outermost line of defence against galactic cosmic rays. This makes it important for us to understand as much as possible about the structure of the boundary to the heliosphere, and how this may vary over time in response to changes in the density of the interstellar medium beyond.

THE PIONEERS

After using a series of spacecraft in heliocentric orbit to study the solar wind in the inner Solar System, NASA's Ames Research Center built two spacecraft to report on the solar wind as they headed to Jupiter. Pioneer 10 was launched on 2 March 1972, and Pioneer 11 on 9 March 1973. In addition to magnetometers and instruments to study charged-particle radiation and plasma waves in interplanetary space and in the Jovian magnetosphere, each spacecraft had an ultraviolet photometer with which to report on neutral hydrogen and helium in interplanetary space and seek an indication of the edge of the heliosphere. As a result of its gravitational 'slingshot' with Jupiter on 4 December 1973, Pioneer 10 was deflected on to a trajectory which would take it out of the Solar System at a speed of 2.38 AU per year in a direction opposite to that of the Sun's motion through interstellar

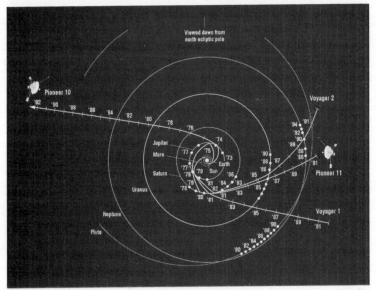

Figure 3. A schematic diagram, looking down from the north ecliptic pole, showing the trajectories of the Pioneer 10 and 11 and Voyager 1 and 2 spacecraft as they exit the Solar System. The orbits of the planets are also shown. (Image courtesy of NASA Ames Research Center.)

Figure 4. An artist's impression of the Pioneer 10 spacecraft, shown looking back towards the inner Solar System from Neptune's orbit, at a distance of 30 AU from the Sun. (Image courtesy of NASA Ames Research Center.)

space and down the tail of the heliosphere (Figure 3). Pioneer 11 used its slingshot with Jupiter on 3 December 1974 to head for Saturn, and the fly-by of Saturn on 1 September 1979 placed it on a trajectory that would cause it to leave the Solar System at a speed of 2.21 AU per year in the direction of the Sun's motion (Figure 3). If the boundary of the heliosphere in this direction were to be close by, there was a fair chance that Pioneer 11 would be able to report on conditions there.

On approaching the boundary, the modulation of galactic cosmic rays by the solar magnetic field and solar activity should decrease and then disappear altogether. In the event, the solar-wind density and magnetic field decreased with increasing range, but there was no sign of an increase in the flux of lower-energy cosmic rays. Some theorists had proposed that the boundary with interstellar space might be somewhere between the orbits of the outer planets, but these new data suggested that it was much further out. Pioneer 10 crossed the orbit of

Neptune on 13 June 1993 (Figure 4), at a distance of 30 AU from the Sun without meeting it, and Pioneer 11 did so on 23 February 1990. The ultraviolet photometers on these spacecraft could observe the glow of sunlight back-scattered by hydrogen and helium near the boundary, and such measurements indicated that the heliopause was at least 50 AU from the Sun. Although Pioneer 11 was heading in a favourable direction, when it fell silent on 30 September 1995 at a heliocentric distance of 44 AU it had not reached the termination shock. Pioneer 10's mission was officially concluded on 31 March 1997 owing to the exhaustion of its power supply, at which time it was at 67 AU, but contact was continued intermittently, with the last data being received on 2 March 2002 at 80 AU. But since this spacecraft was heading down the heliospheric 'tail' no one was surprised that it had not reached the boundary region.

THE VOYAGERS

As a result of its fly-by of Saturn on 13 November 1980, Voyager 1 was deflected 35° north of the ecliptic plane to depart the Solar System at a speed of 3.5 AU per year (see Figure 3). In contrast, Voyager 2 left Saturn in the plane of the ecliptic on a trajectory designed to enable it to undertake the Grand Tour of the outer planets, with a fly-by of Uranus on 24 January 1986 and Neptune on 25 August 1989 (Figure 5), with the last encounter deflecting the spacecraft 48° south of the ecliptic to depart the Solar System at a speed of 3.0 AU per year (see Figure 3). The Voyager Interstellar Mission officially began on 1 January 1990, in the hope of leaving the heliosphere and penetrating the interstellar medium. By the early 1990s the termination shock was expected to be somewhere between 60 and 105 AU, with the heliopause located between 116 and 177 AU. The crossing of the termination shock would be noted by the magnetometer as a sudden increase in the strength of the magnetic field.

The increasing heliocentric distances of the Pioneer and Voyager spacecraft over time are plotted in Figure 6, and these, together with additional data, are tabulated in Table 1 (see p.269).

The main operational limitation on a Voyager spacecraft is power. This was gradually diminishing: in part due to the decay of the plutonium in the radioisotope thermal generator, but primarily due to

Figure 5. An image composite showing the Voyager 2 spacecraft skimming over Neptune's largest moon, Triton, with the planet in the background, during the spacecraft's final encounter with a body in the Solar System. (Image courtesy of NASA/David M. Harland.)

Table 1. Where Are They Now?

	Pioneer 10	Pioneer 11	Voyager 1	Voyager 2
Heliocentric distance (AU)	95.8	76.2	106.5	86.0
Heliocentric speed (km/sec)	12.1	11.5	17.1	15.5
Heliocentric speed (AU/year)	2.55	2.43	3.61	3.28
Ecliptic latitude (degrees)	3.0	14.5	34.9	−32.1
RA (hours)	5.08	18.64	17.12	19.81
Dec (degrees)	25.82	−8.45	12.46	−54.05
Constellation	Taurus	Scutum	Ophiuchus	Telescopium

the degradation of the thermocouples which turn the liberated heat into electricity. As the cameras, infrared spectrometer, and photo-polarimeter were no longer in use, a reduction in the down-link band-width to a data rate of 160 bits per second was still sufficient for the engineering data and most of the continuing science observations. Being far from the Sun, the two spacecraft were well positioned to monitor the ultraviolet glow of interstellar hydrogen penetrating the Solar System. By 1992, the two spacecraft were using different stars for attitude determination (one in the northern sky and the other in the southern sky) to enable the part of the sky that was blocked by the structures on one spacecraft to be visible to the instruments on the other. The ultraviolet data were stored on tape, and then replayed at 600 bits per second. Twice each year, high-time-resolution plasma wave data are transmitted at 1.4 kilobits per second. If all goes well, the two spacecraft should be able to report on particles and fields until about 2020.

In July 1992 the Voyagers began to detect intense low-frequency radio emissions which lasted for several months. Each burst was probably a cloud of plasma that had been ejected by the Sun in a 'coronal mass ejection' some 400 days earlier and had now reached the termination shock. These observations placed the termination shock somewhere between 87 and 133 AU.

On 17 February 1998, after a 20-year chase, Voyager 1 overtook Pioneer 10 as the most distant spacecraft from the Sun – at a distance of 69.4 AU (Figure 6). But the activities of the two Voyagers steadily declined. Later that year, Voyager 2's scan platform was switched off to save power. First, the platform heater was turned off, but since this had

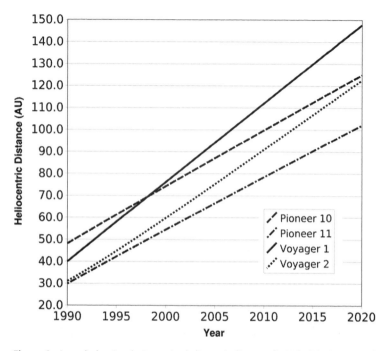

Figure 6. A graph showing the increasing heliocentric distances (in AU) of the Pioneer and Voyager spacecraft as they move away from the Sun. In February 1998, after a 20-year chase, Voyager 1 overtook Pioneer 10 to become the most distant spacecraft from the Sun. (Reproduced with permission from *Robotic Exploration of the Solar System*, Paolo Ulivi and David M. Harland (Springer-Praxis, 2007).)

also been used to keep the sensor of the ultraviolet spectrometer warm, this soon had to be switched off as well. The platform on Voyager 1 was to have been deactivated in 2000, but although it was decided to cease slewing the platform, its heater was left on to enable the ultraviolet spectrometer to continue to operate.

On 1 August 2002, at a distance of 85 AU from the Sun, Voyager 1 noted a large increase in the flux of energetic charged particles. Some of the scientists interpreted this as evidence that the spacecraft had crossed the termination shock; but to others, these data, and the counts of cosmic rays, indicated that the spacecraft was very close to, but had not yet crossed, the shock. Several months later, a surge of solar activity inflated the heliosphere and the spacecraft was once again immersed in the smoothly flowing supersonic solar wind. On 16 December 2004, just as rumours were rife that the Voyager Interstellar Mission might lose its funding, the scientists revealed that at a distance of 94 AU the magnetometer on Voyager 1 was reporting that the magnetic field had tripled – to a strength not seen for 20 years, when the spacecraft was in the much denser solar wind closer to the Sun. This was a clear sign that it had reached the termination shock (Figure 7), because the strength of the magnetic field would increase as the solar wind was compressed upon becoming subsonic. At the same time, plasma-wave oscillations were detected, similar to those which had previously been seen shortly prior to penetrating the shock waves in front of planetary magneto-spheres. Unfortunately the crossing of the termination shock had gone unobserved, since the spacecraft was not being tracked at that time. By the time the change became apparent, it was already in the heliosheath.

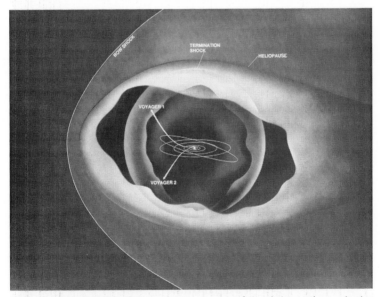

Figure 7. The trajectories of the two Voyager spacecraft in relation to the termination shock and the heliopause. Voyager 1 reached the termination shock towards the end of 2004, at a distance approaching 94 AU, but unfortunately the event had gone unobserved since the spacecraft was not being tracked at that time. Voyager 2 reached the termination shock on 30 August 2007 at a distance of 84 AU, and this time the event was closely monitored. (Image courtesy of NASA Jet Propulsion Laboratory.)

In fact, in mid-2004 the pressure of the solar wind had declined, and as the heliosphere contracted the termination shock washed over the spacecraft several months later. Voyager 2 reached the termination shock on 30 August 2007 at 84 AU, and this time the event was monitored closely. In fact, because the location of the termination shock is constantly changing in response to the Sun's activity, the spacecraft made five crossings. Intriguingly, the shock differed from expectations, in that instead of there being a very abrupt decrease in the speed of the solar wind there was a gradual slowing down ahead of each crossing, and then a relatively small decrease at the termination shock itself. Intriguingly, the energy readings were surprisingly low.

The next major event should be when one of these spacecraft exits the heliosphere and enters interstellar space. (The directions of motion of the Pioneer and Voyager spacecraft within the heliosphere are shown schematically in Figure 8.) The observations of the termination shock suggest that the heliopause is at about 125 AU. To further reduce the power consumption, and so extend the life of the spacecraft, they

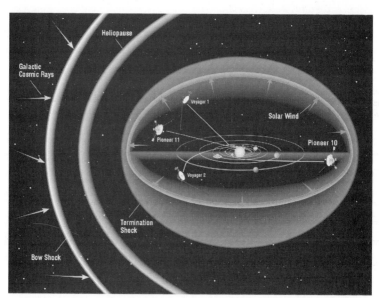

Figure 8. The trajectories of the Pioneer and Voyager spacecraft relative to the 'bow shock' which lies in the direction in which the Sun is moving through interstellar space. (Image courtesy of NASA Ames Research Center.)

will switch off their tape recorders and cease to maintain their high-gain antennae pointing precisely at Earth – but as there will be no taped data to replay at a high data rate the low-gain antennae will be adequate. In a final power-reduction regime, the remaining instruments will be switched off in a sequence designed to maximize scientific productivity at that time. Around 2020 the power supply will no longer be sufficient to run any instruments in parallel with the core systems, and at a heliocentric distance of 145–150 AU both vehicles will suffer power starvation and fall silent.

STEREO

In 2007, instruments on the twin STEREO spacecraft, launched by NASA in 2006 to study the Sun, unexpectedly detected neutral atoms (probably hydrogen) originating from the direction towards which the Sun is travelling. It would appear that the solar wind ions heated in the termination shock exchange electric charge with the cold neutral atoms from the interstellar medium to become energetic neutral atoms which, no longer hindered by magnetic fields, flow back in towards the Sun. This clarified a mystery observed when Voyager 2 crossed the termination shock – i.e. the newly discovered population of ions in the heliosheath contains about 70 per cent of the energy that is dissipated in the termination shock: exactly the amount unaccounted for by Voyager 2's instruments.

IBEX

The Voyagers can provide data for only the locations they sample; they are unable to investigate the shape of the heliosheath and the local processes. To provide a sense of context, NASA decided to launch the Interstellar Boundary Explorer (IBEX) in 2008. This low-cost satellite has an imaging system to make an all-sky survey of the manner in which the energetic neutral atoms arriving from interstellar space interact with the heliosphere.

THE FAR FUTURE

Voyager 1 is travelling in the direction of the constellation Ophiuchus, and in about 18,000 years it will be 63,000 AU from the Sun, or, to express it more conveniently, one light year (Figure 9). And 20,000 years later it will travel within 1.64 light years of the star AC+79 388, some 2,000 years before Pioneer 11 passes it at a similar distance. Over the next 500,000 years Voyager 1 will perform a further three stellar encounters at distances in excess of two light years. In about 296,000 years Voyager 2 will be 4.3 light years from Sirius in Canis Major (currently the brightest star of the terrestrial sky). However, before that, in about 40,000 years, it will make a 1.7-light-year pass of Ross 248. Unless humanity finds itself trapped within the Solar System owing to the impracticability of interstellar travel, these robotic probes may well outlive the species that dispatched them.

Figure 9. An artist's depiction of one of the two Voyager spacecraft in deep space. (Image courtesy of NASA Jet Propulsion Laboratory.)

FURTHER READING

Evans, Ben, with Harland, David M., *NASA's Voyager Missions: Exploring the Outer Solar System and Beyond*, (Springer-Praxis, 2008).

WEB RESOURCES

Voyager: The Interstellar Mission web page at NASA JPL is
http://voyager.jpl.nasa.gov/mission/interstellar.html.
The Heliosphere in the News web page at NASA GSFC is
http://helios.gsfc.nasa.gov/heliosph.html.
The IBEX web page at Southwest Research Institute is
http://www.ibex.swri.edu/.

The Liverpool Telescope: A Unique New Eye on the Universe

MICHAEL BODE

IN THE BEGINNING

The life of an astronomer is no different from any other – you never know how seemingly inconsequential happenings will start a sequence of events that dramatically change the course of your life. For me, I can pinpoint one such event as a five-minute talk twenty years ago at an otherwise forgotten meeting in Preston, Lancashire.

I was then a newly appointed lecturer in the Department of Physics and Astronomy at what is now the University of Central Lancashire. The meeting was part of a visit by the committee that oversaw astronomy provision in the UK on behalf of the forerunner of the Particle Physics and Astronomy Research Council (PPARC – today's Science and Technology Facilities Council, or STFC). Most of the visit of these august folk was devoted to discussion of weighty matters relating to strategy and funding, to which those such as I were not privy. Apart from a rather good dinner, the only other general invitation was to present a selection of the work of my department to the committee. I thus got five minutes to outline my own research which, at that time, as now, focused very much on the study of the sub-class of cataclysmic variable stars known as classical novae.

Most of the talk (say four and a half minutes!) related to our latest observations and their interpretation. At the end, I made what I thought at the time was a rather throwaway remark that observationally, for my sort of science at least, we were not well served by the suite of telescopes to which we then had access. Although increasingly large in aperture and with their instrumentation becoming ever more sensitive and sophisticated, they were still operating in a conventional fashion. Typically, you applied for time through a competitive peer-review process (so far, so good). If the case made were deemed strong enough, you might expect to be awarded three nights on average, anything between six months and a year after first writing the application. You would then travel to the telescope for your observing run, lose perhaps one night to the weather and/or technical problems, return home with the data, analyse them back at base and hopefully publish a worthwhile contribution to the scientific literature in due course.

Such facilities and ways of working are absolutely fine for much of modern astronomy. However, if you wanted to observe something like a nova that erupts unpredictably, get on to it within a day, then follow its evolution in detail for weeks, months, or even years thereafter, conventional operation was relatively useless. Even attempts to overcome this using imaginative schemes such as override programmes were fraught with problems.

Having said my piece, I quietly forgot about it, until a day or so later when I got a call from the secretary to the committee. Would I like to join a panel that they were establishing, chaired by Ron Hilditch of St Andrews University, to look at the procurement of such a telescope for the UK? The deliberations had to be concluded rapidly, as it was hoped to include this in the Ground-Based Plan for British astronomy for the next decade. The Automated Monitoring Telescope, as it was later known, was admittedly only a relatively minor part of the whole (more major items to come out included the upgraded MERLIN radio array centred on Jodrell Bank, and what we now know as the Gemini 8-metre telescopes). However, it was at least included, albeit in fairly modest form. Our panel had in fact recommended initially just the conversion of the 1-metre Jacobus Kapteyn Telescope on La Palma to a service rôle, with a team of dedicated astronomers carrying out programmes in a very flexible way for members of the professional astronomical community. The science would not only cover so-called 'targets of opportunity' such as novae and supernovae, but long-term monitoring of all manner of variable objects (comets and asteroids, stars, active galactic nuclei, and many others), plus simultaneous observations with those carried out by spacecraft (where the scientific pay-offs may be great, but the track record of success had been very patchy).

The next step was to prepare a grant application. Our vision of a manned operation was privately condemned as 'wimpish' by some members of the Ground-Based Plan committee. We therefore explored this further, along with other alternatives, and ultimately focused on the capabilities of a fully robotic system. Now, amateur astronomers were at the forefront here. They had been hooking up their back-garden telescopes to home computers since the late 1970s. Having other lives to lead during the day, this meant that they could still observe their favourite variable stars and keep their jobs (and families) going. The benefits of a robotic system extended further, however, than just their flexibility and convenience. In the professional arena, capital and running costs could be lower, and the instrumental set-up would be consistent from night to night (indeed, it would be counter-productive to change things overly). One group of amateurs in the United States had even started their own company to manufacture commercially robotic telescopes of the scale in which we were interested.

The grant application duly went in. In fact, such was the financial climate at the time that we were encouraged to bid for two telescopes – one in the north and one in the south. Then, perhaps inevitably, the bottom dropped out of the so-called Medium-Projects market as the financial situation of the Research Council suddenly took a rapid turn for the worse (nothing is new!). Only two of the original six projects under this banner were funded, and ours was not one of them.

TO LIVERPOOL

Few parts of the United Kingdom, perhaps even the world, can boast the richness of astronomical heritage possessed by the Merseyside region. Around 1618, the founding father of British astronomy, Jeremiah Horrocks, was born on a farm in Toxteth. In 1639, he used a profound knowledge of the latest astronomical theories, coupled with expertise gained possibly through the manufacture and certainly through the use of precision instruments, to conduct his revolutionary observations of a transit of Venus. These observations were then used to derive the most accurate scale of the Solar System thus far obtained. Horrocks was also the first person to determine that the Moon's orbit around the Earth was in fact an ellipse. Tragically, by 1641 he was dead. Who knows what else he would have gone on to accomplish?

In the following centuries, Liverpool developed into a major port, and, in common with many others, its city fathers helped to found an astronomical observatory which focused on providing accurate time-keeping for navigational purposes. Founded in the early nineteenth century, the Liverpool Observatory later moved across the water to Bidston Hill on the Wirral, where fundamental work in astrometry and timekeeping was continued. By the middle of the twentieth century its function had evolved and the observatory became the Proudman Oceanographic Institute.

The nineteenth century was also the era of the gentleman scientist. Liverpool produced its fair share of these, with several having an astronomical leaning. One of the most notable, and perhaps most relevant in the context of our story, was one William Lassell, who made his money from brewing. In his spare time, however, he built a series of increasingly large and sophisticated reflecting telescopes. One of the most famous was his 24-inch reflector with which he discovered Triton, Neptune's largest moon, only two weeks after the planet itself was discovered in 1846. Ultimately, Lassell decided that the conditions in Liverpool were not ideal and were indeed steadily deteriorating, and his ultimate venture, a 48-inch telescope, was sited on the island of Malta.

There are many other noteworthy facets of the region's astronomical heritage. These include Isaac Roberts, who was a pioneer of astrophotography; Oliver Lodge, the first professor of physics at the University of Liverpool and the first person to suggest that radio waves could be detected from celestial bodies (specifically in this case the Sun); the Liverpool Astronomical Society, which is one of the world's longest-running amateur societies, and in fact the forerunner of the British Astronomical Association.

It was therefore fitting that in late 1991, Liverpool John Moores University (LJMU) decided to establish a chair in astronomy. In February 1992, I moved there to lead the creation of a new research group in the subject and we rapidly gathered together a team of enthusiastic and able scientists. The ambition to realize the procurement of a large robotic telescope had not subsided, and the university was very supportive in the quest. We formed a fundraising committee and were delighted when Sir Patrick Moore agreed to be its chairman. We prepared literature and approached trusts and companies, seeking to raise funds. However, we still thought along the same lines as before, and were pulled up short when one of our British target companies made it plain that they thought the project was '. . . great for British science and education, but lousy for British industry' because we were raising funds effectively to buy an American product. A chance meeting at another of those Research Council committees with Neil Parker, then Head of Technology at the Royal Greenwich Observatory (RGO), had, however, already led to the realization that the RGO (at the time based in Cambridge) had a design for what they called the Future Small Telescope, and together we might be able to design and build the telescope in the UK. All we needed was the cash!

In 1994, Merseyside was declared an 'Objective 1' region of the EU. Significant sums of money became available, targeted at regeneration projects. Fostering the growth of technological industry was one of the aims. We therefore made a bid with the RGO to establish a company on Merseyside to develop a prototype telescope and then become self-sustaining through the winning of commercial contracts for other large

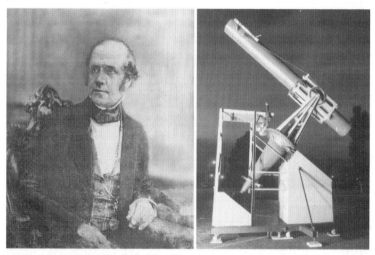

Figure 1 (*Left*). William Lassell (1799–1880) who designed and built the most advanced telescopes of his day. **Figure 1** (*Right*). A replica of Lassell's 24-inch reflector with which he discovered Neptune's largest moon Triton, from the heart of Liverpool, in 1846. The replica was built as part of the 1996 local celebrations marking the 150th anniversary of Neptune's discovery, and that of Triton. (Images courtesy of Liverpool Astronomical Society and the World Museum, Liverpool.)

instruments of this type. Convincing the powers that be that astronomy would create and sustain manufacturing jobs was not easy, of course. We had also decided (like the nineteenth-century astronomer William Lassell before us (Figure 1)) that the region was not the best place to site a new large telescope and wished to put it on an island (La Palma) in the Canaries off the north-west coast of Africa. Despite (perhaps unsurprisingly) being turned down at the first attempt, we persevered, and with the continued support of Sir Patrick, the university, and others, in 1995 we were successful. The project began in earnest with the formal founding of the telescope company – Telescope Technologies Limited (TTL) – in the following year.

TELESCOPE DESIGN AND MANUFACTURE

As well as requiring a fully robotic system, our science goals demanded accurate tracking and pointing, with relatively fast motion on all axes. In addition, the optics were to be of a quality that matched the sub-arcsecond 'seeing' of the chosen site on La Palma. Our partners at the RGO had been responsible for the design of the 4.2-metre William Herschel Telescope, which had been operational at La Palma since the mid-1980s. More recently, they had played a significant role in the 8-metre Gemini project. The basic design of our telescope benefited greatly from this expertise. The development of the robotic system and instrumentation would meanwhile be the province of astronomers and software engineers in what would later become LJMU's Astrophysics Research Institute (ARI). The prototype telescope would have a 2-metre primary mirror and was named the Liverpool Telescope (LT) as an appropriate tribute to the region from which it originated.

Attention was also paid to the design of the building in which the telescope would eventually reside. Conventional domes give good protection from the elements but have several drawbacks. Firstly, a dome traps the warm air that builds up within it in the day and once the slit is opened, this pours out, causing the turbulence that gives rise to degradation of the image quality (so-called 'dome seeing'). You will notice that in modern domes of large telescopes there are shutters and flaps around the sides of the enclosure that are opened at night to maximize the airflow and minimize the effects of dome seeing. In addition, a conventional dome usually rotates more slowly than the telescope it is housing, and this would certainly be true for the relatively fast-moving telescopes we required, thus limiting the speed of response. The RGO and TTL engineers therefore came up with a fully opening (clam-shell) design, which would place the telescope in the open air when observing, and thus it would be able to take full advantage very rapidly of the true image quality of the site and allow the telescope to move unimpaired by the speed of rotation of a dome. On the downside, of course, is the fact that the telescope would now be exposed to wind buffeting, for example. This required the engineers to produce a telescope design that would be relatively rigid so that it would still perform well in strong winds.

We were elated to receive the initial funding that got the project under way, but I remember one seasoned old astronomer at another university telling me, 'Your troubles have just begun!' Indeed, there were many trials and tribulations along the way, not least of which was the government decision in 1997 to close the RGO. This meant that we were faced with trying to retain the core design team from Cambridge by enticing them to move to Liverpool, or we would be forced to abandon the project. With help from the university and the PPARC, we succeeded in the former task and somehow managed to keep the project on track. We were also greatly aided by the generosity of a university benefactor and enthusiast about all things astronomical, Mr Aldham Robarts – a Canadian newspaper publisher living in the UK, who ultimately became chairman of TTL. By this stage, we were building up the Liverpool Telescope team in the ARI with the recruitment of key personnel such as Iain Steele from Southampton and David Carter from RGO (both of whom are still with the ARI in senior positions) and had appointed the first employees of Telescope Technologies Limited. Together with the RGO and PPARC, we had also secured the first commercial contract to build a 2-metre telescope for the Inter-University Centre for Astronomy and Astrophysics (IUCAA) in Pune, India, as the largest and most sophisticated telescope on the Indian sub-continent.

Like the Liverpool Telescope (LT), the IUCAA Telescope would have a 2-metre primary mirror and be capable of being used in Cassegrain or (potentially) Nasmyth modes. Specifications included pointing accuracy of two arcseconds, autoguided tracking, and the ability to mount simultaneously up to five instruments at the Acquisition and Guidance (A&G) box (Figure 2). A 45-degree flat mirror could

Figure 2. The Acquisition and Guidance box is the real 'business end' of the Liverpool Telescope. It lies below the 2-metre primary mirror. This photograph shows the A&G box with the Supernova InfraRed Camera (SupIRCam) attached to the straight-through port, and thus facing towards the camera, with other instruments and electronics boxes arranged around the side ports. (Image courtesy of Stuart Bates.)

deflect the beam entering the A&G box to either one of the four side ports, or move out of the way to allow it to pass to a straight-through position. Thus instruments could be changed in around 30 seconds. Unlike the IUCAA Telescope, however, the LT would have an extra layer of software in its control system. The Robotic Control System (RCS) developed in the ARI takes the place of the human observer to make the LT fully robotic.

Late in 1998, the Astrophysics Research Institute was continuing to grow and moved to a new building on the banks of the Mersey in Birkenhead. A few months later, TTL took residence in a purpose-built unit virtually next door. The TTL building is unique in having the capability to construct up to four 2-metre-class telescopes simultaneously. Each of these can be assembled on a very stable plinth of 1-metre-thick concrete sitting on piles driven 18 metres down to bed-rock. Above each plinth is a slide-off shutter allowing each completed

Figure 3. Inside Telescope Technologies Limited, with three 2-metre telescopes in assembly. Left to right: Faulkes Telescope South, Faulkes Telescope North, and the IUCAA Telescope. Above each telescope is a roll-off shutter allowing on-sky testing. (Image courtesy of Telescope Technologies Limited.)

telescope to be tested on the sky before disassembly and shipping. Following the LT and IUCAA telescopes, two further 2-metre robotic telescopes were built here, this time for the Faulkes Telescopes project (Figure 3), and a 2.4-metre telescope has subsequently been delivered to the Yunnan Observatory, China. The latter is currently the largest optical telescope in Asia. Although many parts of these telescopes had to be procured from further afield (indeed, much of the large optics was sourced from the former Soviet Union), over forty companies in the region were active suppliers to the project.

By May 2001, the LT was at the stage that testing on the sky could be undertaken in Birkenhead. This included the CCD-camera, developed in the ARI and built in conjunction with San Diego State University. We were pleasantly surprised to find that even in Birkenhead, the atmospheric 'seeing' was less than three arcseconds during our tests. We were not so delighted that it changed our minds about siting the telescope on La Palma, however!

A NEW TELESCOPE ON LA PALMA

The island of La Palma is next to the most westerly of the Canaries. It is noted for rising more steeply out of the ocean than any other island, though precisely how this is defined I am not entirely sure. What is certain, however, is that at around 2,400 metres, on the edge of a truly spectacular volcanic caldera, has been established one of the world's most important astronomical observatories. Here more than a dozen nations have chosen to site their telescopes due to the excellent image quality that is obtainable (usually better than 1 arcsecond), dark skies, and many clear nights per year. Indeed, the Spanish have just finished building the largest optical telescope ever constructed and placing it here – the 10.4-metre Gran Telescopio Canarias (GTC), which has a segmented primary mirror.

Although we were developing a fully robotic system, we did not want to place our prototype on a truly inhospitable and underdeveloped site, as might be the case when our systems were more tried and tested. Of the potential observatories around the world, we therefore chose La Palma for the LT, but not only because of its excellence for astronomy. Additional factors were the strong UK presence operating the Isaac Newton Group of telescopes (at that time the William Herschel, Isaac Newton, and Jacobus Kapteyn), links to the RGO, plus the relative ease with which we could access the island from the UK as and when required.

In late 2001, the LT and its enclosure were duly shipped from the UK (appropriately, but coincidentally, from the docks behind the ARI in Birkenhead). Once they arrived at the summit, the first task was to reassemble the enclosure. Unfortunately, the site works themselves were not nearly as complete at this time as we had been led to believe. In addition, the enclosure for the LT had been fabricated by Cammell Laird. At the time, this seemed an excellent outcome – a very local company manufacturing one of the major components of the project. Unfortunately, Cammell Laird went into receivership before the enclosure was completed and we had to retrieve an incomplete product

Figure 4. The Liverpool Telescope is reassembled on the island of La Palma in the Canaries. Here it is seen in its fully opening clam-shell-like enclosure. (Image courtesy of Robert Smith.)

Figure 5. Weighing over 20 tonnes and having a primary mirror 2 metres in diameter, the Liverpool Telescope is the world's largest fully robotic research telescope. (Image courtesy of Jon Marchant.)

Figure 6. A selection of 'first light' images from the Liverpool Telescope and its CCD camera from July 2003. *Left to Right*: the globular cluster M15, the planetary nebula M57, and the spiral galaxy M51.

with virtually non-existent plans as to how to reassemble it. It thus took over a year to reach the point at which reassembly of the telescope inside the clam shell could begin (Figure 4). Even then, we had to re-engineer some of the enclosure's fabric and most of its hydraulic and control systems. Unsurprisingly for a prototype, there were difficulties to be overcome with the telescope as well (Figure 5). However, just over 18 months after arriving at the top of the mountain, the LT saw its 'first light' and we were truly surprised at how well the telescope-camera system behaved at this very early stage of commissioning (Figure 6).

SCIENCE AND EDUCATION

Science operations began in January 2004 alongside continued commissioning of the telescope and its systems. Initially, only the optical camera (the Robotic and Automated Telescope Camera – RATCam) with its 8-position filter wheel was used. Later in 2004, an infrared camera was gradually brought on stream. This had been developed in collaboration with Imperial College, London, as part of a project to observe the light curves of Type 1a supernovae. These objects are, of course, extremely luminous and it had been known for some time that they could be used as beacons ('standard candles') with which to measure distances to very large scales. In fact, observations of these objects in the late 1990s had led astronomers to the astonishing discovery that the expansion of the universe now seemed to be accelerating and for the concept of 'dark energy' to be introduced to help explain this. One reason for wishing to observe these objects in the infrared is that uncertainties introduced by the diminution of starlight caused by dust lying between us and a particular supernova are much reduced compared with those for (shorter-wavelength) visible light. The Supernova InfraRed Camera (SupIRCam) subsequently became fully 'common user' in summer 2005.

The third instrument to be added is a low-resolution optical spectrograph. This device (now named the Meaburn Spectrograph, after its chief designer, Professor John Meaburn of the University of Manchester) is fed by a bundle of fibres that sample an area of sky large enough to ensure that the desired target is always within the aperture they form – an essential feature for a fully-robotic system such as the LT, where even its accurate pointing could not guarantee placing a target on to the narrow entrance slit of a conventional spectrograph every time. The Meaburn Spectrograph was developed in conjunction with the University of Manchester, Jodrell Bank Observatory, and represents a step-change in the instrumental capabilities of robotic telescopes. It has now been joined by a higher-resolution and more sensitive device, FRODOSpec, this time developed in a joint project between LJMU ARI and the University of Southampton. FRODOSpec (the Fibre-fed Robotic Telescope Dual-beam Optical Spectrograph) will be the workhorse spectroscopic instrument of the telescope for many years to come.

In November 2005, a simple ring polarimeter (RINGO) was added to the complement of LT instruments. Designed, built, and commissioned in the ARI in only just over six months, RINGO has a primary mission to perform the earliest polarization measurements of gamma-ray bursts (GRBs), an enigmatic class of extreme astrophysical object that we will return to below. The current instrumentation suite is completed by a fast-readout optical camera known as RISE, developed in conjunction with Queen's University Belfast as another fast-track instrument like RINGO. Installed on the LT in early 2008, RISE is capable of performing very accurate timing measurements in the search for planetary systems around other stars (also see below).

Time on the LT is divided several ways. LJMU has 30 per cent of the time on the telescope. Astronomers at the university, in conjunction with collaborators at other institutions, bid into this competitively twice per year. This biannual application process is also the same for other parties who have access to the telescope for research. The UK professional community have 40 per cent of the time by virtue of STFC's investment in capital and operational costs. This time is administered through the Panel for the Allocation of Telescope Time (PATT) as a national facility. Twenty per cent of the time is guaranteed to Spanish astronomers as part of the site tax, as is five per cent 'International Time' for collaborative projects across the La Palma facilities. This leaves five per cent of the time for 'Public Understanding', which comprises that for the National Schools' Observatory (NSO), other educational, and outreach projects, plus those involving the amateur community. Although five per cent of time does not sound much, this is in fact a significant amount on a telescope as large, capable, and well sited as the LT. We will return to this important part of the LT's mission below.

As envisaged from the outset, the scientific programmes approved and now active on the telescope cover a wide range of front-rank astronomy. Here we give just a few examples, beginning with the Solar System.

As noted above, TTL designed and built the two Faulkes Telescopes (funded by Dr Dill Faulkes, a British software entrepreneur with a PhD in cosmology), now sited in Hawaii and Australia, as clones of the LT, but initially primarily destined to be used for education, rather than research. However, in a project led from Liverpool, we have been using the FTs together with the LT as the prototype of a global network capable of observing variable objects anywhere on the sky, at any time, and doing so continuously for as long as is scientifically important. As part of this RoboNet-1.0 project, the LT took part in the world-wide observations of the effects of the Deep Impact probe on Comet Tempel 1 on 4 July 2005. The LT is also capable of following up Near Earth Objects (NEOs) discovered by other, wider field-of-view instruments and improving our knowledge of their orbits. In March 2004, the LT was in fact almost alone amongst professional facilities in catching a fleeting glimpse of NEO 2004FH as it effectively grazed the Earth at only 43,000 kilometres distance (Figure 7).

More recently, the telescope contributed to observations of the asteroid known as (54509) 2000 PH5 that detected the so-called Yarkovsky-O'Keefe-Radzievskii-Paddack (YORP) effect for the first time and which was reported in companion papers led by astronomers from Queen's University Belfast (QUB) and Cornell University respectively. This effect is believed to alter the way small bodies in the Solar System rotate. The YORP effect takes the form of a torque, due to sunlight hitting the surfaces of asteroids and meteoroids and warming their surfaces, leading to a gentle recoil effect as the heat is emitted. By analogy, if one were to shine light on a propeller over a sufficiently long period, it would start spinning.

Although this is an almost immeasurably weak force, astronomers believe it may be responsible for spinning some asteroids up so fast that they break apart, perhaps leading to the formation of binary asteroids. Others may be slowed down so that they take many days to rotate once. The YORP effect also plays an important role in changing the orbits of asteroids between Mars and Jupiter, including their delivery to planet-crossing orbits. Despite its importance, the effect had never been seen acting on a Solar-System body until now.

Figure 7. NEO 2004FH, caught by the Liverpool Telescope as it streaked past the Earth on 18 March 2004. (Image courtesy of Robert Smith, Jon Marchant, Alan Scott, and Stuart Bates, the ARI, LJMU.)

Moving further out into the universe, the telescope is being used to look for planets around other stars. At the time of the Preston committee meeting, we knew of no such bodies for certain. At the time of writing, there are approaching 300 confirmed examples, and the number is growing rapidly. These have mainly been found by detecting the 'wobble' they cause in their parent star via the regular Doppler shift of the star's spectral lines. This technique has been very successfully applied, but is only sensitive to relatively massive planets in close-in orbits. A few planets have also been detected in transit, as they partially block out their star's light as they pass in front of it as seen from Earth. Again, these planets need to be relatively massive (similar in size at least to Jupiter) for this to be observable from the ground, and such planets are much more likely to be observed if in short-period, close-in orbits. Thus these techniques have found many 'hot Jupiters' but are at present incapable of directly finding 'cool Earths'.

Another way to detect planets is to use a technique known as gravitational microlensing (Figure 8). Here, the light of a distant star is bent by the gravitational field of a nearer massive object lying along the line of sight, and the light from the distant star may seem to be brightened by this. As the two objects are moving, this effect is transient and a flare that might last for a few days or weeks may be seen. If the intervening mass (also a star) has a planet, the gravitational field

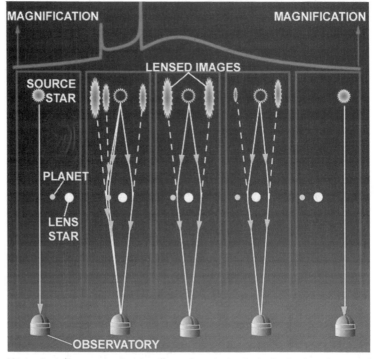

Figure 8. A diagram showing the effects of gravitational microlensing by a foreground star, plus planet, on the observed brightness of a more distant star. The presence of a planet is revealed by a structure on the light curve of the lensed object, which may be very short in duration compared to the main event. (Diagram courtesy of David Bennett, University of Notre Dame, Indiana, USA.)

of the planet will also bend the light of the more distant object and cause a blip that might be relatively bright, but last just an hour or two. Such a method is capable not only of finding cool Jupiter-sized planets around other stars, but is our main hope from the ground of detecting Earth-sized planets. The trick is to catch the blip. The LT is conducting a programme led by astronomers at the University of St Andrews, where the telescope is automatically notified of the onset of a micro-lensing event by one of the small telescope searches that have been active for some years. It then samples the light curve looking for the tell-tale blip, at which time it concentrates on observing this in great detail to help characterize the planet that might be giving rise to it. At the time of writing, the RoboNet project, of which LT is a central part, has participated in the detection of three out of the four extra-solar planets found via microlensing and announced to the world (with more 'in the works'). One of these, given the dull-sounding label of OGLE 2005-BLG-390Lb, turns out to be only a few times the mass of the Earth, and is a cold world orbiting its parent star around 25,000 light years from Earth (Figure 9). Its discovery was undoubtedly a major step on the road to finding other Earth-like planets.

From what has been said above about the early history of the project, it will come as no surprise that we are actively using the LT to observe novae. These come in several varieties under the general head-ing of cataclysmic variables. The telescope is, for example, undertaking projects for different groups attempting to understand more about dwarf novae. Here, two stars (a red dwarf and a white dwarf) are so close together that material is effectively falling from the outer atmos-phere of the red star on to the white dwarf and forming an accretion disc as it does so. For reasons that are still not entirely clear, the mass-transfer rate through the disc increases from time to time and the system is seen to brighten by a few magnitudes before fading away again. The focus of attention is therefore to observe these outbursts at several wavelengths to track what is really happening to the disc. Astronomers at Warwick University are also using the LT as part of an international programme to understand more about the evolutionary track that leads a pair of stars to end up as a cataclysmic binary in the first place. So far, their careful studies of the orbital periods of such stars have shown that their results agree with the best theoretical models, contrary to previous conclusions using what turned out to be biased data.

Figure 9. An artist's impression of the most Earth-like extra-solar planet discovered to date, in terms of its mass and distance from its parent star. It orbits a red dwarf star some 25,000 light years away. OGLE 2005-BLG-390Lʙ has about five times the Earth's mass, and is almost certainly a terrestrial-type planet, made mostly of rock with a metallic core, like the Earth. However, its large orbit and cool parent star must make it a very cold place; its estimated surface temperature is −220°C. OGLE 2005-BLG-390Lb was found by the technique of gravitational microlensing. Its discovery involved a collaboration of three microlensing campaigns, PLANET/RoboNet, OGLE, and MOA, and researchers from 12 countries. (Image courtesy of NASA, ESA, and G. Bacon (STScI).)

Related to the dwarf novae are the classical novae that were the subject of that brief but seminal talk exactly two decades ago. In these objects, the central system is virtually identical to that in dwarf novae, but the rate of transfer of material between the components may be less, for reasons as yet unknown. Classical novae also undergo unpredictable outbursts, but here they are of much greater violence, reaching luminosities up to around 100,000 times that of the Sun at peak, but perhaps occurring only every 10,000 to 100,000 years (compared to dwarf novae, whose outbursts may occur every few weeks). At outburst, they expel around a ten-thousandth of the mass of the Sun into interstellar space at velocities which may be as high as a few thousand kilometres per second.

The LT is observing classical novae in our own galaxy at the rate of two or three a year. In particular, it has been doing so in conjunction with the Spitzer Infrared Space Telescope in a collaboration involving astronomers from the universities of Minnesota, Keele, Central Lancashire, Manchester, and LJMU ARI. The overall goal here is to learn more about the chemistry that goes on in the ejected material, and the subsequent formation of sub-micron-sized dust particles that occurs in many of these objects. Understanding dust formation is crucial to several branches of astronomy, and novae provide real-time laboratories in which this can be studied. It turns out that although most novae are discovered and followed by amateur astronomers, the LT is one of very few professional observatories routinely observing their outbursts in great detail.

In collaboration with colleagues at Jodrell Bank Observatory and San Diego State University, we have been searching for novae in other galaxies by taking images of the target galaxy every other night. In a galaxy the size of the Milky Way, we expect that around thirty classical novae will erupt every year. In our own galaxy, we discover five to ten times fewer, partly because interstellar dust gets in the way for most, and partly because the whole sky is not being monitored all the time, and so some are missed. If we look at another, relatively nearby galaxy, particularly if it is observed face on, we can hope to discover the majority of novae that go off. In addition, they are all essentially at the same distance (that of the parent galaxy), so one great uncertainty in our study of these objects is eliminated. Our work is concentrating on large spiral galaxies, and our aims are to explore the use of classical novae as 'standard candles' in our determination of the distance scale of the Universe, and also to investigate more fully their relation to the evolution of binary stars in general. In a pilot study for this project we discovered four novae in around a month in one of our target galaxies, and now we are discovering and following many more.

Returning now to the supernovae, here LT is undertaking several projects (Figure 10). In one of these, led by astronomers from Queens University in Belfast, the aim is to identify the progenitor stars of newly discovered objects using archival (pre-outburst) images from the Hubble Space Telescope. The LT is used to characterize the light curve to identify which type of supernova each event was in the first place.

Figure 10. An image of supernova 2004C in NGC 3683 observed on the first night of Liverpool-Telescope science operations as part of a programme led by Imperial College, London. This object turned out to be a Type 1c supernova, associated in some instances with gamma-ray bursts or GRBs. (Image courtesy of Dr Seppo Matilla and Professor Peter Meikle.)

Recently, the LT has been part of a combined campaign to monitor an unprecedented 'double supernova', which exploded for its second time in October 2006 in the distant galaxy UGC4904. A global collaboration of astronomers, led by those at QUB, teamed up with Japanese supernova hunter Koichi Itagaki. Both explosions, previously thought to be from two separate objects designated UGC4904-V1 and SN2006jc, were in fact due to the same object, which was also one of the most massive stars known to exist. This is the first time such a double explosion has been observed, and it challenges our understanding of star-deaths.

There is now strong evidence that our own Milky Way galaxy harbours a supermassive black hole at its centre. Unlike the Milky Way, however, there are some galaxies where the black hole at their centre is still apparently gobbling up material in copious amounts, including presumably whole stellar systems. As this material falls down into the black hole, energy is released, and the centres of these systems are not only very luminous, but highly variable. Such active galactic nuclei (AGN) are again the focus of several LT programmes, one of which is led by the University of Southampton. Here, observations have been carried out in conjunction with the Rossi X-ray Timing Explorer (RXTE) satellite. Comparison of variations seen over time with the LT in the optical and those observed in the X-ray with RXTE show quasi-simultaneous variations in these two bands for several objects. Differences in the exact timing of variations in these two wavebands probe what is happening near to the central accreting black hole. Changes in the colour of the optical emission with time are also giving information on the extreme physical conditions in this region.

The most extreme objects that the LT is actively observing are, however, the so-called gamma-ray bursters (GRBs). These were discovered in 1967 by American defence satellites monitoring the nuclear-test-ban treaties. They were looking for gamma radiation that would be given off by clandestine tests in space. What they found were very short bursts of such radiation, but it was soon realized they were occurring too frequently and randomly in the sky to be artificial. In 1973, confident of their findings, the results were made public by the project's scientists at Los Alamos, New Mexico. However, from their discovery until 1997, we did not really know how far away the objects giving rise to these high-energy bursts were, and without this knowledge their true nature was veiled in mystery. One thing was certain, they were evenly scattered across the sky and did not concentrate along the plane of the Milky Way as objects associated with the general stellar population of our galaxy would tend to do. There was a suspicion that they were at very large distances, but a suspicion was all it was.

The breakthrough came when an Italian-Dutch satellite named Beppo-SAX was able to pinpoint the origin of a burst sufficiently accurately for telescopes on the ground to look at the region some hours later to search for anything that had varied. In this way, telescopes of the Isaac Newton Group on La Palma identified an optical counterpart and later the Hubble Space Telescope revealed that this sat in a 'fuzzy blob' that turned out to be a distant galaxy. On its own, this could have been a chance alignment, but over the next few years many so-called 'optical counterparts' have been found, and all appear to lie at cosmological distances. At such distances, the bursts had to be releasing immense energy to be seen to be so bright at Earth. Indeed, it now turns out they are the largest explosions since the Big Bang, vastly out-shining supernovae.

The big question is what causes these titanic explosions, which, although very rare for an individual galaxy, may be going off at the rate of several hundred per day across the universe? Almost all of the optical counterparts so far observed belong to the class of 'long' bursts, where the gamma-ray flash typically lasts tens of seconds. Here, it seems, we may be seeing the results of the collapse of a super-massive star in a 'hypernova' event. The resulting ejected material, moving at near the speed of light, slams into the gas of the circum-burst medium, giving rise to shocks, which lead in turn to the visible afterglow. However, not everyone has agreed with this interpretation. The origin of the other class of 'short' bursts, lasting typically a few seconds, has been less certain. Models involving the coalescence of black holes and neutron stars are the front runners here, but the evidence has been somewhat circumstantial.

On 20 November 2004 a spacecraft was launched that is revolution-izing our understanding of GRBs. The aptly named Swift satellite (a collaboration from the US, UK, and Italy) detects the burst of gamma-rays, then rapidly re-points to image the region, first with its X-ray camera, and then with an optical imager. Increasingly precise positions are fed to the ground, starting only seconds after the burst is first detected. The LT is capable of receiving these alerts automatically. This interrupts the telescope's programme immediately, swings it to the GRB position, configures the correct instrument, and starts an expo-sure. All this occurs within minutes of the burst, when we expect to learn the most about the physics of what is really going on. The Swift satellite is detecting GRBs at the rate of just under a hundred a year. The LT is responding on average to one or two alerts a month from Swift and other gamma-ray satellites (Figure 11). Not only is the interruption and pointing of the telescope and configuration of its instruments fully robotic and done without any human intervention, but the whole process of initial identification and follow-up of any

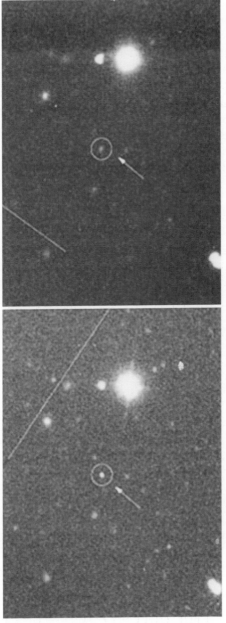

Figure 11. The fading optical afterglow of GRB041006, discovered on 6 October 2004, which was the first gamma-ray burst to be followed up by the Liverpool Telescope. (Images courtesy of Carole Mundell.)

'new' objects in the subsequent images is carried out fully automatically too. Human observers are automatically alerted and then take over the later stages of the process. In May 2005, this led to the LT being the first facility to follow the decline of a burst in several colours throughout the crucial first hour. Then in 2006, the LT-RINGO polarimeter combination provided the earliest polarization measures of a burst, revealing important constraints on the physical circumstances of the explosion, and winning the LT team, led by Carole Mundell and Iain Steele of the ARI, the 2007 *Times Higher Education Supplement* Research Project of the Year award.

Right from the start of the project, we realized that a telescope such as the LT could routinely and efficiently include observations for

Figure 12. A Liverpool-Telescope image of the barred spiral galaxy NGC 7479, which was the first object to be observed by a school (Saints Peter and Paul High Schools, Widnes, Cheshire, UK) using the 'Go Observing' software of the NSO, developed by Andy Newsam, NSO Director, ARI, LJMU.

schools to be scheduled in among its research programmes. With the help of the EU, PPARC, LJMU and Aldham Robarts we launched what became the National Schools' Observatory, whose aim is to enthuse our young people about the study of science, technology, engineering, and mathematics, and a whole host of other subjects, by harnessing the popular appeal of all things to do with space and astronomy. Developed with teachers, the NSO now has over 800 schools as full members, and although there are lots of activities that they can undertake without the telescope, the pinnacle of excitement no doubt comes when a class uses the specially designed 'Go Observing' software to upload observations of targets ranging from the plains and craters on the Moon to distant galaxies (Figure 12), then to see their results and subsequently analyse them, either at school or at home. Several thousand LT-observation requests per year are now being fulfilled for school students by the NSO.

RECENT DEVELOPMENTS AND FUTURE PROSPECTS

The RoboNet project pioneered the use of networks of large robotic telescopes to explore the astrophysical time domain more fully than ever before. The dream we have of developing a fully-fledged global facility is now, however, much nearer to reality with the acquisition of TTL by Las Cumbres Observatory (LCO). Led by California-based software guru Wayne Rosing, LCO now operates the two Faulkes Telescopes and is embarking on the building of a global network of several tens of 0.4-metre and 1-metre telescopes for research and educational use (the Las Cumbres Global Telescope Network – LCOGTN). Still owned and operated by LJMU, the LT and its dedicated team are working very closely with LCO to help to ensure that the new network achieves the success it so richly deserves.

It was always our ambition to bring the work of the Astrophysics Research Institute, and in particular the LT, to the general public. July 2005 saw the opening of the Spaceport Visitor Centre next to the Seacombe terminal of Mersey Ferries. Indeed, it is the result of a unique collaboration between the astronomers at the ARI and the regional transport body, Merseytravel, who operate the world-famous ferries. With the equivalent floor-space area of the National Space Centre in Leicester, and housing many dramatic interactive exhibits, Spaceport showcases the science of our robotic telescopes and is now the public face of the National Schools' Observatory.

In February 2006, the Liverpool Telescope project received a royal seal of approval with the award of a Queen's Anniversary Prize to the university. This was presented by the Queen at Buckingham Palace and is a tribute to the determination, talent, and sheer hard work of all those involved, both in LJMU and among our many collaborators and supporters. Little would I have thought when I stood up and said my short piece in front of that long-forgotten committee all those years ago that our collective efforts would lead to all this.

The Magnetic Astronomers

ALLAN CHAPMAN

Modern astronomers tend to collect, analyse, and interpret every possible kind of energy source that reaches our earth from the universe. This includes all manner of radiation, gravity, strong and weak forces, and, of course, light and magnetism. For many centuries, however, scientists knew of only one form of energy that got through to the Earth: light, and, perhaps, the curious radiant heat of the Sun, which was powerful in deserts, but seemingly imperceptible on mountain tops.

But in AD 1269 a new potential form of celestial force was acknowledged. And this was magnetism. Now philosophers had been vaguely aware of magnetism since classical times, and in 60 BC the Roman writer Lucretius even suggested that the attractive force might have been occasioned by streams of atoms pouring out of a lodestone or piece of natural magnetite rock. And sometime around AD 1160 Europeans began to use simple magnetic compasses for direction finding, based on Chinese prototypes.

AN EXPERIMENTAL SCIENTIST OF TRUE GENIUS

On 8 August 1269, a document was finished and dated that was miles ahead of anything ever previously written about magnetism, and which also saw it as a cosmological force. Its author was a Frenchman, from Picardy in north-eastern France, and he was known as Pierre, or in the Latin and English versions of his name, Petrus and Peter. And as most thirteenth-century people were known solely by their Christian names, with their place of origin or occupation, he was known variously as Pierre de Méharicourt, Petrus Peregrinus, and Peter the Pilgrim. The Latin *peregrinator* could mean pilgrim, traveller, or even crusader. Our modern usage of the word, one might say, is to go on one's *peregrinations*, or wanderings.

But who was Peter? We only wish we had a clue, for with the snapshot exception of his *Epistola Petri Peregrini de Maricourt*, or 'Essay on Magnetism', dated 8 August 1269, sent to his correspondent 'Sygerum de Foucaucourt, Militem' (Siger of Foucaucourt, Soldier), and the reference to his northern French origin, we know nothing whatsoever about him. For it is people like Peter who make the study of history so fascinating, but from the inner details of his large *Epistola* we can say that he was well-travelled, fascinated by machines and inventions, able to write decent Latin, and in early August 1269 was probably working as a military engineer at the siege of Lucera in southern Italy. But most important of all, from our point of view, he fully understood the geocentric astronomy of the day, believed that the Earth and the cosmos were connected magnetically, and was an experimental scientist of true genius. For his *Epistola*, sent from camp to his friend Siger the Soldier, is the true founding document of the science of geomagnetism.

The document narrates a series of experiments, performed by Peter on pieces of magnetite iron stone. Why does every magnet have a north and a south pole which attract and repel respectively? Why, if one breaks a natural magnet in half, do the two bits suddenly develop north and south poles of their own, yet if one cements them back together they resume their behaviour as one magnet? Indeed, he describes most of those experiments on magnets that would now be taught to young children in school, including how to magnetize iron and steel.

He then placed a piece of magnetite into a little cup, to act as a small boat, and floated it in a tub of water, noting that the 'boat' oriented itself to the north. If one graduated the rim of this tub into 360 degrees, or balanced a magnetized slip of iron or a pin within such a graduated circle (as in the manner of a conventional dry compass), then one could use it as an instrument with which to measure the altazimuth risings and settings of astronomical bodies with reference to the magnetic pole. Peter had invented the azimuth compass.

Yet Peter was not only a remarkably learned military engineer who was a pioneer of the experimental method, and who clearly had a firm understanding of medieval geocentric astronomy and the geometry that underlay it, but he was also a philosopher who asked 'big' questions about the cosmos. One such question concerned the source of the northerly and southerly direction of the attraction. Yet surely it was false to assume, he argued, that there was a giant natural magnet at the North Pole, for magnetite stone occurred naturally all across Europe. The power of a given piece of magnetite, moreover, seemed to have more to do with the richness of its iron content than it had with how far north it originated.

And then came the stunning suggestion: could terrestrial magnetism be somehow connected with the heavens and their believed rotation around a fixed Earth? Peter decided that an experiment could be devised to test the theory. One would start by carving a perfect sphere from a block of pure magnetite, to act as a miniature earth (which all educated people in the Middle Ages knew was spherical). After using little needles to establish the precise north and south magnetic points of the sphere, it would be mounted on a polar axis, and adjusted to the exact latitude elevation of the location in question. Peter argued that if this whole apparatus could be perfectly manufactured and adjusted, then the sphere *should* rotate once per day, on its own, in precise synchronicity with the motion of the stars.

He could not get the experiment to work, but felt that with time and patience it should. Of course, we know that he was wrong in terms of his basic physics, but what is amazing about Peter is that he drew such profound conclusions about the Earth and the heavens, and about the nature of motion, from his experiments and speculations. And one might be bold enough to suggest that his polar-mounted sphere was probably the first astronomically-aligned equatorial mount.

ROBERT NORMAN AND THE MAGNETIC 'DIP'

It is a fact of history that when a new science has come into being, most of the original discoveries were made by men who were not part of the formal academic system, but were inspired lateral thinkers. Peter Peregrinus, military engineer and traveller, is an obvious case in point. But another great researcher into magnetism was an ex-sailor, practising as a scientific-instrument maker in the 1580s, in Ratcliff, London, on the north bank of the Thames. And just as Peter remains biographically so tantalizing, so Robert Norman is in many ways equally elusive. But in his two books which narrate his magnetic researches, *The New Attractive* (1581) and *The Safegarde of Saylers* (1584, 1590), we have at least a hint of his background. For Robert Norman tells us that before becoming a maker of high-quality navigational instruments he had served some 20 years at sea, probably as a navigator. After all, Norman lived through the Golden Age of the Elizabethan 'sea dogs', and one wonders under whom he served during those years. Drake, or Ralegh, perhaps? He had certainly learned enough Dutch on the way to enable him to translate navigational books from the Netherlands into English. But otherwise he is a man of mystery, for we know nothing about his birth or death dates, place of origin, or marital status.

But very importantly, he was the first researcher to announce that the Earth's magnetic field was two-dimensional. For in addition to the compass needle's horizontal movement, right to left, Norman found that the Earth's field had a rising and falling, or up-and-down motion. Indeed, if one took one of Norman's 'dip needles', invented by himself – a compass with its steel-pointer needle set in horizontal gimbals within a vertically suspended brass ring – one found that on the Earth's Equator the needle lay horizontal, or tangential, to the Earth's surface. Yet the closer one approached to the North Pole, the more the needle 'dipped' towards the vertical, leaving one to conclude that if ever anybody reached the North or South Pole they would find that the needle stood upright there. It appeared, therefore, that the Earth's magnetic field, whatever its cause might be, acted between the North and South Poles in a series of great vertical arches or curves, that rose up from and returned to the polar points. Norman discovered, for example, that in London the vertical magnetic needle 'dipped' at an angle of 71° 50′. He realized that such needles, carried on ships at sea, could prove useful for finding a vessel's latitude, if only one could make a table of the 'dip' angles between the Equator and the poles. One might even use them in cloudy or foggy weather when it was impossible to get a geographical fix from the Sun, Moon, and stars, for the dip needle, combined with the conventional horizontal compass, gave the navigator a new pair of eyes whereby he could see in the dark, which would help, in particular, to fix his latitude.

And though we know so little about his personal circumstances, we can deduce two things about Robert Norman. For one thing, he displayed, like Peter 300 years earlier, a brilliant gift for experimental research. And secondly, he had most likely built up a very successful business, the proceeds of which generated enough spare cash to give him the leisure to pursue his magnetic researches. Indeed, he was a natural ancestor to that very British tradition of the 'grand amateur' astronomer: men who advanced science and funded their researches out of their own pockets. His instruments came to be so prized, moreover, that nearly a century later Dr Christopher Merret mentions having a damaged dip needle of Norman's repaired and restored back to full working order.

Yet in 1831, a 300-year-old German manuscript letter was translated into English. It was written by one Georg Hartmann, a German priest, astronomer, and experimentalist, and dated 4 March 1544. Hartmann, whose working life was largely spent in Nuremberg, that powerhouse of Renaissance technology, had written to Duke Albert of Prussia, telling of his own recent discovery: that of the magnetic dip. He had made this finding 30-odd years before Robert Norman, yet the German discovery, being contained in a private letter, seems simply to have got filed away, until it came to light in the nineteenth century. Sadly, Hartmann's discovery had no influence whatsoever on the developing science of geomagnetism, so that Robert Norman's work, which he published in print and thereby secured his priority, ranks as an entirely independent find. But modern scholars recognize the magnetic 'dip' as a double discovery.

WILLIAM GILBERT AND A NEW COSMOLOGY

When Robert Norman was conducting his experiments in London around 1580, he might not have been aware of the ongoing magnetic researches of a very successful society physician who was destined to become doctor to Her Majesty Queen Elizabeth I. This was Dr William Gilbert, and in him we encounter, at last, a researcher who is firmly established in the historical record. For Dr Gilbert was born in Colchester in 1540, the son of a successful merchant, was sent to be educated at Cambridge, and later became a Fellow of the prestigious Royal College of Physicians in London. And while he may never have met Robert Norman, he certainly knew of his books and discoveries – as he did of Petrus Peregrinus' *Epistola* – for he acknowledges them approvingly, and in particular Norman's discovery of the magnetic 'dip', in his masterpiece *De Magnete* ('On the Magnet') in 1600.

Gilbert's *De Magnete* in its English translation should be required reading for every student of physics and astronomy. For he not only built on Peter's ideas of tracing the magnetic polarities of a spherical magnet, or 'terrella' ('little earth'), which also incorporated Norman's work on the 'dip', but he set the great magnet of the Earth in a truly cosmological context. Gilbert worked out these ideas, based in part upon his carefully constructed laboratory experiments with spherical magnets, and interpreted them within the context of the most advanced astronomical theories of the Elizabethan age, such as those of Copernicus and Tycho Brahe. He did this in *De Magnete*, and developed them further in *De Mundo* ('On the World and Cosmos'), which was not published until 1651, 48 years after Gilbert's death.

In *De Magnete*, Book VI, Gilbert formulated the idea of a sort of universal magnetism. The Earth was seen as a giant spherical magnet, which, he argued, contrary to Ptolemy, actually *rotated* upon its axis once per day. So was Gilbert a Copernican? It is hard to be sure, but let us not forget that before Galileo's monumental telescopic observations (after 1609), most of the available geometrical proofs were firmly on the side of the Earth being fixed and stationary at the centre of a series of concentric spheres which carried the Sun, Moon, planets, and stars around the Earth. This came not from religious dogma, as is popularly supposed, but from the best available physical and mathematical evidence of the day. The attraction of Copernicanism at this time, however, arose from its capacity to explain the planetary retrogrades and periods more simply and elegantly than could the system of Ptolemy. But the rest of the arguments brought to bear by Copernicus and his subsequent disciples derived more from philosophical speculation, such as the presumed 'naturalness' of everything rotating around the 'lamp' of the universe, than from observational evidence or mathematical proof. And as a cautious and critical thinker, Dr Gilbert would have been aware of the scientific weakness of Copernicanism when it came to physical proof, in contradistinction to its simplicity and elegance, both of which were deeply significant properties for men trained in Greek geometry, as he would have been at St John's College, Cambridge.

By the 1590s, however, when Gilbert was already conducting his laboratory experiments on magnets, the classical universe of Aristotle and Ptolemy was receiving one blow after another. Tycho Brahe's analysis of the position of the brilliant supernova of 1572–3, followed by his work on the movement of the comets of 1577 and 1588, for example, had begun to cast doubt upon both the existence of the crystalline spheres and the long-held belief that astronomical bodies were made up of a different sort of material from the Earth. And it was in the light of these possibilities that Gilbert proposed a new cosmology in *De Mundo*.

For Gilbert came to argue that if the Earth was a magnet, why should not the Sun, Moon, and planets be likewise? And while, as we saw above, Gilbert never declared himself a Copernican, he nonetheless used Copernican assumptions at every turn when discussing the cosmos. Could it be, perhaps, that there were no crystalline spheres, and that the planets rotated under the invisible force of a magnetic flux somehow connected with the Sun? One might even suggest that Mercury moved fastest – being close to the Sun – and distant Saturn the slowest, because of a natural weakening of the Sun's magnetic force as it travelled out further into space. Indeed, was the whole universe awash with magnetic fields that caused all manner of distant motions?

Gilbert's *De Magnete* and wider ideas were incredibly influential in the early seventeenth century, and one man who was deeply impressed by them was Johannes Kepler, who between 1602 and 1609 was struggling to accommodate the oddly eccentric orbit of Mars to the epicyclic circles of Ptolemy, before realizing that the true shape must be an ellipse. Yet how could a planet move around a crystalline ellipse, to speed up and slow down as it approached and receded from the Sun? A magnetic flux from the Sun seemed a much more flexible yet no less precise connective agent between the Sun and a planet. And especially after Thomas Harriot and Galileo discovered, from watching its spots through their newly invented telescopes around 1611, that the Sun really *did* rotate upon its axis, an invisible magnetic emanation spinning out into space seemed at least a plausible agent for the cause of the celestial motions.

So why, one might wonder, did Gilbert leave some of his ideas about astronomical magnetism unpublished at his death? Well, for one thing, Dr Gilbert seems to have died fairly suddenly, at the age of 63, in 1603. Now some might say he delayed because he feared Church persecution, but this argument falls down on two grounds. Firstly, the Roman Catholic Church had not yet developed its stance on Copernicanism, and would not do so until 1616, when Galileo was first warned by the Inquisition not to teach as fact anything which he could not physically prove. Yet far more significant was the plain fact that England was very much of a Protestant country in Queen Elizabeth's reign, and often in a state of open warfare with Catholic Europe and Spain in particular, and the Church of England did not have, nor ever would develop, any prohibitions pertaining to scientific theories. So long as people abstained from criminal or treasonable activities, and did not threaten the peace of the realm, they were left in peace. Quite simply, I would guess that – apart from his fairly sudden death – the reason why Gilbert never published *De Mundo* with its magnetic cosmology was because of his high-profile position as a very successful royal and society physician. For in 1600, unlike today, medicine was a deeply conservative profession, based not in constantly advancing clinical research, but in using the tried and trusted procedures of the classical Greek and Roman medical writers. Conservative doctors were sound and trustworthy doctors. Only fools and quacks came out with outrageous new notions (many of them wrong), and they were never employed by the wealthy. One suspects Gilbert realized that, had he widely broadcast his views about magnets and planets, this might have resulted in his no longer being consulted by the great and the good. And to see the risks involved when high-profile doctors innovated, one has only to look forward 30 years to his royal doctor successor, Dr William Harvey, physician to King Charles I. For when Harvey announced those physiological researches which demonstrated that the blood circulated around the body under the pumping action of the heart, in 1628 – perhaps the greatest single medical discovery of all time – his income fell sharply. For how could you trust a doctor who criticized the ancients and came out with such mad ideas? Most likely Dr Gilbert feared less for his skin than for his purse.

Yet the incredible researches and ideas announced in *De Magnete* came as an exciting breath of fresh air to many physical scientists, who felt that the classical writers were unable to explain the newly discovered phenomena. We have already seen how Kepler was influenced by Gilbert. So was the great French philosopher of the 'mechanical philosophy', René Descartes, and the Englishman Jeremiah Horrocks. Indeed, in his treatise on the transit of Venus of 1639, Horrocks speculated openly about the 'Magnetical and Sympathetical Rayes' of Kepler, as an agent of planetary motion – which were in turn borrowed by Kepler from Gilbert.

THE DISCOVERY OF MAGNETIC VARIATION

In addition to Robert Norman and Dr Gilbert, Elizabethan England was to bring into being a wonderful educational resource which would itself make major contributions to the science of geomagnetism. This was Gresham College, Bishopsgate, in the very heart of the City of London and standing on a site close to the famous 'gherkin' modern office building. The college was established within the great mansion of the late Sir Thomas Gresham, one of the greatest international financiers of the age, following the death of Lady Gresham in 1597. Gresham's massive fortune provided not only a magnificent city property, to be managed jointly by the City and the Mercers' Livery Company, but also a large endowment to pay the salaries of seven professors. These men had to deliver public lectures free of charge to anyone who chose to walk in off the street, making Gresham the world's first college of adult education. Two of the Gresham professorships were in Astronomy and Geometry respectively (then seen as closely linked), and early incumbents of the Chairs included the young Sir Christopher Wren and Dr Robert Hooke, while that group of scientific friends which in 1660 would become the Royal Society first held their meetings in Gresham.

Now Gresham College was intimately bound up with the wealth and prosperity of the City of London, which then, as now, derived largely from overseas and even global trade – be it the export of Cotswold woollen cloth, the import of silk from China, or the sale of stocks and bonds. English merchants of that time were especially attracted by the Americas, and the merchant, privateer, and explorer captains who sailed from the Thames had an active interest in good navigation. So it was not for nothing that Gresham professors began to undertake major researches into the behaviour of the Earth's magnetic field. For why did compasses in the Caribbean, or in Hudson's Bay, Canada, often behave strangely, and not point to astronomical north?

Around 1580, William Borough, an experienced sailor and, later, senior Admiralty official, had begun to study the curious quirks of a compass set up on a stone plinth in his garden in Limehouse, north-east London. He noticed in particular that the needle did not point due north, but a few degrees to the *east*. Then in 1622, Professor Edmund Gunter of Gresham College did a set of fresh compass experiments, but found that the needle pointed considerably more to the west, at 6° east, than it had in Borough's day. In 1634, Gresham Professor Henry Gellibrand repeated the observations, and found a continuing pronounced drift towards the west, his value now being only 4° 5′ east. And then, in 1657, the London navigation and astronomy teacher, Henry Bond, who had been monitoring the Earth's magnetic field since 1633, found that the compass needle now pointed to astronomical north exactly. Bond also found, from an analysis of his own daily readings, that not only was the magnetic north gradually shifting to the west of astronomical north, but that the overall deviation contained a variation within itself.

No one knew why the Earth's magnetic field was behaving in this way, but its study would have two major consequences. Firstly, a knowledge of the drift would aid the security of London's and other nations' seafarers; and secondly, it would further confirm geomagnetism's association with astronomy, by adding more circumstantial evidence to the increasingly accepted Copernican theory. For how could one hope to explain a moving terrestrial magnetic field if the Earth itself was supposed to be fixed, motionless, and unchanging?

THE GREATEST MAGNETIC ASTRONOMER

At this point one encounters the man who was, perhaps, the greatest magnetic astronomer of them all: Edmond Halley. He was himself a child of the burgeoning City of London. Edmond's father was a comfortably-off merchant who seems to have owned a 'country retreat' in then semi-rural Islington. Edmond was educated at St Paul's School, then as now one of the leading schools in England, and when he was sent up to the Queen's College, Oxford, at the age of 17 in 1673, he took with him a private set of scientific instruments which were said to have been the envy of the university. In many ways Halley was a larger-than-life figure: physically and mentally robust, with a vast and enduring energy, sociable, having a good sense of humour, able to charm the birds out of the trees, loving his drink but never a drunkard, and possessing a brain that placed him within the top handful of world scientists of the day. He had already won fame as a cartographer of the southern stars by the age of 22, after spending nearly two years observing on the island of St Helena. And at that same age he was elected

Fellow of the Royal Society, received his Oxford M.A. without examination by Royal Command of King Charles II, and began a triumphal grand tour of learned Europe. And instead of sitting back on his laurels, Halley worked and researched like a Trojan for the next 64 years of his life, dying suddenly in his 86th year while still holding the title of Astronomer Royal. While still a young man in the early 1680s he became a friend of Sir Isaac Newton (Halley being Newton's junior by 14 years), and proofread and personally financed the publication costs of Newton's *Principia* in 1686. (And long before that date, moreover, scientists had come to realize that the force which kept the planets in their orbits was not magnetism, but the newly defined and newly understood force of gravity.)

And in the 1690s, Halley did Great Britain a major diplomatic service when Peter the Great, Czar of all the Russias, made a state visit to England. For the seven-foot-tall Czar, despite being a sometimes cruel autocrat back at home, had a first-class brain and a passion for science, technology, and ships. He also drank like a fish, and loved wild horseplay. Who could be his guide and companion? Why, Dr Halley, no less. The two men seemed to get on like a house on fire, for not only did Halley escort Czar Peter around the Royal Navy dockyards and scientific and diplomatic London, but they also got up to drunken pranks together. During one of their sessions, at Sayes Court House, Deptford, the Czar and the astronomer took turns at giving each other rides around the gardens in a wheelbarrow! It seems that Edmond Halley was the only member of the British 'establishment' who could keep up with Czar Peter.

But on his more serious side, Halley was fascinated by the great patterns that appeared to underpin the whole of nature, from the evaporation of the oceans to produce rainfall over mountains to the behaviour of comets. In addition to being an experimentalist and observer, he was an instinctive science historian; and from his schooldays onwards he regularly amassed data about historical scientific observations, and sought out patterns and regularities that might be susceptible to mathematical analysis. The discovery, which brought him enduring fame, of the cyclical nature of the bright comet of 1682 (the return of which he announced in 1705) was an excellent case in point, and based upon a meticulous search through the historical record for comet appearances combined with a mathematical analysis of its perihelion orbit.

Halley was already making detailed geomagnetic observations while still a schoolboy, for in 1672, when he was 16, he established the compass variation in London at 2° 30' *west* of astronomical north, and being familiar with the prior work of Borough, Gunter, and Gellibrand, pointed out in a major paper to the Royal Society on geomagnetism in 1692 that in the 112 years which had elapsed between Borough's Limehouse observations around 1580 and his own day, the compass variation had swung through 17 degrees of a circle towards the west.

Yet Halley was not only an astronomer of genius, he was also, perhaps, the true founding father of geophysics in the widest sense. For it was Halley's researches into the trade winds in the 1680s that were to lay the foundations of the science of global meteorology, while his work on the saltiness of the seas led him to suggest that the Earth was vastly old, and had even been repeatedly hit and transformed by impacts from space, during the time of the 'old Chaos', after the Creation, but before God planted the Garden of Eden.

THE VOYAGES OF THE *PARAMORE*

Possessing as Halley did the instincts of an experimental physicist, he began to consider, and to model, possible causal agents for the Earth's magnetic field, for its variations, and for its now quite conspicuous westerly drift. And in a previous Royal Society paper of 1683, he had posited 'that there are in the Earth Four such Magnetical Points or Poles which occasion the great variety and seeming irregularity which is observed in the variations of the Compas.' For at this stage Halley was considering the idea that the Earth had a dense inner core of possibly ferrous rocks, surrounded by an outer, shell-like mantle upon which we live. Both of these concentric spheres would have two magnetic poles, yet if the mantle rotated at a slightly different rate from the core, the result would be a drift and a variation in the ensuing magnetic field. In later papers he proposed that there might even be several mantle-shells, concentrically rotating within each other. He further suggested that the outer mantle might be only about 500 miles thick, and even wondered if there could be an atmosphere, with inhabitants, in the gap between, enjoying the benefits of an unknown form of light. Yet Halley the pragmatist pulls himself up sharp, declaring 'this is not to be esteemed as an Argument'.

As an administrative officer of the Royal Society – serving as its Clerk – Edmond Halley was in an ideal position to have ready access to all manner of scientific data that poured into the Society: from travellers, sea-captains, scientists, and all kinds of observers across the globe. And by the early 1690s, he had become especially fascinated by reports – confirming what he would have witnessed at first hand on his own St Helena astronomical voyage of 1676–8 – of how very strangely the compass behaved in certain parts of the Atlantic Ocean. He felt that the accurate mapping of these magnetic lines would not only add greatly to our knowledge of the Earth and heavens, but do a major service to maritime safety. What was needed was to send a Royal Navy expedition to comb the Atlantic, preferably from the Arctic to the Antarctic, between the European, African, and American continents. And with his combination of scientific reputation, charm, and friends in high places, he persuaded the Admiralty to commission what would turn out to be the first ever purely scientific naval expedition in British history, which sailed from Portsmouth in the autumn of 1698.

Yet what was remarkable was that the captain of H.M.S. *Paramore*, a 60-foot three-masted vessel with a crew of 20 men, was not some experienced and grizzled commander, but Dr Edmond Halley himself. A man, indeed, who had only previously been to sea in the capacity of a passenger, and had never carried the King's commission, or had the responsibilities of command. And considering the expected length and danger of the *Paramore*'s cruise, this in itself is truly amazing. Indeed, one can fully understand why his officers, who no doubt were slowly clawing their way up the promotion ladder, did not take kindly to serving under a landlubber Fellow of the Royal Society who had suddenly been given full Captain's rank above their heads.

After being brought around from the Thames in stormy seas, and having to refit in Portsmouth, H.M.S. *Paramore* finally headed out into the Atlantic in November 1698. Sailing down almost to North Africa, she then crossed the Atlantic, and sailed into the Caribbean. And whenever storms permitted, Halley took magnetic and astronomical bearings, comparing the behaviour and direction of the compasses against exact astronomical sights, and collecting data for a magnetic chart of the mid- and north Atlantic.

But problems were thick on the ground. The weather seems to have been very poor, and Halley had constant trouble with his officers; and when he returned to England the following July, he had his Lieutenant,

Edward Harrison, court-martialled, though it seems that the court did not uphold Halley's charges. Halley had hoped to take *Paramore* down into the south Atlantic to measure the behaviour of the compass in waters around the south polar seas, but, because of weather conditions, that had to be postponed until *Paramore*'s second voyage, which took place over 1699 and 1700. On this second voyage, Halley made maritime history, on 1 February 1700, by reaching the latitude of 52° 24' south of the Equator in mid-Atlantic, hitting ice, and sailing close to three giant icebergs, each as high as Beachy Head. *Paramore* often groped her way through thick sea fogs, and as Halley recorded, even when the Sun did appear, 'he had not force enough to warm the Air, but the Thermometer continu'd below the freezing point.'[1] He brought *Paramore* due north of what later explorers of the Antarctic continent would name 'Halley Bay' in Edmond's honour. But finding it impossible to get further south, Halley put *Paramore* around on to a northerly course, though it still took days of sailing before the temperature crept above freezing. Returning home after a year in some of the loneliest and most freezing seas in the world, in which he enjoyed incredible good luck and risked enormous dangers, Halley had a body of magnetic data unrivalled by any other scientist or explorer to date. In 1701 he published his famous magnetic chart of the Atlantic Ocean, in the drawing of which he used, for the first time on a printed map, those 'isogonic' contour lines linking places of a similar magnetic characteristic. And while Halley may not have invented the contour idea, every subsequent map- or graph-maker has him to thank for publicizing this clear and elegant method of highlighting places possessing equal properties – of magnetism, mountain height, population density, or density of galaxy or radiation distribution – on all manner of charts.

UNDERSTANDING THE NORTHERN LIGHTS

Edmond Halley was not by nature a speculative scientist, preferring to interpret meticulously marshalled data and draw conclusions that were as mathematically based as possible. A wonderful example of how his mind worked was demonstrated in 1716, when he witnessed the most

1. *The Three Voyages of Edmond Halley in the Paramore*, p. 161.

spectacular aurora borealis in living memory. Starting at about 7 p.m. on 6 March 1716 (or 17 March 1716, according to the modern calendar), the sky blazed over London, and he made careful drawings of what he saw. And being the methodical man that he was, Halley began by searching for records of earlier aurorae. He says no such conspicuous lights had been witnessed since those which appeared in France in September 1621, and which the French astronomer Pierre Gassendi had styled 'Aurora Borealis', or Northern Lights, because no matter where an observer was stationed the lights always appeared in the northern sky. Then having combed the historical record for bright lights before 1621, Halley set about the task of collating observations of the current aurora of 1716, obtaining his data from across the British Isles and Europe, and from the logs of returned sea captains who had seen it on the high seas. Indeed, Halley's organizational skill in marshalling and interpreting all manner of scientific data was truly breathtaking, and what he did with the spectacular aurora of 1716 was simply characteristic of his thoroughness. But what conclusions did he draw?

Well, when all of his reports were in he concluded, that the aurora had been observed across a zone 30° in longitude by 50° in latitude, and irrespective of an observer's location it was always in the north. And no matter where you were, the brilliant arcs of the aurora seemed to correspond with the known arcs of the Earth's magnetic field for that region. Halley, along with other scientists, already knew that the Earth's magnetic pole did not correspond to its astronomical pole, which led him to explain why aurorae were more commonly seen in Greenland (which in those days, in the less precise use of the term, included vast tracts of northern Canada), Norway, and countries closest to the magnetic pole.

But central to Halley's conclusion was that auroral phenomena were intimately connected to the Earth's magnetic field. And when he did allow himself to speculate a little, he suggested that the light might be somehow produced when the magnetic 'Effluvia' from the presumed air-space between the Earth's outer mantle and core escaped into the atmosphere, and moved along the curved lines of the magnetic field. Of course, no one in Halley's day had any knowledge of those solar magnetic storms that played a major role in the generation of aurorae, and would not do so, indeed, until the nineteenth century; but Halley's perceived association between the aurora borealis and geomagnetism was an insight of genius, based upon a meticulous interpretation of evidence.

It would not be until the nineteenth century that geomagnetism once again really entered the astronomical limelight. For by then, not only had there been massive development in astronomical instrumentation, but also in the related sciences of chemistry, optics, and electrical physics, which were already in an advanced state. And in the wake of the violent solar storm of 1–2 September 1859, which interrupted electric telegraph systems and produced spectacular auroral displays worldwide, the Sun's status as the most powerful magnet in the Solar System was dramatically confirmed.

So let us not forget that it was in medieval Europe that the first non-optical form of energy to be recognized by scientists first came to be studied, and that all sorts of men, from military engineers, practical navigators, and instrument-makers to astronomy professors and cosmologists, ranked amongst the first magnetic astronomers.

FURTHER READING

Chapman, Allan, 'Petrus Peregrinus', 'Robert Norman', 'Georg Hartmann', 'Giambattista Della Porta', and 'William Gilbert', in *Encyclopedia of Geomagnetism and Paleomagnetism*, ed. David Gubbins and Emilio Herrero-Bervera (Springer, 2007).

Chapman, Allan, 'Gresham College: Scientific Instruments and the Advancement of Useful Knowledge in Seventeenth-Century England', *Bulletin of the Scientific Instrument Society*, 56 (1998), pp. 6–13.

Clark, Stuart, *The Sun Kings. The Unexpected Tragedy of Richard Carrington and the Tale of How Modern Astronomy Began* (Princeton and Oxford University presses, 2007).

Cook, Sir Alan, *Edmond Halley. Charting the Heavens and the Seas* (Clarendon Press, 1998).

Gellibrand, Henry, *A Discourse Mathematical on the Variation of the Magneticall Needle. Together with its diminution lately discovered* (London, 1635).

Gilbert, William, *De Magnete* (1600; English translation: Dover, 1958).

Halley, Edmond, 'A Theory of the Variation of the Magnetical Compass', *Philosophical Transactions of the Royal Society* 13, no. 148 (1683), pp. 208–21.

Halley, Edmond, 'An Account of the cause of the Change of the Variation of the Magnetical Needle', *Philosophical Transactions of the Royal Society* 16, no. 195 (1692), pp. 563–78.

Halley, Edmond, 'An Account of the surprizing Appearance of the Lights seen in the Air on the sixth of March last', *Philosophical Transactions of the Royal Society* 29, no. 347 (1716), pp. 406–28.

Ronan, Colin, *Edmond Halley: Genius in Eclipse* (Macdonald, 1970).

Taylor, Eva G. R., *The Mathematical Practitioners of Tudor and Stuart England 1485–1714* (Cambridge University Press, 1954, 1968).

Thompson, Silvanus P. (ed), *Epistle of Petrus Peregrinus of Maricourt, to Sygerum of Foucaucourt, soldier, concerning the magnet.* English translation, London, 1902.

Thrower, Norman, J. W. (ed), *The Three Voyages of Edmond Halley in the Paramore, 1698–1701*, (The Hakluyt Society, 1981). Reproduces Halley's sailing logs for H.M.S. *Paramore*, and includes large-scale reproductions of his magnetic charts.

Ward, John, *Lives of the Professors of Gresham College* (1740; reprint by Johnson Reprint Corporation, 1967).

Part III

Miscellaneous

Some Interesting Variable Stars

JOHN ISLES

All variable stars are of potential interest, and hundreds of them can be observed with the slightest optical aid – even with a pair of binoculars. The stars in the list that follows include many that are popular with amateur observers, as well as some less well-known objects that are nevertheless suitable for study visually. The periods and ranges of many variables are not constant from one cycle to another, and some are completely irregular.

Finder charts are given after the list for those stars marked with an asterisk. These charts are adapted with permission from those issued by the Variable Star Section of the British Astronomical Association. Apart from the eclipsing variables and others in which the light changes are purely a geometrical effect, variable stars can be divided broadly into two classes: the pulsating stars, and the eruptive or cataclysmic variables.

Mira (Omicron Ceti) is the best-known member of the long-period subclass of pulsating red-giant stars. The chart is suitable for use in estimating the magnitude of Mira when it reaches naked-eye brightness – typically from about a month before the predicted date of maximum until two or three months after maximum. Predictions for Mira and other stars of its class follow the section of finder charts.

The semi-regular variables are less predictable, and generally have smaller ranges. V Canum Venaticorum is one of the more reliable ones, with steady oscillations in a six-month cycle. Z Ursae Majoris, easily found with binoculars near Delta, has a large range, and often shows double maxima owing to the presence of multiple periodicities in its light changes. The chart for Z is also suitable for observing another semi-regular star, RY Ursae Majoris. These semi-regular stars are mostly red giants or supergiants.

The RV Tauri stars are of earlier spectral class than the semi-regulars, and in a full cycle of variation they often show deep minima and double maxima that are separated by a secondary minimum. U Monocerotis is one of the brightest RV Tauri stars.

Among eruptive variable stars is the carbon-rich supergiant R Coronae Borealis. Its unpredictable eruptions cause it not to brighten, but to fade. This happens when one of the sooty clouds that the star throws out from time to time happens to come in our direction and blots out most of the star's light from our view. Much of the time R Coronae is bright enough to be seen in binoculars, and the chart can be used to estimate its magnitude. During the deepest minima, however, the star needs a telescope of 25-cm or larger aperture to be detected.

CH Cygni is a symbiotic star – that is, a close binary comprising a red giant and a hot dwarf star that interact physically, giving rise to outbursts. The system also shows semi-regular oscillations, and sudden fades and rises that may be connected with eclipses.

Observers can follow the changes of these variable stars by using the comparison stars whose magnitudes are given below each chart. Observations of variable stars by amateurs are of scientific value, provided they are collected and made available for analysis. This is done by several organizations, including the British Astronomical Association (see the list of astronomical societies in this volume), the American Association of Variable Star Observers (25 Birch Street, Cambridge, Mass. 02138), and the Royal Astronomical Society of New Zealand (PO Box 3181, Wellington).

Star	RA		Declination		Range	Type	Period	Spectrum
	h	m	°	′			(days)	
R Andromedae	00	24.0	+38	35	5.8–14.9	Mira	409	S
W Andromedae	02	17.6	+44	18	6.7–14.6	Mira	396	S
U Antliae	10	35.2	−39	34	5–6	Irregular	—	C
Theta Apodis	14	05.3	−76	48	5–7	Semi-regular	119	M
R Aquarii	23	43.8	−15	17	5.8–12.4	Symbiotic	387	M+Pec
T Aquarii	20	49.9	−05	09	7.2–14.2	Mira	202	M
R Aquilae	19	06.4	+08	14	5.5–12.0	Mira	284	M
V Aquilae	19	04.4	−05	41	6.6–8.4	Semi-regular	353	C
Eta Aquilae	19	52.5	+01	00	3.5–4.4	Cepheid	7.2	F–G
U Arae	17	53.6	−51	41	7.7–14.1	Mira	225	M
R Arietis	02	16.1	+25	03	7.4–13.7	Mira	187	M
U Arietis	03	11.0	+14	48	7.2–15.2	Mira	371	M
R Aurigae	05	17.3	+53	35	6.7–13.9	Mira	458	M
Epsilon Aurigae	05	02.0	+43	49	2.9–3.8	Algol	9892	F+B
R Boötis	14	37.2	+26	44	6.2–13.1	Mira	223	M

Star	RA		Declination		Range	Type	Period (days)	Spectrum
	h	m	°	′				
X Camelopardalis	04	45.7	+75	06	7.4−14.2	Mira	144	K−M
R Cancri	08	16.6	+11	44	6.1−11.8	Mira	362	M
X Cancri	08	55.4	+17	14	5.6−7.5	Semi-regular	195?	C
R Canis Majoris	07	19.5	−16	24	5.7−6.3	Algol	1.1	F
VY Canis Majoris	07	23.0	−25	46	6.5−9.6	Unique	—	M
S Canis Minoris	07	32.7	+08	19	6.6−13.2	Mira	333	M
R Canum Ven.	13	49.0	+39	33	6.5−12.9	Mira	329	M
*V Canum Ven.	13	19.5	+45	32	6.5−8.6	Semi-regular	192	M
R Carinae	09	32.2	−62	47	3.9−10.5	Mira	309	M
S Carinae	10	09.4	−61	33	4.5−9.9	Mira	149	K−M
I Carinae	09	45.2	−62	30	3.3−4.2	Cepheid	35.5	F−K
Eta Carinae	10	45.1	−59	41	−0.8−7.9	Irregular	—	Pec
R Cassiopeiae	23	58.4	+51	24	4.7−13.5	Mira	430	M
S Cassiopeiae	01	19.7	+72	37	7.9−16.1	Mira	612	S
W Cassiopeiae	00	54.9	+58	34	7.8−12.5	Mira	406	C
Gamma Cas.	00	56.7	+60	43	1.6−3.0	Gamma Cas.	—	B
Rho Cassiopeiae	23	54.4	+57	30	4.1−6.2	Semi-regular	—	F−K
R Centauri	14	16.6	−59	55	5.3−11.8	Mira	546	M
S Centauri	12	24.6	−49	26	7−8	Semi-regular	65	C
T Centauri	13	41.8	−33	36	5.5−9.0	Semi-regular	90	K−M
S Cephei	21	35.2	+78	37	7.4−12.9	Mira	487	C
T Cephei	21	09.5	+68	29	5.2−11.3	Mira	388	M
Delta Cephei	22	29.2	+58	25	3.5−4.4	Cepheid	5.4	F−G
Mu Cephei	21	43.5	+58	47	3.4−5.1	Semi-regular	730	M
U Ceti	02	33.7	−13	09	6.8−13.4	Mira	235	M
W Ceti	00	02.1	−14	41	7.1−14.8	Mira	351	S
*Omicron Ceti	02	19.3	−02	59	2.0−10.1	Mira	332	M
R Chamaeleontis	08	21.8	−76	21	7.5−14.2	Mira	335	M
T Columbae	05	19.3	−33	42	6.6−12.7	Mira	226	M
R Comae Ber.	12	04.3	+18	47	7.1−14.6	Mira	363	M
*R Coronae Bor.	15	48.6	+28	09	5.7−14.8	R Coronae Bor.	—	C
S Coronae Bor.	15	21.4	+31	22	5.8−14.1	Mira	360	M
T Coronae Bor.	15	59.6	+25	55	2.0−10.8	Recurrent nova	—	M+Pec
V Coronae Bor.	15	49.5	+39	34	6.9−12.6	Mira	358	C
W Coronae Bor.	16	15.4	+37	48	7.8−14.3	Mira	238	M
R Corvi	12	19.6	−19	15	6.7−14.4	Mira	317	M
R Crucis	12	23.6	−61	38	6.4−7.2	Cepheid	5.8	F−G
R Cygni	19	36.8	+50	12	6.1−14.4	Mira	426	S
U Cygni	20	19.6	+47	54	5.9−12.1	Mira	463	C
W Cygni	21	36.0	+45	22	5.0−7.6	Semi-regular	131	M

Star	RA		Declination		Range	Type	Period (days)	Spectrum
	h	m	°	′				
RT Cygni	19	43.6	+48	47	6.0–13.1	Mira	190	M
SS Cygni	21	42.7	+43	35	7.7–12.4	Dwarf nova	50±	K+Pec
*CH Cygni	19	24.5	+50	14	5.6–9.0	Symbiotic	—	M+B
Chi Cygni	19	50.6	+32	55	3.3–14.2	Mira	408	S
R Delphini	20	14.9	+09	05	7.6–13.8	Mira	285	M
U Delphini	20	45.5	+18	05	5.6–7.5	Semi-regular	110?	M
EU Delphini	20	37.9	+18	16	5.8–6.9	Semi-regular	60	M
Beta Doradûs	05	33.6	−62	29	3.5–4.1	Cepheid	9.8	F–G
R Draconis	16	32.7	+66	45	6.7–13.2	Mira	246	M
T Eridani	03	55.2	−24	02	7.2–13.2	Mira	252	M
R Fornacis	02	29.3	−26	06	7.5–13.0	Mira	389	C
R Geminorum	07	07.4	+22	42	6.0–14.0	Mira	370	S
U Geminorum	07	55.1	+22	00	8.2–14.9	Dwarf nova	105±	Pec+M
Zeta Geminorum	07	04.1	+20	34	3.6–4.2	Cepheid	10.2	F–G
Eta Geminorum	06	14.9	+22	30	3.2–3.9	Semi-regular	233	M
S Gruis	22	26.1	−48	26	6.0–15.0	Mira	402	M
S Herculis	16	51.9	+14	56	6.4–13.8	Mira	307	M
U Herculis	16	25.8	+18	54	6.4–13.4	Mira	406	M
Alpha Herculis	17	14.6	+14	23	2.7–4.0	Semi-regular	—	M
68, u Herculis	17	17.3	+33	06	4.7–5.4	Algol	2.1	B+B
R Horologii	02	53.9	−49	53	4.7–14.3	Mira	408	M
U Horologii	03	52.8	−45	50	6–14	Mira	348	M
R Hydrae	13	29.7	−23	17	3.5–10.9	Mira	389	M
U Hydrae	10	37.6	−13	23	4.3–6.5	Semi-regular	450?	C
VW Hydri	04	09.1	−71	18	8.4–14.4	Dwarf nova	27±	Pec
R Leonis	09	47.6	+11	26	4.4–11.3	Mira	310	M
R Leonis Minoris	09	45.6	+34	31	6.3–13.2	Mira	372	M
R Leporis	04	59.6	−14	48	5.5–11.7	Mira	427	C
Y Librae	15	11.7	−06	01	7.6–14.7	Mira	276	M
RS Librae	15	24.3	−22	55	7.0–13.0	Mira	218	M
Delta Librae	15	01.0	−08	31	4.9–5.9	Algol	2.3	A
R Lyncis	07	01.3	+55	20	7.2–14.3	Mira	379	S
R Lyrae	18	55.3	+43	57	3.9–5.0	Semi-regular	46?	M
RR Lyrae	19	25.5	+42	47	7.1–8.1	RR Lyrae	0.6	A–F
Beta Lyrae	18	50.1	+33	22	3.3–4.4	Eclipsing	12.9	B
U Microscopii	20	29.2	−40	25	7.0–14.4	Mira	334	M
*U Monocerotis	07	30.8	−09	47	5.9–7.8	RV Tauri	91	F–K
V Monocerotis	06	22.7	−02	12	6.0–13.9	Mira	340	M
R Normae	15	36.0	−49	30	6.5–13.9	Mira	508	M
T Normae	15	44.1	−54	59	6.2–13.6	Mira	241	M

Star	RA		Declination		Range	Type	Period (days)	Spectrum
	h	m	°	'				
R Octantis	05	26.1	−86	23	6.3−13.2	Mira	405	M
S Octantis	18	08.7	−86	48	7.2−14.0	Mira	259	M
V Ophiuchi	16	26.7	−12	26	7.3−11.6	Mira	297	C
X Ophiuchi	18	38.3	+08	50	5.9−9.2	Mira	329	M
RS Ophiuchi	17	50.2	−06	43	4.3−12.5	Recurrent nova	—	OB+M
U Orionis	05	55.8	+20	10	4.8−13.0	Mira	368	M
W Orionis	05	05.4	+01	11	5.9−7.7	Semi-regular	212	C
Alpha Orionis	05	55.2	+07	24	0.0−1.3	Semi-regular	2335	M
S Pavonis	19	55.2	−59	12	6.6−10.4	Semi-regular	381	M
Kappa Pavonis	18	56.9	−67	14	3.9−4.8	W Virginis	9.1	G
R Pegasi	23	06.8	+10	33	6.9−13.8	Mira	378	M
X Persei	03	55.4	+31	03	6.0−7.0	Gamma Cas.	—	O9.5
Beta Persei	03	08.2	+40	57	2.1−3.4	Algol	2.9	B
Zeta Phoenicis	01	08.4	−55	15	3.9−4.4	Algol	1.7	B+B
R Pictoris	04	46.2	−49	15	6.4−10.1	Semi-regular	171	M
RS Puppis	08	13.1	−34	35	6.5−7.7	Cepheid	41.4	F−G
L² Puppis	07	13.5	−44	39	2.6−6.2	Semi-regular	141	M
T Pyxidis	09	04.7	−32	23	6.5−15.3	Recurrent nova	7000±	Pec
U Sagittae	19	18.8	+19	37	6.5−9.3	Algol	3.4	B+G
WZ Sagittae	20	07.6	+17	42	7.0−15.5	Dwarf nova	1900±	A
R Sagittarii	19	16.7	−19	18	6.7−12.8	Mira	270	M
RR Sagittarii	19	55.9	−29	11	5.4−14.0	Mira	336	M
RT Sagittarii	20	17.7	−39	07	6.0−14.1	Mira	306	M
RU Sagittarii	19	58.7	−41	51	6.0−13.8	Mira	240	M
RY Sagittarii	19	16.5	−33	31	5.8−14.0	R Coronae Bor.	—	G
RR Scorpii	16	56.6	−30	35	5.0−12.4	Mira	281	M
RS Scorpii	16	55.6	−45	06	6.2−13.0	Mira	320	M
RT Scorpii	17	03.5	−36	55	7.0−15.2	Mira	449	S
Delta Scorpii	16	00.3	−22	37	1.6−2.3	Irregular	—	B
S Sculptoris	00	15.4	−32	03	5.5−13.6	Mira	363	M
R Scuti	18	47.5	−05	42	4.2−8.6	RV Tauri	146	G−K
R Serpentis	15	50.7	+15	08	5.2−14.4	Mira	356	M
S Serpentis	15	21.7	+14	19	7.0−14.1	Mira	372	M
T Tauri	04	22.0	+19	32	9.3−13.5	T Tauri	—	F−K
SU Tauri	05	49.1	+19	04	9.1−16.9	R Coronae Bor.	—	G
Lambda Tauri	04	00.7	+12	29	3.4−3.9	Algol	4.0	B+A
R Trianguli	02	37.0	+34	16	5.4−12.6	Mira	267	M
R Ursae Majoris	10	44.6	+68	47	6.5−13.7	Mira	302	M
T Ursae Majoris	12	36.4	+59	29	6.6−13.5	Mira	257	M
*Z Ursae Majoris	11	56.5	+57	52	6.2−9.4	Semi-regular	196	M

Star	RA		Declination		Range	Type	Period (days)	Spectrum
	h	m	°	'				
*RY Ursae Majoris	12	20.5	+61	19	6.7–8.3	Semi-regular	310?	M
U Ursae Minoris	14	17.3	+66	48	7.1–13.0	Mira	331	M
R Virginis	12	38.5	+06	59	6.1–12.1	Mira	146	M
S Virginis	13	33.0	−07	12	6.3–13.2	Mira	375	M
SS Virginis	12	25.3	+00	48	6.0–9.6	Semi-regular	364	C
R Vulpeculae	21	04.4	+23	49	7.0–14.3	Mira	137	M
Z Vulpeculae	19	21.7	+25	34	7.3–8.9	Algol	2.5	B+A

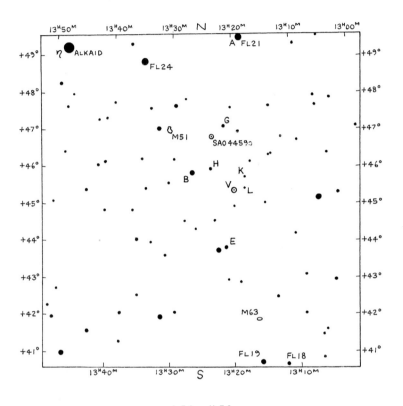

V CANUM VENATICORUM   13h 19.5m +45° 32′ (2000)

A 5.1	H 7.8
B 5.9	K 8.4
E 6.5	L 8.6
G 7.1	

o (MIRA) CETI   02h 19.3m −02° 59′ (2000)

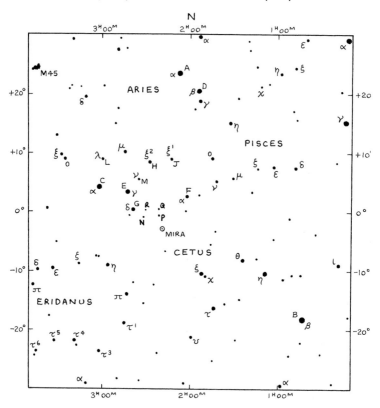

A 2.2	J 4.4
B 2.4	L 4.9
C 2.7	M 5.1
D 3.0	N 5.4
E 3.6	P 5.5
F 3.8	Q 5.7
G 4.1	R 6.1
H 4.3	

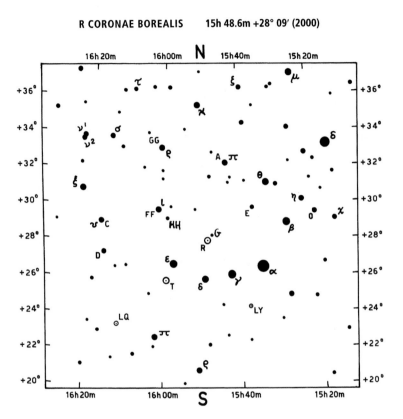

R CORONAE BOREALIS   15h 48.6m +28° 09′ (2000)

FF 5.0   C 5.8
GG 5.4   D 6.2
A 5.6   E 6.5
        HH 7.1
         G 7.4

CH CYGNI   **19h 24.5m +50° 14' (2000)**

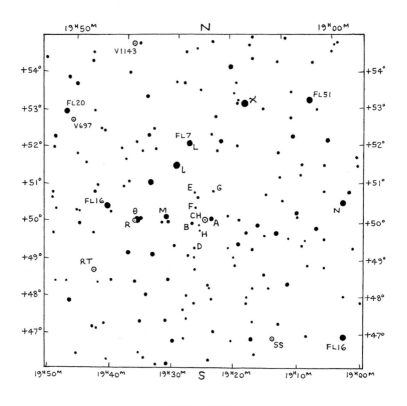

N 5.4	D 8.0
M 5.5	E 8.1
L 5.8	F 8.5
A 6.5	G 8.5
B 7.4	H 9.2

U MONOCEROTIS   07h 30.8m −09° 47′ (2000)

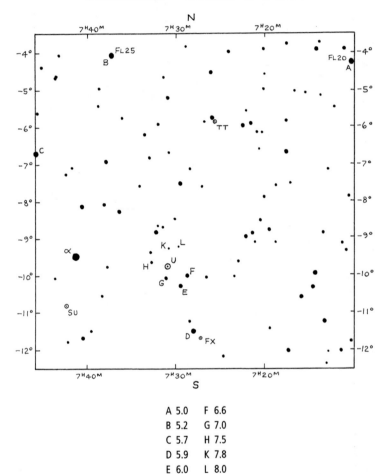

A 5.0   F 6.6
B 5.2   G 7.0
C 5.7   H 7.5
D 5.9   K 7.8
E 6.0   L 8.0

RY URSAE MAJORIS 12h 20.5m +61° 19′ (2000)
Z URSAE MAJORIS 11h 56.5m +57° 52′ (2000)

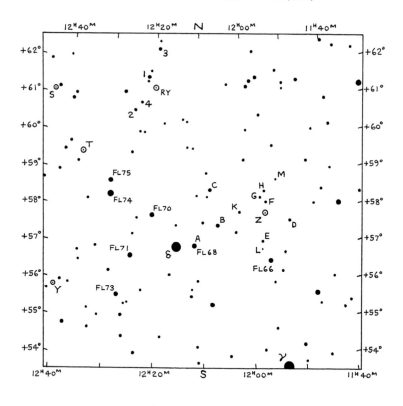

A 6.5	F 8.6	M 9.1
B 7.2	G 8.7	1 6.9
C 7.6	H 8.8	2 7.4
D 8.0	K 8.9	3 7.7
E 8.3	L 9.0	4 7.8

Mira Stars: Maxima, 2009

JOHN ISLES

Below are the predicted dates of maxima for Mira stars that reach magnitude 7.5 or brighter at an average maximum. Individual maxima can in some cases be brighter or fainter than average by a magnitude or more, and all dates are only approximate. The positions, extreme ranges, and mean periods of these stars can be found in the preceding list of interesting variable stars.

Star	Mean Magnitude at Maximum	Dates of Maxima
R Andromedae	6.9	24 Aug
W Andromedae	7.4	28 Jun
R Aquilae	6.1	17 Sep
R Boötis	7.2	16 Jul
R Cancri	6.8	25 Aug
S Canis Minoris	7.5	4 Dec
R Carinae	4.6	20 Mar
S Carinae	5.7	4 Jan, 2 Jun, 29 Oct
R Centauri	5.8	12 Sep
T Cephei	6.0	1 Jan
U Ceti	7.5	20 Jul
Omicron Ceti	3.4	18 Nov
T Columbae	7.5	28 Feb, 11 Oct
S Coronae Borealis	7.3	19 Sep
V Coronae Borealis	7.5	22 Jan
R Corvi	7.5	7 Feb, 21 Dec
RT Cygni	7.3	23 Jan, 1 Aug
Chi Cygni	5.2	27 Dec
R Geminorum	7.1	26 Dec
U Herculis	7.5	21 Nov
R Hydrae	4.5	2 Nov

Star	Mean Magnitude at Maximum	Dates of Maxima
R Leonis	5.8	10 Sep
R Leonis Minoris	7.1	3 Jan
RS Librae	7.5	14 Jul
V Monocerotis	7.0	29 May
T Normae	7.4	5 Aug
V Ophiuchi	7.5	13 Oct
X Ophiuchi	6.8	3 Jan, 27 Nov
U Orionis	6.3	15 Feb
R Sagittarii	7.3	18 Mar, 13 Dec
RR Sagittarii	6.8	20 Nov
RT Sagittarii	7.0	3 Jul
RU Sagittarii	7.2	16 Feb, 14 Oct
RR Scorpii	5.9	7 Mar, 13 Dec
RS Scorpii	7.0	1 Apr
S Sculptoris	6.7	2 Jan, 30 Dec
R Serpentis	6.9	18 Sep
R Trianguli	6.2	6 Sep
R Ursae Majoris	7.5	6 Apr
R Virginis	6.9	10 Mar, 3 Aug, 26 Dec
S Virginis	7.0	4 Feb

Some Interesting Double Stars

BOB ARGYLE

The positions, angles, and separations given below correspond to epoch 2008.0.

No.	RA		Declin-ation		Star	Magni-tudes	Separa-tion	PA	Cata-logue	Comments
	h	m	°	′			arcsec	°		
1	00	31.5	−62	58	β Tuc	4.4, 4.8	27.1	169	LCL 119	Both again difficult doubles.
2	00	49.1	+57	49	η Cas	3.4, 7.5	13.2	321	Σ60	Easy. Creamy, bluish. P = 480 years.
3	00	55.0	+23	38	36 And	6.0, 6.4	1.0	322	Σ73	P = 168 years. Both yellow. Slowly opening.
4	01	13.7	+07	35	ζ Psc	5.6, 6.5	23.1	63	Σ100	Yellow, reddish-white.
5	01	39.8	−56	12	p Eri	5.8, 5.8	11.6	189	Δ5	Period = 483 years.
6	01	53.5	+19	18	γ Ari	4.8, 4.8	7.5	1	Σ180	Very easy. Both white.
7	02	02.0	+02	46	α Psc	4.2, 5.1	1.8	265	Σ202	Binary, period = 933 years.
8	02	03.9	+42	20	γ And	2.3, 5.0	9.6	63	Σ205	Yellow, blue. Relatively fixed.
					γ2 And	5.1, 6.3	0.3	100	OΣ38	BC. Needs 30 cm. Closing.
9	02	29.1	+67	24	ι Cas AB	4.9, 6.9	2.6	230	Σ262	AB is long period binary. P = 620 years.
					ι Cas AC	4.9, 8.4	7.2	118		
10	02	33.8	−28	14	ω For	5.0, 7.7	10.8	245	HJ 3506	Common proper motion.

No.	RA		Declination		Star	Magnitudes	Separation	PA	Catalogue	Comments
	h	m	°	′			arcsec	°		
11	02	43.3	+03	14	γ Cet	3.5, 7.3	2.3	298	Σ299	Not too easy.
12	02	58.3	−40	18	θ Eri	3.4, 4.5	8.3	90	PZ 2	Both white.
13	02	59.2	+21	20	ε Ari	5.2, 5.5	1.4	208	Σ333	Closing slowly. P = 350 years? Both white.
14	03	00.9	+52	21	Σ331 Per	5.3, 6.7	12.0	85	–	Fixed.
15	03	12.1	−28	59	α For	4.0, 7.0	5.2	300	HJ 3555	P = 269 years. B variable?
16	03	48.6	−37	37	f Eri	4.8, 5.3	8.2	215	Δ16	Pale yellow. Fixed.
17	03	54.3	−02	57	32 Eri	4.8, 6.1	6.9	348	Σ470	Fixed.
18	04	32.0	+53	55	1 Cam	5.7, 6.8	10.3	308	Σ550	Fixed.
19	04	50.9	−53	28	ι Pic	5.6, 6.4	12.4	58	Δ18	Good object for small apertures. Fixed.
20	05	13.2	−12	56	κ Lep	4.5, 7.4	2.0	357	Σ661	Visible in 7.5 cm. Slowly closing.
21	05	14.5	−08	12	β Ori	0.1, 6.8	9.5	204	Σ668	Companion once thought to be close double.
22	05	21.8	−24	46	41 Lep	5.4, 6.6	3.4	93	HJ 3752	Deep yellow pair in a rich field.
23	05	24.5	−02	24	η Ori	3.8, 4.8	1.7	78	DA 5	Slow moving binary.
24	05	35.1	+09	56	λ Ori	3.6, 5.5	4.3	44	Σ738	Fixed.
25	05	35.3	−05	23	θ Ori AB	6.7, 7.9	8.6	32	Σ748	Trapezium in M42.
					θ Ori CD	5.1, 6.7	13.4	61		
26	05	38.7	−02	36	σ Ori AC	4.0, 10.3	11.4	238	Σ762	Quintuple. A is a close double.
					σ Ori ED	6.5, 7.5	30.1	231		
27	05	40.7	−01	57	ζ Ori	1.9, 4.0	2.6	166	Σ774	Can be split in 7.5 cm. Long period binary.
28	06	14.9	+22	30	η Gem	var, 6.5	1.6	255	β1008	Well seen with 20 cm. Primary orange.

No.	RA		Declin-ation		Star	Magni-tudes	Separa-tion	PA	Cata-logue	Comments
	h	m	°	′			arcsec	°		
29	06	46.2	+59	27	12 Lyn AB	5.4, 6.0	1.9	69	Σ948	AB is binary, P = 706 years.
					12 Lyn AC	5.4, 7.3	8.7	309		
30	07	08.7	−70	30	γ Vol	3.9, 5.8	14.1	298	Δ42	Very slow binary.
31	07	16.6	−23	19	h3945 CMa	4.8, 6.8	26.8	51	−	Contrasting colours.
32	07	20.1	+21	59	δ Gem	3.5, 8.2	5.6	228	Σ1066	Not too easy. Yellow, pale blue.
33	07	34.6	+31	53	α Gem	1.9, 2.9	4.6	58	Σ1110	Widening. Easy with 7.5 cm.
34	07	38.8	−26	48	κ Pup	4.5, 4.7	9.8	318	H III 27	Both white.
35	08	12.2	+17	39	ζ Cnc AB	5.6, 6.0	1.0	42	Σ1196	Period (AB) = 60 years. Near maximum separation.
					ζ Cnc AB-C	5.0, 6.2	5.9	69	Σ1196	Period (AB-C) = 1,150 years.
36	08	44.7	−54	43	δ Vel	2.1, 5.1	0.6	313	I 10	Difficult close pair. Period = 142 years.
37	08	46.8	+06	25	ε Hyd	3.3, 6.8	2.9	305	Σ1273	PA slowly increasing. A is a very close pair.
38	09	18.8	+36	48	38 Lyn	3.9, 6.6	2.6	226	Σ1334	Almost fixed.
39	09	47.1	−65	04	μ Car	3.1, 6.1	5.0	129	RMK 11	Fixed. Fine in small telescopes.
40	10	20.0	+19	50	γ Leo	2.2, 3.5	4.6	126	Σ1424	Binary, period = 619 years. Both orange.
41	10	32.0	−45	04	s Vel	6.2, 6.5	13.5	218	PZ 3	Fixed.
42	10	46.8	−49	26	μ Vel	2.7, 6.4	2.6	55	R 155	P = 138 years. Near widest separation.

No.	RA		Declin-ation		Star	Magni-tudes	Separa-tion	PA	Cata-logue	Comments
	h	m	°	′			arcsec	°		
43	10	55.6	+24	45	54 Leo	4.5, 6.3	6.6	111	Σ1487	Slowly widening. Pale yellow and white.
44	11	18.2	+31	32	ξ UMa	4.3, 4.8	1.6	219	Σ1523	Binary, 60 years. Needs 7.5 cm.
45	11	23.9	+10	32	ι Leo	4.0, 6.7	1.9	101	Σ1536	Binary, period = 186 years.
46	11	32.3	−29	16	N Hya	5.8, 5.9	9.4	210	H III 96	Fixed.
47	12	14.0	−45	43	D Cen	5.6, 6.8	2.8	243	RMK 14	Orange and white. Closing.
48	12	24.4	+25	35	Σ1639 CBe	6.7, 7.8	1.8	324	–	Slow binary.
49	12	26.6	−63	06	α Cru	1.4, 1.9	4.0	114	Δ252	Third star in a low power field.
50	12	41.5	−48	58	γ Cen	2.9, 2.9	0.4	330	HJ 4539	Period = 84 years. Closing. Both yellow.
51	12	41.7	−01	127	γ Vir	3.5, 3.5	1.2	31	Σ1670	Periastron in 2005. Now widening quickly.
52	12	46.3	−68	06	β Mus	3.7, 4.0	1.3	49	R 207	Both white. Closing slowly. P = 383 years.
53	12	54.6	−57	11	μ Cru	4.3, 5.3	34.9	17	Δ126	Fixed. Both white.
54	12	56.0	+38	19	α CVn	2.9, 5.5	19.3	229	Σ1692	Easy. Yellow, bluish.
55	13	22.6	−60	59	J Cen	4.6, 6.5	60.0	343	Δ133	Fixed. A is a close pair.
56	13	24.0	+54	56	ζ UMa	2.3, 4.0	14.4	152	Σ1744	Very easy. Naked-eye pair with Alcor.
57	13	51.8	−33	00	3 Cen	4.5, 6.0	7.7	102	H III 101	Both white. Closing slowly.
58	14	39.6	−60	50	α Cen	0.0, 1.2	7.5	241	RHD 1	Finest pair in the sky. P = 80 years. Closing.

No.	RA		Declin-ation		Star	Magni-tudes	Separa-tion	PA	Cata-logue	Comments
	h	m	°	′			arcsec	°		
59	14	41.1	+13	44	ζ Boo	4.5, 4.6	0.6	295	Σ1865	Both white. Closing – highly inclined orbit.
60	14	45.0	+27	04	ε Boo	2.5, 4.9	2.9	344	Σ1877	Yellow, blue. Fine pair.
61	14	46.0	−25	27	54 Hya	5.1, 7.1	8.3	122	H III 97	Closing slowly.
62	14	49.3	−14	09	μ Lib	5.8, 6.7	1.8	6	β106	Becoming wider. Fine in 7.5 cm.
63	14	51.4	+19	06	ξ Boo	4.7, 7.0	6.1	309	Σ1888	Fine contrast. Easy.
64	15	03.8	+47	39	44 Boo	5.3, 6.2	1.7	59	Σ1909	Period = 206 years. Beginning to close.
65	15	05.1	−47	03	π Lup	4.6, 4.7	1.7	64	HJ 4728	Widening.
66	15	18.5	−47	53	μ Lup AB	5.1, 5.2	1.0	320	HJ 4753	AB closing. Underobserved.
					μ Lup AC	4.4, 7.2	22.7	127	Δ180	AC almost fixed.
67	15	23.4	−59	19	γ Cir	5.1, 5.5	0.8	1	HJ 4757	Closing. Needs 20 cm. Long period binary.
68	15	32.0	+30	17	η CrB	5.6, 5.9	0.6	158	Σ1937	Both yellow. P = 41 yrs. Will be widening.
69	15	34.8	+10	33	δ Ser	4.2, 5.2	4.0	173	Σ1954	Long period binary.
70	15	35.1	−41	10	γ Lup	3.5, 3.6	0.8	277	HJ 4786	Binary. Period = 190 years. Needs 20 cm.
71	15	56.9	−33	58	ξ Lup	5.3, 5.8	10.2	49	PZ 4	Fixed.
72	16	14.7	+33	52	σ CrB	5.6, 6.6	7.2	237	Σ2032	Long period binary. Both white.
73	16	29.4	−26	26	α Sco	1.2, 5.4	2.6	277	GNT 1	Red, green. Difficult from mid-northern latitudes.

No.	RA		Declin-ation		Star	Magni-tudes	Separa-tion	PA	Cata-logue	Comments
	h	m	°	′			arcsec	°		
74	16	30.9	+01	59	λ Oph	4.2, 5.2	1.4	36	Σ2055	P = 129 years. Fairly difficult in small apertures.
75	16	41.3	+31	36	ζ Her	2.9, 5.5	1.1	187	Σ2084	Period = 34 years. Now widening. Needs 20 cm.
76	17	05.3	+54	28	μ Dra	5.7, 5.7	2.3	7	Σ2130	Period = 672 years.
77	17	14.6	+14	24	α Her	var, 5.4	4.6	103	Σ2140	Red, green. Long period binary.
78	17	15.3	−26	35	36 Oph	5.1, 5.1	5.0	142	SHJ 243	Period = 471 years.
79	17	23.7	+37	08	ρ Her	4.6, 5.6	4.1	319	Σ2161	Slowly widening.
80	18	01.5	+21	36	95 Her	5.0, 5.1	6.5	257	Σ2264	Colours thought variable in C19.
81	18	05.5	+02	30	70 Oph	4.2, 6.0	5.6	132	Σ2272	Opening. Easy in 7.5 cm.
82	18	06.8	−43	25	h5014 CrA	5.7, 5.7	1.7	3	–	Period = 450 years. Needs 10 cm.
83	18	35.9	+16	58	OΣ358 Her	6.8, 7.0	1.5	150	–	Period = 380 years.
84	18	44.3	+39	40	ε¹ Lyr	5.0, 6.1	2.4	348	Σ2382	Quadruple system with ε². Both pairs
85	18	44.3	+39	40	ε² Lyr	5.2, 5.5	2.4	79	Σ2383	visible in 7.5 cm.
86	18	56.2	+04	12	θ Ser	4.5, 5.4	22.4	104	Σ2417	Fixed. Very easy.
87	19	06.4	−37	04	γ CrA	4.8, 5.1	1.3	17	HJ 5084	Beautiful pair. Period = 122 years.
88	19	30.7	+27	58	β Cyg AB	3.1, 5.1	34.3	54	Σ I 43	Glorious. Yellow, blue-greenish.
					β Cyg Aa	3.1, 5.2	0.4	101	MCA 55	Aa. Period = 97 years. Closing.

No.	RA		Declination		Star	Magnitudes	Separation	PA	Catalogue	Comments
	h	m	°	′			arcsec	°		
89	19	45.0	+45	08	δ Cyg	2.9, 6.3	2.7	221	Σ2579	Slowly widening. Period = 780 years.
90	19	48.2	+70	16	ε Dra	3.8, 7.4	3.2	19	Σ2603	Slow binary.
91	20	46.7	+16	07	γ Del	4.5, 5.5	9.1	265	Σ2727	Easy. Yellowish. Long period binary.
92	20	59.1	+04	18	ε Equ AB	6.0, 6.3	0.5	284	Σ2737	Fine triple. AB is closing.
					ε Equ AC	6.0, 7.1	10.3	66		
93	21	06.9	+38	45	61 Cyg	5.2, 6.0	31.2	150	Σ2758	Nearby binary. Both orange. Period = 659 years.
94	21	13.7	+64	24	H I 48 Cep	7.2, 7.3	0.5	241	–	Period = 82 years. Widening rapidly.
95	21	19.9	−53	27	θ Ind	4.5, 7.0	7.0	271	HJ 5258	Pale yellow and reddish. Long period binary.
96	21	44.1	+28	45	μ Cyg	4.8, 6.1	1.7	315	Σ2822	Period = 789 years.
97	22	03.8	+64	37	ξ Cep	4.4, 6.5	8.3	274	Σ2863	White and blue. Long period binary.
98	22	26.6	−16	45	53 Aqr	6.4, 6.6	1.3	35	SHJ 345	Long period binary; periastron in 2023.
99	22	28.8	−00	01	ζ Aqr	4.3, 4.5	2.2	175	Σ2909	Period = 587 years. Slowly widening.
100	23	59.5	+33	43	Σ3050 And	6.6, 6.6	2.1	335	–	Period = 350 years.

Some Interesting Nebulae, Clusters, and Galaxies

Object	RA		Declina-tion		Remarks
	h	m	°	′	
M31 Andromedae	00	40.7	+41	05	Andromeda Galaxy, visible to naked eye.
H VIII 78 Cassiopeiae	00	41.3	+61	36	Fine cluster, between Gamma and Kappa Cassiopeiae.
M33 Trianguli	01	31.8	+30	28	Spiral. Difficult with small apertures.
H VI 33−4 Persei, C14	02	18.3	+56	59	Double cluster; Sword-handle.
Δ142 Doradus	05	39.1	−69	09	Looped nebula round 30 Doradus. Naked eye. In Large Magellanic Cloud.
M1 Tauri	05	32.3	+22	00	Crab Nebula, near Zeta Tauri.
M42 Orionis	05	33.4	−05	24	Orion Nebula. Contains the famous Trapezium, Theta Orionis.
M35 Geminorum	06	06.5	+24	21	Open cluster near Eta Geminorum.
H VII 2 Monocerotis, C50	06	30.7	+04	53	Open cluster, just visible to naked eye.
M41 Canis Majoris	06	45.5	−20	42	Open cluster, just visible to naked eye.
M47 Puppis	07	34.3	−14	22	Mag. 5.2. Loose cluster.
H IV 64 Puppis	07	39.6	−18	05	Bright planetary in rich neighbourhood.
M46 Puppis	07	39.5	−14	42	Open cluster.
M44 Cancri	08	38	+20	07	Praesepe. Open cluster near Delta Cancri. Visible to naked eye.
M97 Ursae Majoris	11	12.6	+55	13	Owl Nebula, diameter 3′. Planetary.
Kappa Crucis, C94	12	50.7	−60	05	'Jewel Box'; open cluster, with stars of contrasting colours.
M3 Can. Ven.	13	40.6	+28	34	Bright globular.
Omega Centauri, C80	13	23.7	−47	03	Finest of all globulars. Easy with naked eye.
M80 Scorpii	16	14.9	−22	53	Globular, between Antares and Beta Scorpii.
M4 Scorpii	16	21.5	−26	26	Open cluster close to Antares.

Object	RA		Declina-tion		Remarks
	h	m	°	′	
M13 Herculis	16	40	+36	31	Globular. Just visible to naked eye.
M92 Herculis	16	16.1	+43	11	Globular. Between Iota and Eta Herculis.
M6 Scorpii	17	36.8	−32	11	Open cluster; naked eye.
M7 Scorpii	17	50.6	−34	48	Very bright open cluster; naked eye.
M23 Sagittarii	17	54.8	−19	01	Open cluster nearly 50′ in diameter.
H IV 37 Draconis, C6	17	58.6	+66	38	Bright planetary.
M8 Sagittarii	18	01.4	−24	23	Lagoon Nebula. Gaseous. Just visible with naked eye.
NGC 6572 Ophiuchi	18	10.9	+06	50	Bright planetary, between Beta Ophiuchi and Zeta Aquilae.
M17 Sagittarii	18	18.8	−16	12	Omega Nebula. Gaseous. Large and bright.
M11 Scuti	18	49.0	−06	19	Wild Duck. Bright open cluster.
M57 Lyrae	18	52.6	+32	59	Ring Nebula. Brightest of planetaries.
M27 Vulpeculae	19	58.1	+22	37	Dumb-bell Nebula, near Gamma Sagittae.
H IV 1 Aquarii, C55	21	02.1	−11	31	Bright planetary, near Nu Aquarii.
M15 Pegasi	21	28.3	+12	01	Bright globular, near Epsilon Pegasi.
M39 Cygni	21	31.0	+48	17	Open cluster between Deneb and Alpha Lacertae. Well seen with low powers.

(M = Messier number; NGC = New General Catalogue number; C = Caldwell number.)

Our Contributors

Professor Chris Kitchin was formerly Director of the University of Hertfordshire Observatory. He is an astrophysicist with a great eagerness in encouraging a popular interest in astronomy. He is the author of several books, and appears regularly on television.

Martin Mobberley is one of the UK's most active imagers of comets, planets, asteroids, variable stars, novae and supernovae, and served as President of the British Astronomical Association from 1997 to 1999. In 2000 he was awarded the Association's Walter Goodacre Award. He is the author of six astronomy books published by Springer as well as three children's space-exploration books published by Top That Publishing.

Pete Lawrence has been a keen amateur astronomer since the mid-1960s. He qualified with a degree in Physics with Astrophysics from the University of Leicester in the early 1980s and subsequently became interested in digital-imaging and processing techniques. His images now regularly appear all over the world, on the Internet, in magazines, and in books. He currently writes for the BBC *Sky at Night* magazine as their resident imaging expert, observation guide, and equipment reviewer. He is also a regular contributor to *The Sky at Night* television programme.

Dr Ralph D. Lorenz is a planetary scientist at the Johns Hopkins University Applied Physics Laboratory in Laurel, Maryland, USA, with particular interest in Titan, astrobiology, space exploration systems, and climate. He is co-author of *Titan Unveiled*, *Space Systems Failures* and several other books.

Professor Greg Parker is Professor of Photonics in the School of Electronics and Computer Science at the University of Southampton, UK. By day he carries out research into optical nanodevices called photonic quasicrystals, but by night he is a keen amateur astrophotographer. Greg has published over 120 refereed journal papers in solid-state physics and optics, two books (a solid-state physics textbook and an astrophotography book), and has filed over a dozen patents. He is a C.Eng., C.Phys., and F.Inst.P., and is currently building his own mini-WASP array at his New Forest Observatory.

Professor Fred Watson is Astronomer-in-Charge of the Anglo-Australian Observatory at Coonabarabran in north-western New South Wales, and a well-known broadcaster on Australian radio. He is a regular contributor to the *Yearbook of Astronomy*, and his recent books include *Universe* (for which he was chief consultant), *Stargazer: The Life and Times of the Telescope*, and *Why Is Uranus Upside Down? And Other Questions About the Universe*. In 2006 he was awarded the Australian Government Eureka Prize for Promoting Understanding of Science. Visit Fred's website at http://fredwatson.com.au/.

Dr David M. Harland gained his BSc in astronomy in 1977 and a doctorate in computational science. Subsequently, he has taught computer science, worked in industry, and managed academic research. In 1995 he 'retired' and has since published many books on space themes.

Professor Mike Bode is Director of the Astrophysics Research Institute of Liverpool John Moores University and the university's Professor of Astrophysics. He has appeared regularly on BBC Television's *The Sky at Night* and has previously contributed articles on novae and lunar transients to the *Yearbook of Astronomy*. His latest book on *Classical Novae* (co-edited with Professor Aneurin Evans of the University of Keele) has recently been published by Cambridge University Press.

Dr Allan Chapman, of Wadham College, Oxford, is probably Britain's leading authority on the history of astronomy. He has published many research papers and several books, as well as numerous popular accounts. He is a frequent and welcome contributor to the *Yearbook*.

Astronomical Societies in the British Isles

British Astronomical Association
Assistant Secretary: Burlington House, Piccadilly, London W1V 9AG.
Meetings: Lecture Hall of Scientific Societies, Civil Service Commission Building, 23 Savile Row, London W1. Last Wednesday each month (Oct.–June), 5 p.m. and some Saturday afternoons.

Association for Astronomy Education
Secretary: Teresa Grafton, The Association for Astronomy Education, c/o The Royal Astronomical Society, Burlington House, Piccadilly, London W1V 0NL.

Astronomical Society of Edinburgh
Secretary: Graham Rule, 105/19 Causewayside, Edinburgh EH9 1QG.
Website: www.roe.ac.uk/asewww/; *Email:* asewww@roe.ac.uk
Meetings: City Observatory, Calton Hill, Edinburgh. 1st Friday each month, 8 p.m.

Astronomical Society of Glasgow
Secretary: Mr David Degan, 5 Hillside Avenue, Alexandria, Dunbartonshire G83 0BB.
Website: www.astronomicalsocietyofglasgow.org.uk
Meetings: Royal College, University of Strathclyde, Montrose Street, Glasgow. 3rd Thursday each month, Sept.–Apr., 7.30 p.m.

Astronomical Society of Haringey
Secretary: Jerry Workman, 91 Greenslade Road, Barking, Essex IG11 9XF.
Meetings: Palm Court, Alexandra Palace, 3rd Wednesday each month, 8 p.m.

Astronomy Ireland
Secretary: Tony Ryan, PO Box 2888, Dublin 1, Eire.
Website: www.astronomy.ie; *Email:* info@astronomy.ie
Meetings: 2nd Monday of each month. Telescope meetings every clear Saturday.

Federation of Astronomical Societies
Secretary: Clive Down, 10 Glan-y-Llyn, North Cornelly, Bridgend, County Borough CF33 4EF.
Email: clivedown@btinternet.com

Junior Astronomical Society of Ireland
Secretary: K. Nolan, 5 St Patrick's Crescent, Rathcoole, Co. Dublin.
Meetings: The Royal Dublin Society, Ballsbridge, Dublin 4. Monthly.

Society for Popular Astronomy
Secretary: Guy Fennimore, 36 Fairway, Keyworth, Nottingham NG12 5DU.
Website: www.popastro.com; *Email:* SPAstronomy@aol.com
Meetings: Last Saturday in Jan., Apr., July, Oct., 2.30 p.m. in London.

Webb Society
Treasurer/Membership Secretary: Steve Rayner, 10 Meon Close, Tadley RG26 4HN.

Aberdeen and District Astronomical Society
Secretary: Ian C. Giddings, 95 Brentfield Circle, Ellon, Aberdeenshire AB41 9DB.
Meetings: Robert Gordon's Institute of Technology, St Andrew's Street, Aberdeen.
Fridays, 7.30 p.m.

Abingdon Astronomical Society (was **Fitzharry's Astronomical Society**)
Secretary: Chris Holt, 9 Rutherford Close, Abingdon, Oxon OX14 2AT.
Website: www.abingdonastro.org.uk; *Email:* info@abingdonastro.co.uk
Meetings: All Saints' Methodist Church Hall, Dorchester Crescent, Abingdon, Oxon.
2nd Monday Sept.–June, 8 p.m. and additional beginners' meetings and observing
evenings as advertised.

Altrincham and District Astronomical Society
Secretary: Derek McComiskey, 33 Tottenham Drive, Manchester M23 9WH.
Meetings: Timperley Village Club. 1st Friday Sept.–June, 8 p.m.

Andover Astronomical Society
Secretary: Mrs S. Fisher, Staddlestones, Aughton, Kingston, Marlborough, Wiltshire
SN8 3SA.
Meetings: Grately Village Hall. 3rd Thursday each month, 7.30 p.m.

Astra Astronomy Section
Secretary: c/o Duncan Lunan, Flat 65, Dalraida House, 56 Blythswood Court,
Anderston, Glasgow G2 7PE.
Meetings: Airdrie Arts Centre, Anderson Street, Airdrie. Weekly.

Astrodome Mobile School Planetarium
Contact: Peter J. Golding, 53 City Way, Rochester, Kent ME1 2AX.
Website: www.astrodome.clara.co.uk; *Email:* astrodome@clara.co.uk

Aylesbury Astronomical Society
Secretary: Alan Smith, 182 Marley Fields, Leighton Buzzard, Bedfordshire LU7 8WN.
Meetings: 1st Monday in month at 8 p.m., venue in Aylesbury area. Details from
Secretary.

Bassetlaw Astronomical Society
Secretary: Andrew Patton, 58 Holding, Worksop, Notts S81 0TD.
Meetings: Rhodesia Village Hall, Rhodesia, Worksop, Notts. 2nd and 4th Tuesdays of
month at 7.45 p.m.

Batley & Spenborough Astronomical Society
Secretary: Robert Morton, 22 Links Avenue, Cleckheaton, West Yorks BD19 4EG.
Meetings: Milner K. Ford Observatory, Wilton Park, Batley. Every Thursday, 8 p.m.

Bedford Astronomical Society
Secretary: Mrs L. Harrington, 24 Swallowfield, Wyboston, Bedfordshire MK44 3AE.
Website: www.observer1.freeserve.co.uk/bashome.html
Meetings: Bedford School, Burnaby Rd, Bedford. Last Wednesday each month.

Bingham & Brooks Space Organization
Secretary: N. Bingham, 15 Hickmore's Lane, Lindfield, West Sussex.

Birmingham Astronomical Society
Contact: P. Bolas, 4 Moat Bank, Bretby, Burton-on-Trent DE15 0QJ.
Website: www.birmingham-astronomical.co.uk; *Email:* pbolas@aol.com
Meetings: Room 146, Aston University. Last Tuesday of month. Sept.–June (except
Dec., moved to 1st week in Jan.).

Blackburn Leisure Astronomy Section
Secretary: Mr H. Murphy, 20 Princess Way, Beverley, East Yorkshire HU17 8PD.
Meetings: Blackburn Leisure Welfare. Mondays, 8 p.m.

Blackpool & District Astronomical Society
> *Secretary:* Terry Devon, 30 Victory Road, Blackpool, Lancashire FY1 3JT.
> *Website:* www.blackpoolastronomy.org.uk; *Email:* info@blackpoolastronomy.org.uk
> *Meetings:* St Kentigern's Social Centre, Blackpool. 1st Wednesday of the month,
> 7.45 p.m.

Bolton Astronomical Society
> *Secretary:* Peter Miskiw, 9 Hedley Street, Bolton, Lancashire BL1 3LE.
> *Meetings:* Ladybridge Community Centre, Bolton. 1st and 3rd Tuesdays Sept.–May,
> 7.30 p.m.

Border Astronomy Society
> *Secretary:* David Pettitt, 14 Sharp Grove, Carlisle, Cumbria CA2 5QR.
> *Website:* www.members.aol.com/P3pub/page8.html
> *Email:* davidpettitt@supanet.com
> *Meetings:* The Observatory, Trinity School, Carlisle. Alternate Thursdays, 7.30 p.m.,
> Sept.–May.

Boston Astronomers
> *Secretary:* Mrs Lorraine Money, 18 College Park, Horncastle, Lincolnshire LN9 6RE.
> *Meetings:* Blackfriars Arts Centre, Boston. 2nd Monday each month, 7.30 p.m.

Bradford Astronomical Society
> *Contact:* Mrs J. Hilary Knaggs, 6 Meadow View, Wyke, Bradford BD12 9LA.
> *Website:* www.bradford-astro.freeserve.co.uk/index.htm
> *Meetings:* Eccleshill Library, Bradford. Alternate Mondays, 7.30 p.m.

Braintree, Halstead & District Astronomical Society
> *Secretary:* Mr J. R. Green, 70 Dorothy Sayers Drive, Witham, Essex CM8 2LU.
> *Meetings:* BT Social Club Hall, Witham Telephone Exchange. 3rd Thursday each
> month, 8 p.m.

Breckland Astronomical Society (was **Great Ellingham and District Astronomy Club**)
> *Contact:* Martin Wolton, Willowbeck House, Pulham St Mary, Norfolk IP21 4QS.
> *Meetings:* Great Ellingham Recreation Centre, Watton Road (B1077), Great
> Ellingham, 2nd Friday each month, 7.15 p.m.

Bridgend Astronomical Society
> *Secretary:* Clive Down, 10 Glan-y-Llyn, Broadlands, North Cornelly, Bridgend
> County CF33 4EF.
> *Email:* clivedown@btinternet.com
> *Meetings:* Bridgend Bowls Centre, Bridgend. 2nd Friday, monthly, 7.30 p.m.

Bridgwater Astronomical Society
> *Secretary:* Mr G. MacKenzie, Watergore Cottage, Watergore, South Petherton,
> Somerset TA13 5JQ.
> *Website:* www.ourworld.compuserve.com/hompages/dbown/Bwastro.htm
> *Meetings:* Room D10, Bridgwater College, Bath Road Centre, Bridgwater. 2nd
> Wednesday each month, Sept.–June.

Bridport Astronomical Society
> *Secretary:* Mr G.J. Lodder, 3 The Green, Walditch, Bridport, Dorset DT6 4LB.
> *Meetings:* Walditch Village Hall, Bridport. 1st Sunday each month, 7.30 p.m.

Brighton Astronomical and Scientific Society
> *Secretary:* Ms T. Fearn, 38 Woodlands Close, Peacehaven, East Sussex BN10 7SF.
> *Meetings:* St John's Church Hall, Hove. 1st Tuesday each month, 7.30 p.m.

Bristol Astronomical Society
Secretary: Dr John Pickard, 'Fielding', Easter Compton, Bristol BS35 5SJ.
Meetings: Frank Lecture Theatre, University of Bristol Physics Dept., alternate Fridays in term time, and Westbury Park Methodist Church Rooms, North View, other Fridays.

Callington Community Astronomy Group
Secretary: Beccy Watson. *Tel:* 07732 945671
Email: Beccyboo@kimwatson99.fsnet.co.uk
Website: www.callington-astro.org.uk
Meetings: Callington Space Centre, Callington Community College, Launceston Road, Callington, Cornwall PL17 7DR. 1st and 3rd Saturday of each month, 7.30 p.m., Sept.–July.

Cambridge Astronomical Society
Secretary: Brian Lister, 80 Ramsden Square, Cambridge CB4 2BL.
Meetings: Institute of Astronomy, Madingley Road. 3rd Friday each month.

Cardiff Astronomical Society
Secretary: D.W.S. Powell, 1 Tal-y-Bont Road, Ely, Cardiff CF5 5EU.
Meetings: Dept. of Physics and Astronomy, University of Wales, Newport Road, Cardiff. Alternate Thursdays, 8 p.m.

Castle Point Astronomy Club
Secretary: Andrew Turner, 3 Canewdon Hall Close, Canewdon, Rochford, Essex SS4 3PY.
Meetings: St Michael's Church Hall, Daws Heath. Wednesdays, 8 p.m.

Chelmsford Astronomers
Secretary: Brendan Clark, 5 Borda Close, Chelmsford, Essex.
Meetings: Once a month.

Chester Astronomical Society
Secretary: Mrs S. Brooks, 39 Halton Road, Great Sutton, South Wirral LL66 2UF.
Meetings: All Saints' Parish Church, Chester. Last Wednesday each month except Aug. and Dec., 7.30 p.m.

Chester Society of Natural Science, Literature and Art
Secretary: Paul Braid, 'White Wing', 38 Bryn Avenue, Old Colwyn, Colwyn Bay LL29 8AH.
Email: p.braid@virgin.net
Meetings: Once a month.

Chesterfield Astronomical Society
President: Mr D. Blackburn, 71 Middlecroft Road, Stavely, Chesterfield, Derbyshire S41 3XG. Tel: 07909 570754.
Website: www.chesterfield-as.org.uk
Meetings: Barnet Observatory, Newbold, each Friday.

Clacton & District Astronomical Society
Secretary: C. L. Haskell, 105 London Road, Clacton-on-Sea, Essex.

Cleethorpes & District Astronomical Society
Secretary: C. Illingworth, 38 Shaw Drive, Grimsby, South Humberside.
Meetings: Beacon Hill Observatory, Cleethorpes. 1st Wednesday each month.

Cleveland & Darlington Astronomical Society
Contact: Dr John McCue, 40 Bradbury Rd., Stockton-on-Tees, Cleveland TS20 1LE.
Meetings: Grindon Parish Hall, Thorpe Thewles, near Stockton-on-Tees. 2nd Friday, monthly.

Cork Astronomy Club
> *Secretary:* Charles Coughlan, 12 Forest Ridge Crescent, Wilton, Cork, Eire.
> *Meetings:* 1st Monday, Sept.–May (except bank holidays).

Cornwall Astronomical Society
> *Secretary:* J.M. Harvey, 1 Tregunna Close, Porthleven, Cornwall TR13 9LW.
> *Meetings:* Godolphin Club, Wendron Street, Helston, Cornwall. 2nd and 4th
> Thursday of each month, 7.30 for 8 p.m.

Cotswold Astronomical Society
> *Secretary:* Rod Salisbury, Grove House, Christchurch Road, Cheltenham,
> Gloucestershire GL50 2PN.
> *Website:* www.members.nbci.com/CotswoldAS
> *Meetings:* Shurdington Church Hall, School Lane, Shurdington, Cheltenham. 2nd
> Saturday each month, 8 p.m.

Coventry & Warwickshire Astronomical Society
> *Secretary:* Steve Payne, 68 Stonebury Avenue, Eastern Green, Coventry CV5 7FW.
> *Website:* www.cawas.freeserve.co.uk; *Email:* sjp2000@thefarside57.freeserve.co.uk
> *Meetings:* The Earlsdon Church Hall, Albany Road, Earlsdon, Coventry. 2nd Friday,
> monthly, Sept.–June.

Crawley Astronomical Society
> *Secretary:* Ron Gamer, 1 Pevensey Close, Pound Hill, Crawley, West Sussex
> RH10 7BL.
> *Meetings:* Ifield Community Centre, Ifield Road, Crawley. 3rd Friday each month,
> 7.30 p.m.

Crayford Manor House Astronomical Society
> *Secretary:* Roger Pickard, 28 Appletons, Hadlow, Kent TM1 0DT.
> *Meetings:* Manor House Centre, Crayford. Monthly during term time.

Crewkerne and District Astronomical Society (CADAS)
> *Chairman:* Kevin Dodgson, 46 Hermitage Street, Crewkerne, Somerset TA18 8ET.
> *Email:* crewastra@aol.com

Croydon Astronomical Society
> *Secretary:* John Murrell, 17 Dalmeny Road, Carshalton, Surrey.
> *Meetings:* Lecture Theatre, Royal Russell School, Combe Lane, South Croydon.
> Alternate Fridays, 7.45 p.m.

Derby & District Astronomical Society
> *Secretary:* Ian Bennett, Freers Cottage, Sutton Lane, Etwall.
> *Web site:* www.derby-astro-soc.fsnet/index.html;
> *Email:* bennett.lovatt@btinternet.com
> *Meetings:* Friends Meeting House, Derby. 1st Friday each month, 7.30 p.m.

Doncaster Astronomical Society
> *Secretary:* A. Anson, 15 Cusworth House, St James Street, Doncaster DN1 3AY
> *Web site:* www.donastro.freeserve.co.uk; *Email:* space@donastro.freeserve.co.uk
> *Meetings:* St George's Church House, St George's Church, Church Way, Doncaster.
> 2nd and 4th Thursday of each month, commencing at 7.30 p.m.

Dumfries Astronomical Society
> *Secretary:* Mr J. Sweeney, 3 Lakeview, Powfoot, Annan DG13 5PG.
> *Meetings:* Gracefield Arts Centre, Edinburgh Road, Dumfries. 3rd Tuesday Aug.–
> May, 7.30 p.m.

Dundee Astronomical Society

Secretary: G. Young, 37 Polepark Road, Dundee, Tayside DD1 5QT.

Meetings: Mills Observatory, Balgay Park, Dundee. 1st Friday each month, 7.30 p.m. Sept.–Apr.

Easington and District Astronomical Society

Secretary: T. Bradley, 52 Jameson Road, Hartlepool, Co. Durham.

Meetings: Easington Comprehensive School, Easington Colliery. Every 3rd Thursday throughout the year, 7.30 p.m.

East Antrim Astronomical Society

Secretary: Stephen Beasant

Website: www.eaas.co.uk

Meetings: Ballyclare High School, Ballyclare, County Antrim. First Monday each month.

Eastbourne Astronomical Society

Secretary: Peter Gill, 18 Selwyn House, Selwyn Road, Eastbourne, East Sussex BN21 2LF.

Meetings: Willingdon Memorial Hall, Church Street, Willingdon. One Saturday per month, Sept.–July, 7.30 p.m.

East Riding Astronomers

Secretary: Tony Scaife, 15 Beech Road, Elloughton, Brough, North Humberside HU15 1JX.

Meetings: As arranged.

East Sussex Astronomical Society

Secretary: Marcus Croft, 12 St Mary's Cottages, Ninfield Road, Bexhill-on-Sea, East Sussex.

Website: www.esas.org.uk

Meetings: St Marys School, Wrestwood Road, Bexhill. 1st Thursday of each month, 8 p.m.

Edinburgh University Astronomical Society

Secretary: c/o Dept. of Astronomy, Royal Observatory, Blackford Hill, Edinburgh.

Ewell Astronomical Society

Secretary: Richard Gledhill, 80 Abinger Avenue, Cheam SM2 7LW.

Website: www.ewell-as.co.uk

Meetings: St Mary's Church Hall, London Road, Ewell. 2nd Friday of each month except August, 7.45 p.m.

Exeter Astronomical Society

Secretary: Tim Sedgwick, Old Dower House, Half Moon, Newton St Cyres, Exeter, Devon EX5 5AE.

Meetings: The Meeting Room, Wynards, Magdalen Street, Exeter. 1st Thursday of month.

Farnham Astronomical Society

Secretary: Laurence Anslow, 'Asterion', 18 Wellington Lane, Farnham, Surrey GU9 9BA.

Meetings: Central Club, South Street, Farnham. 2nd Thursday each month, 8 p.m.

Foredown Tower Astronomy Group

Secretary: M. Feist, Foredown Tower Camera Obscura, Foredown Road, Portslade, East Sussex BN41 2EW.

Meetings: At the above address, 3rd Tuesday each month. 7 p.m. (winter), 8 p.m. (summer).

Greenock Astronomical Society
Secretary: Carl Hempsey, 49 Brisbane Street, Greenock.
Meetings: Greenock Arts Guild, 3 Campbell Street, Greenock.

Grimsby Astronomical Society
Secretary: R. Williams, 14 Richmond Close, Grimsby, South Humberside.
Meetings: Secretary's home. 2nd Thursday each month, 7.30 p.m.

Guernsey: La Société Guernesiasie Astronomy Section
Secretary: Debby Quertier, Lamorna, Route Charles, St Peter Port, Guernsey GY1 1QS.
and Jessica Harris, Keanda, Les Sauvagees, St Sampson's, Guernsey GY2 4XT.
Meetings: Observatory, Rue du Lorier, St Peter's. Tuesdays, 8 p.m.

Guildford Astronomical Society
Secretary: A. Langmaid, 22 West Mount, The Mount, Guildford, Surrey GU2 5HL.
Meetings: Guildford Institute, Ward Street, Guildford. 1st Thursday each month except Aug., 7.30 p.m.

Gwynedd Astronomical Society
Secretary: Mr Ernie Greenwood, 18 Twrcelyn Street, Llanerchymedd, Anglesey LL74 8TL.
Meetings: Dept. of Electronic Engineering, Bangor University. 1st Thursday each month except Aug., 7.30 p.m.

The Hampshire Astronomical Group
Secretary: Geoff Mann, 10 Marie Court, 348 London Road, Waterlooville, Hampshire PO7 7SR.
Website: www.hantsastro.demon.co.uk; *Email:* Geoff.Mann@hazleton97.fsnet.co.uk
Meetings: 2nd Friday, Clanfield Memorial Hall, all other Fridays Clanfield Observatory.

Hanney & District Astronomical Society
Secretary: Bob Church, 47 Upthorpe Drive, Wantage, Oxfordshire OX12 7DG.
Meetings: Last Thursday each month, 8 p.m.

Harrogate Astronomical Society
Secretary: Brian Bonser, 114 Main Street, Little Ouseburn TO5 9TG.
Meetings: National Power HQ, Beckwith Knowle, Harrogate. Last Friday each month.

Hastings and Battle Astronomical Society
Secretary: K.A. Woodcock, 24 Emmanuel Road, Hastings, East Sussex TN34 3LB.
Email: keith@habas.freeserve.co.uk
Meetings: Herstmonceux Science Centre. 2nd Saturday of each month, 7.30 p.m.

Havering Astronomical Society
Secretary: Frances Ridgley, 133 Severn Drive, Upminster, Essex RM14 1PP.
Meetings: Cranham Community Centre, Marlborough Gardens, Upminster, Essex. 3rd Wednesday each month except July and Aug., 7.30 p.m.

Heart of England Astronomical Society
Secretary: John Williams, 100 Stanway Road, Shirley, Solihull B90 3JG.
Website: www.members.aol.com/hoeas/home.html; *Email:* hoeas@aol.com
Meetings: Furnace End Village, over Whitacre, Warwickshire. Last Thursday each month, except June, July & Aug., 8 p.m.

Hebden Bridge Literary & Scientific Society, Astronomical Section
Secretary: Peter Jackson, 44 Gilstead Lane, Bingley, West Yorkshire BD16 3NP.
Meetings: Hebden Bridge Information Centre. Last Wednesday, Sept.–May.

Herschel Astronomy Society
Secretary: Kevin Bishop, 106 Holmsdale, Crown Wood, Bracknell, Berkshire RG12 3TB.
Meetings: Eton College. 2nd Friday each month, 7.30 p.m.

Highlands Astronomical Society
Secretary: Richard Green, 11 Drumossie Avenue, Culcabock, Inverness IV2 3SJ.
Meetings: The Spectrum Centre, Inverness. 1st Tuesday each month, 7.30 p.m.

Hinckley & District Astronomical Society
Secretary: Mr S. Albrighton, 4 Walnut Close, The Bridleways, Hartshill, Nuneaton, Warwickshire CV10 0XH.
Meetings: Burbage Common Visitors Centre, Hinckley. 1st Tuesday Sept.–May, 7.30 p.m.

Horsham Astronomy Group (was **Forest Astronomical Society**)
Secretary: Dan White, 32 Burns Close, Horsham, West Sussex RH12 5PF.
Email: secretary@horshamastronomy.com
Meetings: 1st Wednesday each month.

Howards Astronomy Club
Secretary: H. Ilett, 22 St George's Avenue, Warblington, Havant, Hampshire.
Meetings: To be notified.

Huddersfield Astronomical and Philosophical Society
Secretary: Lisa B. Jeffries, 58 Beaumont Street, Netherton, Huddersfield, West Yorkshire HD4 7HE.
Email: l.b.jeffries@hud.ac.uk
Meetings: 4a Railway Street, Huddersfield. Every Wednesday and Friday, 7.30 p.m.

Hull and East Riding Astronomical Society
President: Sharon E. Long
Email: charon@charon.karoo.co.uk
Website: http://www.heras.org.uk
Meetings: The Wilberforce Building, Room S25, University of Hull, Cottingham Road, Hull. 2nd Monday each month, Sept.–May, 7.30–9.30 p.m.

Ilkeston & District Astronomical Society
Secretary: Mark Thomas, 2 Elm Avenue, Sandiacre, Nottingham NG10 5EJ.
Meetings: The Function Room, Erewash Museum, Anchor Row, Ilkeston. 2nd Tuesday monthly, 7.30 p.m.

Ipswich, Orwell Astronomical Society
Secretary: R. Gooding, 168 Ashcroft Road, Ipswich.
Meetings: Orwell Park Observatory, Nacton, Ipswich. Wednesdays, 8 p.m.

Irish Astronomical Association
President: Terry Moseley, 31 Sunderland Road, Belfast BT6 9LY, Northern Ireland.
Email: terrymosel@aol.com
Meetings: Ashby Building, Stranmillis Road, Belfast. Alternate Wednesdays, 7.30 p.m.

Irish Astronomical Society
Secretary: James O'Connor, PO Box 2547, Dublin 15, Eire.
Meetings: Ely House, 8 Ely Place, Dublin 2. 1st and 3rd Monday each month.

Isle of Man Astronomical Society
Secretary: James Martin, Ballaterson Farm, Peel, Isle of Man IM5 3AB.
Email: ballaterson@manx.net
Meetings: Isle of Man Observatory, Foxdale. 1st Thursday of each month, 8 p.m.

Isle of Wight Astronomical Society
> *Secretary:* J. W. Feakins, 1 Hilltop Cottages, High Street, Freshwater, Isle of Wight.
> *Meetings:* Unitarian Church Hall, Newport, Isle of Wight. Monthly.

Keele Astronomical Society
> *Secretary:* Natalie Webb, Department of Physics, University of Keele, Keele, Staffordshire ST5 5BG.
> *Meetings:* As arranged during term time.

Kettering and District Astronomical Society
> *Asst. Secretary:* Steve Williams, 120 Brickhill Road, Wellingborough, Northamptonshire.
> *Meetings:* Quaker Meeting Hall, Northall Street, Kettering, Northamptonshire. 1st Tuesday each month, 7.45 p.m.

King's Lynn Amateur Astronomical Association
> *Secretary:* P. Twynman, 17 Poplar Avenue, RAF Marham, King's Lynn.
> *Meetings:* As arranged.

Lancaster and Morecambe Astronomical Society
> *Secretary:* Mrs E. Robinson, 4 Bedford Place, Lancaster LA1 4EB.
> *Email:* ehelenerob@btinternet.com
> *Meetings:* Church of the Ascension, Torrisholme. 1st Wednesday each month except July and Aug.

Knowle Astronomical Society
> *Secretary:* Nigel Foster, 21 Speedwell Drive, Balsall Common, Coventry, West Midlands CV7 7AU.
> *Meetings:* St George & St Theresa's Parish Centre, 337 Station Road, Dorridge, Solihull, West Midlands B93 8TZ. 1st Monday of each month (+/– 1 week for Bank Holidays) except August.

Lancaster University Astronomical Society
> *Secretary:* c/o Students' Union, Alexandra Square, University of Lancaster.
> *Meetings:* As arranged.

Laymans Astronomical Society
> *Secretary:* John Evans, 10 Arkwright Walk, The Meadows, Nottingham.
> *Meetings:* The Popular, Bath Street, Ilkeston, Derbyshire. Monthly.

Leeds Astronomical Society
> *Secretary:* Mark A. Simpson, 37 Roper Avenue, Gledhow, Leeds LS8 1LG.
> *Meetings:* Centenary House, North Street. 2nd Wednesday each month, 7.30 p.m.

Leicester Astronomical Society
> *Secretary:* Dr P.J. Scott, 21 Rembridge Close, Leicester LE3 9AP.
> *Meetings:* Judgemeadow Community College, Marydene Drive, Evington, Leicester. 2nd and 4th Tuesdays each month, 7.30 p.m.

Letchworth and District Astronomical Society
> *Secretary:* Eric Hutton, 14 Folly Close, Hitchin, Hertfordshire.
> *Meetings:* As arranged.

Lewes Amateur Astronomers
> *Secretary:* Christa Sutton, 8 Tower Road, Lancing, West Sussex BN15 9HT.
> *Meetings:* The Bakehouse Studio, Lewes. Last Wednesday each month.

Limerick Astronomy Club
> *Secretary:* Tony O'Hanlon, 26 Ballycannon Heights, Meelick, Co. Clare, Eire.
> *Meetings:* Limerick Senior College, Limerick. Monthly (except June and Aug.), 8 p.m.

Lincoln Astronomical Society
Secretary: David Swaey, 'Everglades', 13 Beaufort Close, Lincoln LN2 4SF.
Meetings: The Lecture Hall, off Westcliffe Street, Lincoln. 1st Tuesday each month.

Liverpool Astronomical Society
Secretary: Mr K. Clark, 31 Sandymount Drive, Wallasey, Merseyside L45 0LJ.
Meetings: Lecture Theatre, Liverpool Museum. 3rd Friday each month, 7 p.m.

Norman Lockyer Observatory Society
Secretary: G.E. White, PO Box 9, Sidmouth EX10 0YQ.
Website: www.ex.ac.uk/nlo/; *Email:* g.e.white@ex.ac.uk
Meetings: Norman Lockyer Observatory, Sidmouth. Fridays and 2nd Monday each month, 7.30 p.m.

Loughton Astronomical Society
Secretary: Charles Munton, 14a Manor Road, Wood Green, London N22 4YJ.
Meetings: 1st Theydon Bois Scout Hall, Loughton Lane, Theydon Bois. Weekly.

Lowestoft and Great Yarmouth Regional Astronomers (LYRA) Society
Secretary: Simon Briggs, 28 Sussex Road, Lowestoft, Suffolk.
Meetings: Community Wing, Kirkley High School, Kirkley Run, Lowestoft. 3rd Thursday each month, 7.30 p.m.

Luton Astronomical Society
Secretary: Mr G. Mitchell, Putteridge Bury, University of Luton, Hitchin Road, Luton.
Website: www.lutonastrosoc.org.uk; *Email:* user998491@aol.com
Meetings: Univ. of Luton, Putteridge Bury (except June, July and August), or Someries Junior School, Wigmore Lane, Luton (July and August only), last Thursday each month, 7.30–9.00 p.m.

Lytham St Annes Astronomical Association
Secretary: K.J. Porter, 141 Blackpool Road, Ansdell, Lytham St Anne's, Lancashire.
Meetings: College of Further Education, Clifton Drive South, Lytham St Anne's. 2nd Wednesday monthly Oct.–June.

Macclesfield Astronomical Society
Secretary: Mr John H. Thomson, 27 Woodbourne Road, Sale, Cheshire M33 3SY
Website: www.maccastro.com; *Email:* jhandlc@yahoo.com
Meetings: Jodrell Bank Science Centre, Goostrey, Cheshire. 1st Tuesday of every month, 7 p.m.

Maidenhead Astronomical Society
Secretary: Tim Haymes, Hill Rise, Knowl Hill Common, Knowl Hill, Reading RG10 9YD.
Meetings: Stubbings Church Hall, near Maidenhead. 1st Friday Sept.–June.

Maidstone Astronomical Society
Secretary: Stephen James, 4 The Cherry Orchard, Haddow, Tonbridge, Kent.
Meetings: Nettlestead Village Hall. 1st Tuesday in the month except July and Aug., 7.30 p.m.

Manchester Astronomical Society
Secretary: Mr Kevin J. Kilburn FRAS, Godlee Observatory, UMIST, Sackville Street, Manchester M60 1QD.
Website: www.u-net.com/ph/mas/; *Email:* kkilburn@globalnet.co.uk
Meetings: At the Godlee Observatory. Thursdays, 7 p.m., except below.
Free Public Lectures: Renold Building UMIST, third Thursday Sept.–Mar., 7.30 p.m.

Mansfield and Sutton Astronomical Society
Secretary: Angus Wright, Sherwood Observatory, Coxmoor Road, Sutton-in-Ashfield, Nottinghamshire NG17 5LF.
Meetings: Sherwood Observatory, Coxmoor Road. Last Tuesday each month, 7.30 p.m.

Mexborough and Swinton Astronomical Society
Secretary: Mark R. Benton, 14 Sandalwood Rise, Swinton, Mexborough, South Yorkshire S64 8PN.
Website: www.msas.org.uk; *Email:* mark@masas.f9.co.uk
Meetings: Swinton WMC. Thursdays, 7.30 p.m.

Mid-Kent Astronomical Society
Secretary: Peter Parish, 30 Wooldeys Road, Rainham, Kent ME8 7NU.
Meetings: Bredhurst Village Hall, Hurstwood Road, Bredhurst, Kent. 2nd and last Fridays each month except August, 7.45 p.m.
Website: www.mkas-site.co.uk

Milton Keynes Astronomical Society
Secretary: Mike Leggett, 19 Matilda Gardens, Shenley Church End, Milton Keynes MK5 6HT.
Website: www.mkas.org.uk; *Email:* mike-pat-leggett@shenley9.fsnet.co.uk
Meetings: Rectory Cottage, Bletchley. Alternate Fridays.

Moray Astronomical Society
Secretary: Richard Pearce, 1 Forsyth Street, Hopeman, Elgin, Moray, Scotland.
Meetings: Village Hall Close, Co. Elgin.

Newbury Amateur Astronomical Society (NAAS)
Secretary: Mrs Monica Balstone, 37 Mount Pleasant, Tadley RG26 4BG.
Meetings: United Reformed Church Hall, Cromwell Place, Newbury. 1st Friday of month, Sept.–June.

Newcastle-on-Tyne Astronomical Society
Secretary: C.E. Willits, 24 Acomb Avenue, Seaton Delaval, Tyne and Wear.
Meetings: Zoology Lecture Theatre, Newcastle University. Monthly.

North Aston Space & Astronomical Club
Secretary: W.R. Chadburn, 14 Oakdale Road, North Aston, Sheffield.
Meetings: To be notified.

Northamptonshire Natural History Society (Astronomy Section)
Secretary: R.A. Marriott, 24 Thirlestane Road, Northampton NN4 8HD.
Email: ram@hamal.demon.co.uk
Meetings: Humfrey Rooms, Castilian Terrace, Northampton. 2nd and last Mondays, most months, 7.30 p.m.

Northants Amateur Astronomers
Secretary: Mervyn Lloyd, 76 Havelock Street, Kettering, Northamptonshire.
Meetings: 1st and 3rd Tuesdays each month, 7.30 p.m.

North Devon Astronomical Society
Secretary: P.G. Vickery, 12 Broad Park Crescent, Ilfracombe, Devon EX34 8DX.
Meetings: Methodist Hall, Rhododendron Avenue, Sticklepath, Barnstaple. 1st Wednesday each month, 7.15 p.m.

North Dorset Astronomical Society
Secretary: J.E.M. Coward, The Pharmacy, Stalbridge, Dorset.
Meetings: Charterhay, Stourton, Caundle, Dorset. 2nd Wednesday each month.

North Downs Astronomical Society
Secretary: Martin Akers, 36 Timber Tops, Lordswood, Chatham, Kent ME5 8XQ.
Meetings: Vigo Village Hall. 3rd Thursday each month. 7.30 p.m.

North-East London Astronomical Society
Secretary: Mr B. Beeston, 38 Abbey Road, Bush Hill Park, Enfield EN1 2QN.
Meetings: Wanstead House, The Green, Wanstead. 3rd Sunday each month (except Aug.), 3 p.m.

North Gwent and District Astronomical Society
Secretary: Jonathan Powell, 14 Lancaster Drive, Gilwern, nr Abergavenny, Monmouthshire NP7 0AA.
Meetings: Gilwern Community Centre. 15th of each month, 7.30 p.m.

North Staffordshire Astronomical Society
Secretary: Duncan Richardson, Halmerend Hall Farm, Halmerend, Stoke-on-Trent, Staffordshire ST7 8AW.
Email: dwr@enterprise.net
Meetings: 21st Hartstill Scout Group HQ, Mount Pleasant, Newcastle-under-Lyme ST5 1DR. 1st Tuesday each month (except July and Aug.), 7–9.30 p.m.

Northumberland Astronomical Society
Contact: Dr Adrian Jametta, 1 Lake Road, Hadston, Morpeth, Northumberland NE65 9TF.
Email: adrian@themoon.co.uk
Website: www.nastro.org.uk
Meetings: Hauxley Nature Reserve (near Amble). Last Thursday of every month (except December), 7.30 pm. Additional meetings and observing sessions listed on website.
Tel: 07984 154904

North Western Association of Variable Star Observers
Secretary: Jeremy Bullivant, 2 Beaminster Road, Heaton Mersey, Stockport, Cheshire.
Meetings: Four annually.

Norwich Astronomical Society
Secretary: Dave Balcombe, 52 Folly Road, Wymondham, Norfolk NR18 0QR.
Website: www.norwich.astronomical.society.org.uk
Meetings: Seething Observatory, Toad Lane, Thwaite St Mary, Norfolk. Every Friday, 7.30 p.m.

Nottingham Astronomical Society
Secretary: C. Brennan, 40 Swindon Close, The Vale, Giltbrook, Nottingham NG16 2WD.
Meetings: Djanogly City Technology College, Sherwood Rise (B682). 1st and 3rd Thursdays each month, 7.30 p.m.

Oldham Astronomical Society
Secretary: P.J. Collins, 25 Park Crescent, Chadderton, Oldham.
Meetings: Werneth Park Study Centre, Frederick Street, Oldham. Fortnightly, Friday.

Open University Astronomical Society
Secretary: Dr Andrew Norton, Department of Physics and Astronomy, The Open University, Walton Hall, Milton Keynes MK7 6AA.
Website: www.physics.open.ac.uk/research/astro/a_club.html
Meetings: Open University, Milton Keynes. 1st Tuesday of every month, 7.30 p.m.

Orpington Astronomical Society
   Secretary: Dr Ian Carstairs, 38 Brabourne Rise, Beckenham, Kent BR3 2SG.
   Meetings: High Elms Nature Centre, High Elms Country Park, High Elms Road,
   Farnborough, Kent. 4th Thursday each month, Sept.–July, 7.30 p.m.

Papworth Astronomy Club
   Contact: Keith Tritton, Magpie Cottage, Fox Street, Great Gransden, Sandy,
   Bedfordshire SG19 3AA.
   Email: kpt2@tutor.open.ac.uk
   Meetings: Bradbury Progression Centre, Church Lane, Papworth Everard, nr
   Huntingdon. 1st Wednesday each month, 7 p.m.

Peterborough Astronomical Society
   Secretary: Sheila Thorpe, 6 Cypress Close, Longthorpe, Peterborough.
   Meetings: 1st Thursday every month, 7.30 p.m.

Plymouth Astronomical Society
   Secretary: Alan G. Penman, 12 St Maurice View, Plympton, Plymouth, Devon
   PL7 1FQ.
   Email: oakmount12@aol.com
   Meetings: Glynis Kingham Centre, YMCA Annex, Lockyer Street, Plymouth. 2nd
   Friday each month, 7.30 p.m.

PONLAF
   Secretary: Matthew Hepburn, 6 Court Road, Caterham, Surrey CR3 5RD.
   Meetings: Room 5, 6th floor, Tower Block, University of North London. Last Friday
   each month during term time, 6.30 p.m.

Port Talbot Astronomical Society (formerly **Astronomical Society of Wales**)
   Secretary: Mr J. Hawes, 15 Lodge Drive, Baglan, Port Talbot, West Glamorgan
   SA12 8UD.
   Meetings: Port Talbot Arts Centre. 1st Tuesday each month, 7.15 p.m.

Portsmouth Astronomical Society
   Secretary: G.B. Bryant, 81 Ringwood Road, Southsea.
   Meetings: Monday, fortnightly.

Preston & District Astronomical Society
   Secretary: P. Sloane, 77 Ribby Road, Wrea Green, Kirkham, Preston, Lancashire.
   Meetings: Moor Park (Jeremiah Horrocks) Observatory, Preston. 2nd Wednesday,
   last Friday each month, 7.30 p.m.

Reading Astronomical Society
   Secretary: Mrs Ruth Sumner, 22 Anson Crescent, Shinfield, Reading RG2 8JT.
   Meetings: St Peter's Church Hall, Church Road, Earley. 3rd Friday each month,
   7 p.m.

Renfrewshire Astronomical Society
   Secretary: Ian Martin, 10 Aitken Road, Hamilton, South Lanarkshire ML3 7YA.
   Website: www.renfrewshire-as.co.uk; *Email:* RenfrewAS@aol.com
   Meetings: Coats Observatory, Oakshaw Street, Paisley. Fridays, 7.30 p.m.

Rower Astronomical Society
   Secretary: Mary Kelly, Knockatore, The Rower, Thomastown, Co. Kilkenny, Eire.

St Helens Amateur Astronomical Society
   Secretary: Carl Dingsdale, 125 Canberra Avenue, Thatto Heath, St Helens,
   Merseyside WA9 5RT.
   Meetings: As arranged.

Salford Astronomical Society
Secretary: Mrs Kath Redford, 2 Albermarle Road, Swinton, Manchester M27 5ST.
Meetings: The Observatory, Chaseley Road, Salford. Wednesdays.

Salisbury Astronomical Society
Secretary: Mrs R. Collins, 3 Fairview Road, Salisbury, Wiltshire SP1 1JX.
Meetings: Glebe Hall, Winterbourne Earls, Salisbury. 1st Tuesday each month.

Sandbach Astronomical Society
Secretary: Phil Benson, 8 Gawsworth Drive, Sandbach, Cheshire.
Meetings: Sandbach School, as arranged.

Sawtry & District Astronomical Society
Secretary: Brooke Norton, 2 Newton Road, Sawtry, Huntingdon, Cambridgeshire PE17 5UT.
Meetings: Greenfields Cricket Pavilion, Sawtry Fen. Last Friday each month.

Scarborough & District Astronomical Society
Secretary: Mrs S. Anderson, Basin House Farm, Sawdon, Scarborough, North Yorkshire.
Meetings: Scarborough Public Library. Last Saturday each month, 7–9 p.m.

Scottish Astronomers Group
Secretary: Dr Ken Mackay, Hayford House, Cambusbarron, Stirling FK7 9PR.
Meetings: North of Hadrian's Wall, twice yearly.

Sheffield Astronomical Society
Secretary: Darren Swindels, 102 Sheffield Road, Woodhouse, Sheffield, South Yorkshire S13 7EU.
Website: www.sheffieldastro.org.uk; *Email:* info@sheffieldastro.org.uk
Meetings: Twice monthly at Mayfield Environmental Education Centre, David Lane, Fulwood, Sheffield S10, 7.30–10 p.m.

Shetland Astronomical Society
Secretary: Peter Kelly, The Glebe, Fetlar, Shetland ZE2 9DJ.
Email: theglebe@zetnet.co.uk
Meetings: Fetlar, Fridays, Oct.–Mar.

Shropshire Astronomical Society
Contact: Mr David Woodward, 20 Station Road, Condover, Shrewsbury, Shropshire SY5 7BQ.
Website: http://www.shropshire-astro.com; *Email:* jacquidodds@ntlworld.com
Meetings: Quarterly talks at the Gateway Arts and Education Centre, Chester Street, Shrewsbury and monthly observing meetings at Rodington Village Hall.

Sidmouth and District Astronomical Society
Secretary: M. Grant, Salters Meadow, Sidmouth, Devon.
Meetings: Norman Lockyer Observatory, Salcombe Hill. 1st Monday in each month.

Solent Amateur Astronomers
Secretary: Ken Medway, 443 Burgess Road, Swaythling, Southampton SO16 3BL.
Web site: www.delscope.demon.co.uk;
Email: kenmedway@kenmedway.demon.co.uk
Meetings: Room 8, Oaklands Community School, Fairisle Road, Lordshill, Southampton. 3rd Tuesday each month, 7.30 p.m.

Southampton Astronomical Society

> *Secretary:* John Thompson, 4 Heathfield, Hythe, Southampton SO45 5BJ.
> *Web site:* www.home.clara.net/lmhobbs/sas.html;
> *Email:* John.G.Thompson@Tesco.net
> *Meetings:* Conference Room 3, The Civic Centre, Southampton. 2nd Thursday each month (except Aug.), 7.30 p.m.

South Downs Astronomical Society

> *Secretary:* J. Green, 46 Central Avenue, Bognor Regis, West Sussex PO21 5HH.
> *Website:* www.southdowns.org.uk
> *Meetings:* Chichester High School for Boys. 1st Friday in each month (except Aug.).

South-East Essex Astronomical Society

> *Secretary:* C.P. Jones, 29 Buller Road, Laindon, Essex.
> *Website:* www.seeas.dabsol.co.uk/; *Email:* cpj@cix.co.uk
> *Meetings:* Lecture Theatre, Central Library, Victoria Avenue, Southend-on-Sea. Generally 1st Thursday in month, Sept.–May, 7.30 p.m.

South-East Kent Astronomical Society

> *Secretary:* Andrew McCarthy, 25 St Paul's Way, Sandgate, near Folkestone, Kent CT20 3NT.
> *Meetings:* Monthly.

South Lincolnshire Astronomical & Geophysical Society

> *Secretary:* Ian Farley, 12 West Road, Bourne, Lincolnshire PE10 9PS.
> *Meetings:* Adult Education Study Centre, Pinchbeck. 3rd Wednesday each month, 7.30 p.m.

Southport Astronomical Society

> *Secretary:* Patrick Brannon, Willow Cottage, 90 Jacksmere Lane, Scarisbrick, Ormskirk, Lancashire L40 9RS.
> *Meetings:* Monthly Sept.–May, plus observing sessions.

Southport, Ormskirk and District Astronomical Society

> *Secretary:* J.T. Harrison, 92 Cottage Lane, Ormskirk, Lancashire L39 3NJ.
> *Meetings:* Saturday evenings, monthly, as arranged.

South Shields Astronomical Society

> *Secretary:* c/o South Tyneside College, St George's Avenue, South Shields.
> *Meetings:* Marine and Technical College. Each Thursday, 7.30 p.m.

South Somerset Astronomical Society

> *Secretary:* G. McNelly, 11 Laxton Close, Taunton, Somerset.
> *Meetings:* Victoria Inn, Skittle Alley, East Reach, Taunton, Somerset. Last Saturday each month, 7.30 p.m.

South-West Hertfordshire Astronomical Society

> *Secretary:* Tom Walsh, 'Finches', Coleshill Lane, Winchmore Hill, Amersham, Buckinghamshire HP7 0NP.
> *Meetings:* Rickmansworth. Last Friday each month, Sept.–May.

Stafford and District Astronomical Society

> *Secretary:* Miss L. Hodkinson, 6 Elm Walk, Penkridge, Staffordshire ST19 5NL.
> *Meetings:* Weston Road High School, Stafford. Every 3rd Thursday, Sept.–May, 7.15 p.m.

Stirling Astronomical Society

> *Secretary:* Hamish MacPhee, 10 Causewayhead Road, Stirling FK9 5ER.
> *Meetings:* Smith Museum & Art Gallery, Dumbarton Road, Stirling. 2nd Friday each month, 7.30 p.m.

Stoke-on-Trent Astronomical Society
Secretary: M. Pace, Sundale, Dunnocksfold, Alsager, Stoke-on-Trent.
Meetings: Cartwright House, Broad Street, Hanley. Monthly.

Stratford-upon-Avon Astronomical Society
Secretary: Robin Swinbourne, 18 Old Milverton, Leamington Spa, Warwickshire CV32 6SA.
Meetings: Tiddington Home Guard Club. 4th Tuesday each month, 7.30 p.m.

Sunderland Astronomical Society
Contact: Don Simpson, 78 Stratford Avenue, Grangetown, Sunderland SR2 8RZ.
Meetings: Friends Meeting House, Roker. 1st, 2nd and 3rd Sundays each month.

Sussex Astronomical Society
Secretary: Mrs C.G. Sutton, 75 Vale Road, Portslade, Sussex.
Meetings: English Language Centre, Third Avenue, Hove. Every Wednesday, 7.30–9.30 p.m., Sept.–May.

Swansea Astronomical Society
Secretary: Dr Michael Morales, 238 Heol Dulais, Birch Grove, Swansea SA7 9LH.
Website: www.crysania.co.uk/sas/astro/star
Meetings: Lecture Room C, Science Tower, University of Swansea. 2nd and 4th Thursday each month from Sept.–June, 7 p.m.

Tavistock Astronomical Society
Secretary: Mrs Ellie Coombes, Rosemount, Under Road, Gunnislake, Cornwall PL18 9JL.
Meetings: Science Laboratory, Kelly College, Tavistock. 1st Wednesday each month, 7.30 p.m.

Thames Valley Astronomical Group
Secretary: K.J. Pallet, 82a Tennyson Street, South Lambeth, London SW8 3TH.
Meetings: As arranged.

Thanet Amateur Astronomical Society
Secretary: P.F. Jordan, 85 Crescent Road, Ramsgate.
Meetings: Hilderstone House, Broadstairs, Kent. Monthly.

Torbay Astronomical Society
Secretary: Tim Moffat, 31 Netley Road, Newton Abbot, Devon TQ12 2LL.
Meetings: Torquay Boys' Grammar School, 1st Thursday in month; and Town Hall, Torquay, 3rd Thursday in month, Oct.–May, 7.30 p.m.

Tullamore Astronomical Society
Secretary: Tom Walsh, 25 Harbour Walk, Tullamore, Co. Offaly, Eire.
Website: www.iol.ie/seanmck/tas.htm; *Email:* tcwalsh25@yahoo.co.uk
Meetings: Order of Malta Lecture Hall, Tanyard, Tullamore, Co. Offaly, Eire. Mondays at 8 p.m., every fortnight.

Tyrone Astronomical Society
Secretary: John Ryan, 105 Coolnafranky Park, Cookstown, Co. Tyrone, Northern Ireland.
Meetings: Contact Secretary.

Usk Astronomical Society
Secretary: Bob Wright, 'Llwyn Celyn', 75 Woodland Road, Croesyceiliog, Cwmbran NP44 2OX.
Meetings: Usk Community Education Centre, Maryport Street, Usk. Every Thursday during school term, 7 p.m.

Vectis Astronomical Society
Secretary: Rosemary Pears, 1 Rockmount Cottages, Undercliff Drive, St Lawrence, Ventnor, Isle of Wight PO38 1XG.
Website: www.wightskies.fsnet.co.uk/main.html;
Email: may@tatemma.freeserve.co.uk
Meetings: Lord Louis Library Meeting Room, Newport. 4th Friday each month except Dec., 7.30 p.m.

Vigo Astronomical Society
Secretary: Robert Wilson, 43 Admers Wood, Vigo Village, Meopham, Kent DA13 0SP.
Meetings: Vigo Village Hall. As arranged.

Walsall Astronomical Society
Secretary: Bob Cleverley, 40 Mayfield Road, Sutton Coldfield B74 3PZ.
Meetings: Freetrade Inn, Wood Lane, Pelsall North Common. Every Thursday.

Wellingborough District Astronomical Society
Secretary: S.M. Williams, 120 Brickhill Road, Wellingborough, Northamptonshire.
Meetings: Gloucester Hall, Church Street, Wellingborough. 2nd Wednesday each month, 7.30 p.m.

Wessex Astronomical Society
Secretary: Leslie Fry, 14 Hanhum Road, Corfe Mullen, Dorset.
Meetings: Allendale Centre, Wimborne, Dorset. 1st Tuesday of each month.

West Cornwall Astronomical Society
Secretary: Dr R. Waddling, The Pines, Pennance Road, Falmouth, Cornwall TR11 4ED.
Meetings: Helston Football Club, 3rd Thursday each month, and St Michall's Hotel, 1st Wednesday each month, 7.30 p.m.

West of London Astronomical Society
Secretary: Duncan Radbourne, 28 Tavistock Road, Edgware, Middlesex HA8 6DA.
Website: www.wocas.org.uk
Meetings: Monthly, alternately in Uxbridge and North Harrow. 2nd Monday in month, except Aug.

West Midlands Astronomical Association
Secretary: Miss S. Bundy, 93 Greenridge Road, Handsworth Wood, Birmingham.
Meetings: Dr Johnson House, Bull Street, Birmingham. As arranged.

West Yorkshire Astronomical Society
Secretary: Pete Lunn, 21 Crawford Drive, Wakefield, West Yorkshire.
Meetings: Rosse Observatory, Carleton Community Centre, Carleton Road, Pontefract. Each Tuesday, 7.15 p.m.

Whitby and District Astronomical Society
Secretary: Rosemary Bowman, The Cottage, Larpool Drive, Whitby, North Yorkshire YO22 4ND.
Meetings: Whitby Mission, Seafarers' Centre, Haggersgate, Whitby. 1st Tuesday of the month, 7.30 p.m.

Whittington Astronomical Society
Secretary: Peter Williamson, The Observatory, Top Street, Whittington, Shropshire.
Meetings: The Observatory. Every month.

Wiltshire Astronomical Society
Secretary: Simon Barnes, 25 Woodcombe, Melksham, Wiltshire SN12 6HA.
Meetings: St Andrew's Church Hall, Church Lane, off Forest Road, Melksham, Wiltshire.

Wolverhampton Astronomical Society
Secretary: Mr M. Bryce, Iona, 16 Yellowhammer Court, Kidderminster, Worcestershire DY10 4RR.
Website: www.wolvas.org.uk; *Email:* michaelbryce@wolvas.org.uk
Meetings: Beckminster Methodist Church Hall, Birches Barn Road, Wolverhampton. Alternate Mondays, Sept.–Apr., extra dates in summer, 7.30 p.m.

Worcester Astronomical Society
Secretary: Mr S. Bateman, 12 Bozward Street, Worcester WR2 5DE.
Meetings: Room 117, Worcester College of Higher Education, Henwick Grove, Worcester. 2nd Thursday each month, 8 p.m.

Worthing Astronomical Society
Contact: G. Boots, 101 Ardingly Drive, Worthing, West Sussex BN12 4TW.
Website: www.worthingastro.freeserve.co.uk;
Email: gboots@observatory99.freeserve.co.uk
Meetings: Heene Church Rooms, Heene Road, Worthing. 1st Wednesday each month (except Aug.), 7.30 p.m.

Wycombe Astronomical Society
Secretary: Mr P. Treherne, 34 Honeysuckle Road, Widmer End, High Wycombe, Buckinghamshire HP15 6BW.
Meetings: Woodrow High House, Amersham. 3rd Wednesday each month, 7.45 p.m.

The York Astronomical Society
Contact: Hazel Collett, Public Relations Officer
Tel: 07944 751277
Website: www.yorkastro.freeserve.co.uk; *Email:* info@yorkastro.co.uk
Meetings: The Knavesmire Room, York Priory Street Centre, Priory Street, York. 1st and 3rd Friday of each month (except Aug.), 8 p.m.

Any society wishing to be included in this list of local societies or to update details, including any website addresses, is invited to write to the Editor (c/o Pan Macmillan, 20 New Wharf Road, London N1 9RR), so that the relevant information may be included in the next edition of the *Yearbook*.

The William Herschel Society maintains the museum established at 19 New King Street, Bath BA1 2BL – the only surviving Herschel House. It also undertakes activities of various kinds. New members would be welcome; those interested are asked to contact the Membership Secretary at the museum.

The South Downs Planetarium (Kingsham Farm, Kingsham Road, Chichester, West Sussex PO19 8RP) is now fully operational. For further information, visit www.southdowns.org.uk/sdpt or telephone (01243) 774400